MODERN ASTROPHYSICS
A memorial to Otto STRUVE

Astrophysique Moderne
à la mémoire d'Otto STRUVE
communications rassemblées par
Margherita HACK

Otto Struve 1897-1963 *(reproduced by courtesy of Sky and Telescope)*

MODERN ASTROPHYSICS

A memorial to Otto Struve

by M. HACK

N.T. BOBROVNIKOFF, M. RUDKJØBING, E.R. MUSTEL, D. CLARKE, M. DAEHLER, J.E. MACK, J. RING, J.O. STONER, F.E. ROACH, B.T. LYNDS, W.W. MORGAN, R. CANAVAGGIA, E. BÖHM-VITENSE, D.H. MCNAMARA, G.E. MATTHEWS, A. VAN HOOF, W.J. LUYTEN, G. WALLERSTEIN, M. HACK, B. STRÖMGREN, P. SWINGS, K.D. ABHYANKAR, S.S. HUANG, J. SAHADE, J.A. HYNEK, O.C. WILSON, R.H. WOLFE, Jr., H.G. HORAK, N.W. STORER, V. KOURGANOFF, V.L. GINZBURG, S.B. PIKELNER, P. PIŞMIŞ, K.F. OGORODNIKOV, G. REAVES, B. VORONTSOV-VELYAMINOV

1967

GAUTHIER-VILLARS, PARIS
GORDON AND BREACH, NEW YORK

CONTENTS

I met Otto STRUVE for the first time in 1955 at the IX symposium of the International Astronomical Union in Dublin. The next year when I worked at Berkeley for a few months I had many stimulating conversations with him. We talked about the exciting problems of some very peculiar stars, which to him were like old family friends.

In 1959 I had the good fortune to be invited again to Berkeley, and for a whole year I had the opportunity of discussing with STRUVE every kind of problem stellar spectroscopy could offer—the subject matter of the book which we were writing together. During these sessions I fully appreciated the simplicity with which he could explain any complicated problem. He had a remarkable talent for giving clear physical explanations to observational facts.

I met him again in 1961 at the IAU meeting held in Berkeley, and then went for a short time to Green Bank where he was director. At this time he seemed very different from the energetic man I had known two years before. Poor health was already eating away his strength. The final collaboration between STRUVE and myself was at the Institute for Advanced Study in Princeton from October to December 1962. He looked tired and unwell, seeming much older than his sixty-five years, but it did not then occur to me that this would be the last time I would see him. I was making plans with him for the future to which he listened kindly but perhpas a bit absently. He had been to John HOPKINS for a medical check up, and probably suspected or already knew the extent of his illness. Three months later I read in an Italian newspaper the sad news of his death.

From Professor Pol SWINGS, one of his best friends, came the idea that we collect scientific papers from astronomers who have worked with STRUVE into a memorial book in his honor. I am deeply grateful to Professor SWINGS for inviting me to act as editor of this volume and have participated in this capacity as a modest tribute to the memory of a great scientist and a great man, Otto STRUVE.

Margherita HACK

Trieste, September 1965.

Dedicated to the memory

of

Otto STRUVE

Born August 12, 1897 in Kharkov, Russia
Deceased April 6, 1963 in Berkeley, California

Otto STRUVE *was the last of six astronomers in the family* : Friedrich George Wilhelm STRUVE (1793-1864) *was the first. He had a son,* Otto Wilhelm (1819-1905) *who succeeded his father as director of the Pulkovo Observatory. Two sons of* Otto Wilhelm, HERMAN (1854-1920) *and* LUDWIG (1858-1920) *became astronomers and each had a son,* GEORGE (1886-1920) *and* OTTO (1897-1963) *who also became astronomers. With Otto ends the Struve dinasty in astronomy.*

After having fought on the Turkish front during the first World War, Otto STRUVE *returned to his studies at the University of Kharkov where he was graduated and became an instructor. During the Russian revolution he endured many hardships in Constantinople, being at one point obliged to work in very humble positions always close to starvation. Finally in 1921 an invitation came from Professor* E. B. FROST, *director of Yerkes Observatory to join their staff. Eleven years later* STRUVE *became director of Yerkes, and in 1939 he founded and directed the McDonald Observatory. In 1950 he was appointed professor of astronomy at the University of California in Berkeley. From 1952 to 1955 he was president of the International Astronomical Union. In 1959 he accepted the directorship of the National Radio Observatory at Green Bank. For reasons of poor health he resigned this post in 1962 and, freed from administrative duties, became a professor at the California Institute of Technology in Pasadena and at the Institute for Advanced Study in Princeton.*

He has left contributions in almost every field of modern astrophysics. He devoted special attention to research in stellar rotation, physical processes explaining emission lines, turbulence effects in stellar atmospheres, physics of interstellar matter, physics and evolution of close binaries. Every month his articles in Sky and Telescope *described the more recent and interesting advances in astrophysics, giving original interpretations to recent observational results, or explaining in clear physical terms the new theories in astrophysics.*

He has published close to a thousand papers and five books, among which we remember especially the stimulating book on Stellar Evolution, *and his last book,* Astronomy of the Twentieth Century, *in collaboration with Velta Zebergs, one of his young assistants.*

Pre-telescopic topography of the moon

N. T. Bobrovnikoff

Ohio State University, Columbus, Ohio

The opinion that no worthwhile observation of the surface of the moon is possible with the naked eye was expressed already by Hevelius. Nevertheless a linear magnification of Mars of about 100 near opposition shows its disk to be of approximately the same angular size as the disk of the moon appears to the unaided eye. Consequently, pre-telescopic observers of the moon were not as handicapped as we imagine them to be. What they did record there and what they failed to record is the topic of the present discussion. But first of all, what can be seen on the moon with the naked eye ?

An interesting experiment was conducted by C. Flammarion [1900]. He asked a number of people to make drawings of the moon as seen with the unaided eye, with 49 persons submitting 58 sketches. One drawing shows Tycho with its system of rays and with a dark nimbus separating the crater itself from the converging rays. This feature is not easy to see even in a telescope. Obviously we cannot forget maps of the moon, but some drawings were made by children who presumably never looked at such a map.

Mare Crisium (diameter 3′) was recorded by 32 people. One observer stated that it is to him a conspicuous feature on the moon, which is also my impression. It is rather surprising that one third of the observers missed it altogether.

Tycho was recorded by five people, and Copernicus by four, that is one person in ten may be expected to see these features. Yet W. H. Pickering maintained that we cannot see Tycho with the unaided eye, and what is taken for Tycho is the bright spot to the west of Crater Hell. Actually all craters are below the resolving power of the normal human eye and what we see as Kepler or Copernicus are the convergent rays of these craters.

W. H. Pickering [1915, 1925] gives a list of ten objects on the moon of increasing difficulty as seen with the unaided eye. The easiest object on his list is Copernicus, while Kepler is No. 4. The Altai Mountains are No. 10. Mare Crisium is not mentioned, apparently on the assumption that the maria are always seen.

At first quarter the terminator of the moon is conspicuously notched by the string of walled plains and craters, Ptolomaeus to Walther, in the

southern part, and by the Apennines and Alps in the northern. Obviously
previous knowledge, acuity of the eye, and the state of the atmosphere determine what can be recognized on the moon with the naked eye. If we take
the ten conspicuous maria and Pickering's ten objects it is clear that one can
see on the moon at least 20 details, and an exceptionnaly good eye could
recognize probably twice as many.

We are now ready to apply these considerations to the really observed
features of the moon. We shall leave out the pre-historic and aboriginal
descriptions of the spots, even though they do show that the moon was
observed by the primitive peoples at least to the extent that the permanency
and invariability of the spots were recognized. There are surprisingly few
motives in these identifications of the spots with terrestrial objects (such as a
rabbit or a hare), but the matter has already been thoroughly discussed by
HARLEY [1885] and more recently in a series of articles by anthropologist
H. KUNIKE [1926-1934].

Despite Aristotle's sharp separation of the terrestrial from celestial physics,
the idea that the surface of the moon is of the same character as the surface
of the earth was rather common in antiquity. We know that the Pythago-
reans not only imagined plains and mountains on the moon, but even postulated that lunar men and animals should be 15 times as large as their
terrestrial counterparts (PLUTARCH, *De Placita*, Ch. 30). We may assume
that some real observations of the details of the lunar surface were the basis
of such speculations.

There is an indication of such observations in the story of the Hyperboreans
told by Diodorus Siculus (**II**, ch. 47). They were supposed to live beyond
the land of the Celts on a fertile island of an unusually temperate climate,
presumably Britain:

> "They say also that the moon, as viewed from this island, appears
> to be but a little distance from the earth and have upon it prominences,
> like those on the earth, which are visible to the eye" C. H. OLDFATHER'S
> *translation, Loeb Classical Library.*

The basis for this assertion is perhaps the appearance of the winter full,
nearly circumpolar, moon at higher latitudes, as I have frequently seen it,
in a latitude 60° N. The moon for a long time glides along the horizon and
just before and after sunset appears to have unusually prominent details on
its disk.

The only treatise dealing with the topography of the moon that has reached
us from the Graeco-Roman times is that of PLUTARCH, *De Facie in Orbis
Lunae* of which the modern translation by H. Cherniss, *Loeb Classical*

Library is here quoted. This book has had a curious history. Kepler not only translated it but wrote a commentary on it nearly as long as the original of Plutarch. Deslambre docs not deign to notice it, while to DUHEM (*Le système* **2**, p. 360) it was "a work of genius. " It is hardly known to modern astronomers, but one writer (SAMBURSKY, 1950) manages to see in it "the beginning of astrophysics. "

Of course, it is nothing of the sort. PLUTARCH of CHAERONEA (*A. D.*, 46-120) was a publicist specializing in biographies of great men, and took pains to put down the current ideas about the moon, as, indeed, he says himself at the very beginning of his essay. He did an excellent job, probably better than a modern reporter would do with a similar material, but we would hardly call it astrophysics. If we include under that term speculations about the nature of celestial bodies, PLATO and his successors were astrophysicists.

There are many surprising things in PLUTARCH besides the spots on the moon. NEWTON's first law of motion is practically stated (933 D), something like a law of gravitation is mentioned (924E), the solar corona is described (932B), and different colors of the eclipsed moon are noted (933F). From the wrong premise that the moon, being a celestial body, must have its earthy substance diluted by fire, he comes to the correct conclusion that its average density must be less than the average density of the earth (923D). But on the main subject of discussion Plutarch is rather vague.

The participants in the discussion (Lamprias usually taken to represent Plutarch's on views) quote poet Agesianax (920E and 921B), describing on the moon a maiden's face with blue eyes from which we may conclude that the ancients noticed the difference in coloration in different parts of the moon, but no more. Toward the end (944B) the spots on the moon are specifically mentioned and the largest (perhaps our Oceanus Procellarum plus Mare Imbrium) is called Hecate's Recess. The part of the moon that is always turned toward the heavens is called the Elysian Fields. We may infer from all this that PLUTARCH understood that the moon always keeps the same side toward the earth, certainly not a great achievement.

Various theories of lunar spots are quoted. Apollonides, one of the participants, objects to the idea that they are produced by shadows saying that each spot is larger than half the digit, that is 1/24 of the lunar diameter. This would make them larger than 1'15", the limit of the resolving power of a very sharp human eye.

Plutarch is clever enough to reject the suggestion that the spots on the moon are simply an illusion, pointing out that the sharper the vision the more definite are thc spots (920C). We come here across a curious motive frequent in subsequent discussions of the spots which were irreconcilable with ARISTOTLE'S theory. The moon must be perfect as all celestial bodies are, therefore its spots are produced by some extraneous agent such as clouds between us and the moon. During the Middle Ages this was connected with theology. Alexander NECKAM, a foster brother of Richard COEUR DE LION, expressed the ecclesiastical belief that the moon was created spotless and the spots appeared on it as a consequence of the fall of man and will go at the Last Judgment.

The most prevalent idea of this sort was the moon's being a mirror and reflecting terrestrial landscape as mentioned in the second quotation from Agesianax. We have a reminder of this in our nomenclature of the lunar mountains introduced by HEVELIUS. Observing the moon through a telescope he rejected the idea of reflection; yet he could see in the moon a curious resemblance to the Mediterranean region both in size and in the distribution of features, *Selenographia*, page 323.

This is as much as we can possibly extract from Plutarch. No map of the moon is mentioned and it is doubtful that there was any available in antiquity. Alexander Humboldt thought that Anaxagoras compiled a map, but this seems to be based on a misreading of PLUTARCH, WOHLWILL, I, page 254. In fact, the most that Plutarch says about it, *Placita*, II, Ch. 25, is to repeat the idea of Anaxagoras and Democritus: "the moon is a solid condensed and fiery body, in which there are champaign countries, mountains and valleys."

We have to go nine centuries from Plutarch's time to find another investigator of the moon who with much greater justice has been called the first astrophysicist (KOHL, 1925). This is Al Haitham, known in the West as ALHAZEN (965-1039). His reputation (quite deserved) was such that Hevelius placed him alongside of Galileo on the frontispiece of his Selenographia.

ALHAZEN'S, *On the Light of the Moon* (translation by K. KOHL, [1925]) is a rather thorough scientific report on the use of an apparatus by means of which different portions of the moon were studied one at a time. ALHAZEN even employed assistants to insure the reliability of his results. He carried out experiments with light reflected from metallic spheres and proved to his satisfaction that the moon does not have specular reflection. He and subsequent authors such as Roger BACON down to Galileo denied that the moon shines by a reflected light. By this they meant the absence of a specular reflection of the sun which would give just one bright spot on the surface of the moon and not a general illumination. In place of this ALHAZEN introduces the idea of a self-luminous moon, that is the moon absorbing the light of the sun and diffusing it in every direction. At least this is what the text appears to mean, but it may imply also some sort of fluorescence.

The lunar spots are discussed in various places of the essay and the usual theories of their origin are refuted. Especially interesting is the theory that the spotted moon is actually a very small body which we dimly see through a large crystalline sphere. Duhem came across this theory, (*Le Système*, 3, pages 442-460, in a notation to the manuscript of Bernard of Verdun, late 13th century) and considered it unique. It was evidently well known to Alhazen who uses occultations to refute it. He says he observed occultations repeatedly (especially of Venus) and stars, when they are touched by the preceding limb of the moon, disappear instantly which could not be the case if they were occulted by a transparent globe. Yet he failed to make the obvious deductions from this fact: that the moon cannot have any sizeable atmosphere, that apparent diameters of stars are very small and certainly not several minutes of arc as was commonly thought at his time and, finally, that there is appreciable difference between the apparent diameter of stars and planets. But in a case like this we should exercise caution in coming to conclusions.

Obviously ALHAZEN was an excellent observer and had a sharp eye. He noticed, for instance, (KOHL, page 378) that the edges of the moon are brighter than the middle, yet he never mentions the earthlight and the color of the eclipsed moon even when it would be useful for his argument. One would assume that he never noticed these phenomena. But in the other treatise on the moon ALHAZEN emphasises these very things.

The manuscript of ALHAZEN'S, *On the Nature of the Spots that are visible on the Surface of the Moon* (translation by C. SCHOY, [1925]) was found only in 1920. This is a much shorter and more elementary discussion of matters contained in the first treatise and is devoted mostly to the refutation of the already mentioned theories. Alhazen comes to the conclusion that the spots must be ascribed to the difference in reflectivity (albedo) of the various portions of the moon. This is a perfectly correct conclusion even though he thinks that spots are denser matter which absorbs less of the solar light, and therefore emit less light. We note that ALHAZEN begins this treatise with a statement that no changes whatever have been seen on the moon, and repeats this several times in the course of his discussion. He must have had then some record of the spots, that is simply maps of the moon, to be so sure of this, yet he nowhere mentions such records.

ALHAZEN influenced the West not so much directly as through Arabic philosophers ABRAHAM ibn EZRA [1092-1167] and especially through "the commentator", that is AVERROES [1126-1198]. Roger BACON's disquisition on the moon, *Opus Majus*; *Opus Tertium*, Cap. 37, follows ALHAZEN almost verbatim.

The contemporary of Roger BACON, Albertus MAGNUS [1193-1277] seems to have been the only medieval scholar who looked at the moon in order to see the spots for himself. In his *De generatione et corruptione* he gives a rather detailed description of them, (STEIN [1950]) in which three great figures are distinguished: the dragon, the tree and the man. It is possible to identify the head of the dragon with Sinus Medii, its neck with Mare Nubium and its tail with Mare Humorum. The trunk of the tree is Mare Vaporum and its folliage consists of parts of Oceanus Procellarum and Mare Imbrium. The head of the man is formed by Mare Imbrium, his body by Mare Serenitatis and Mare Tranquilitatis, and his legs by Mare Foecunditatis and Mare Nectaris.

In the following centuries discussion of spots on the moon became a favorite topic with philosophers, on account of the "démenti perpétuel", to borrow DUHEM's expression (*Le Système*, 9, pp. 409-430), that is the impossibility to reconcile their existence with the Aristotelian theory. EVEN BEATRICE could not give DANTE a satisfactory account of their existence (*Paradiso*, **II**). The greatest philosopher of the Paris school, Jean BURIDAN [1295-1366] in his commentary on ARISTOTLE devotes a chapter to the spots (*Questiones*, **II**, 19). He is repeated almost word by word by Albert of SAXONY [1368], and Nicole ORESME [1320-1382]. All this is simply a rehash of old opinions based on second and third hand information. It is hard to believe they ever looked at the moon themselves.

In Leonardo DA VINCI [1452-1519] we recognize something quite different. He not only looked at the moon but made drawings of its spots to see if they change with time. In the following the standard abbreviations of Leonardo's manuscripts are used:

Paris A, D, C...	*K*
Codice Atlantico	*CA*
British Museum	*BM*
Earl of Leicester	*Leic.*

We may recall that over 5,000 sheets of Leonardo's notes have survived and it is definitely known that many have disappeared since his death. Some, but by no means all, references to astronomy are reproduced in standard collections by J. P. RICHTER [1939] and E. MacCURDY [1938].

Unfortunately Leonardo's detailed drawings of the moon have not been preserved. There is one on a small scale (*Leic 2*) representing the new moon with some markings on the dark side. Perhaps the curve of Mare Imbrium can be made out. At any rate this drawing is the only pre-telescopic picture of the moon that we have at our disposal.

We may also note here that LEONARDO mentions glasses which he used to study the moon (*CA 190*): *Fa occhiali da vedere la luna grande.* This probably refers to the real image produced by a lens and seen with-out an eye-piece. A certain amount of magnification can be thus obtained depending on the ratio of the focal length of the lens (or mirror) to the distance of the image from the eye for distinct vision. With a certain proficiency of manipulation it is possible to obtain sharp but fleeting images. W. HERSCHEL discovered this way the sixth satellite of Saturn (*Enceladus*) while testing his new 40-foot reflecting telescope, (ARGENTIERI [1916]).

However, D. ARGENTIERI insists that Leonardo used not only this type of a telescope (which Argentieri duplicated from Leonardo's description, F 25) but also an ordinary two-lens telescope a hundred years before GALILEO. If this is so, some of LEONARDO's pictures of the moon were not made with the naked eye.

LEONARDO follows the precedent by enumerating and criticizing the existing theories of the lunar spots. In this, as DUHEM has shown [1906-1913] he follows Albert of SAXONY very closely. But LEONARDO says definitely *(BM 16)* that he repeatedly observed the spots and found them variable. On the other hand he seems to say also that they do not change at all (F 84; F 85). This contradiction is easily resolved. LEONARDO thought, contrary to later thinking, that the dark spots were continents and were, of course, permanent. They seem to be variable on account of the lunar clouds drifting over them. Anyone trying to make out the spots on the moon would readily see the basis of LEONARDO's opinion. The spots do seem to be of variable intensity owing to the state of the atmosphere and position of the moon in respect to the horizon. Even with the telescope Hevelius (*Selenographia*, p. 137) found them strongly variable in color, and KEPLER described a storm on the moon observed by MAESTLIN [1605] (*Notae in Somnium, No, 223*).

We have now come to the debatable subject of the lumen cinereum, or earthlight on the moon. It seems that the English term is somewhat premature. There is no doubt that the major part of this light is indeed due to the reflected light of the earth, yet it shows surprising variation in intensity that cannot be explained on this basis. Perhaps some luminescence of the lunar surface is involved, and it is better to refer to this phenomenon by its old name, lumen cinereum (ashy light), as in other languages.

LEONARDO DA VINCI was the first to suggest the correct explanation of the major part of the lumen cinereum (*CA 243; Leic 2*). He carefully observed it by covering up the bright crescent, and noticed the "silver thread" (so called from its description in COLERIDGE'S Dejection), when the dusky limb of the moon appears to be brighter than its middle. This is mostly a contrast effect. I find that the silver thread is more noticeable with the naked eye than through the binoculars. It is not a new phenomenon as suggested by some writers who could not trace it further back than GALILEO (*Gaythorpe, 1934*). It was mentioned already by ALHAZEN (*Schoy*, 1925).

The description of the lumen cinereum by LEONARDO DA VINCI is very similar to that in BURIDAN and Albert of SAXONY. BURIDAN (*Quaest.* **II**: 19) however, uses this phenomenon to argue that the moon must have some light of its own besides that reflected from the sun:

Sed dubitatio est utrum luna, praeter illuminationem eius a sole, habeat aliquam lucem; et forte non est bene demonstrabile utrum sic aut non sic. Dicunt tamen aliqui quod ipsa habet de se aliquam lucem licet multum diminutam, quia quando luna est crescens per tres vel quattuor dies post coniuctionem, adhuc apparet nobis circulus secundum partem non illuminatam a sole, quod non esset si nullam lucem haberet nisi a sole.

After quoting various explanations of this phenomenon (including the refracted light of the sun!) he does not come to any definite conclusion. None of these writers say anything about the spots seen on the dark side of the moon. From more than 40 years of observation of the lumen cinereum PLASSMANN [1924] found that they are seen distinctly very seldom and only when the lumen cinereum is very bright, of intensity 9 or 10 in the ten step scale of brightness. I have seen them with the naked eye but never distinctly enough to be sure that they are the same as seen on the full moon. Presumably with a really good eye they could be seen definitely enough to settle this question.

We have only one reference to their being seen so (NAU, [1900]) by Bar HEBRAEUS in the 13th Century. He uses them as an argument against a perfectly correct theory of Nassiredin of the inequality of illumination (or as we would say now the difference in the albedo) of the different parts of the moon. The sun cannot have anything to do with this as we see the identical spots on the full moon which is illuminated by the sun and on the new moon which is certainly not.

From this little bit of history of the topography of the moon we conclude that the ancients and medieval people never utilized the full power of the unaided human eye. They never made maps of the moon to see if there really were any changes there. This was regretted by GILBERT, the discoverer of geomagnetism, but it is not known that GILBERT himself did anything about it (WOHLWILL, **I**, p. 254). Observations of occultations were common in antiquity beginning with ARISTOTLE, yet neither ARISTOTLE nor anybody else for 2,000 years realized the potentialities of the occultation method that could have given them much better values of the apparent diameter of stars and planets than the preposterous values of 3' or 2' for first magnitude stars used even by Tycho BRAHE.

This, as we recall, was for him one of the strongest arguments against the heliocentric theory. The occultation method to overcome the low resolving power of the instrument is used with striking success by modern radio astronomy.

That the moon was not diligently observed in antiquity is evident from the fact that Ptolemy missed the variation of the lunar orbit with its coefficient of 39'5. This means simply that he did not observe the moon except at conjunctions, oppositions and quadratures. When systematic observations of the moon were organized for the first time by Tycho BRAHE, this and also a much smaller effect of the annual equation were immediately discovered.

It was then not lack of telescopes but the absence of observational method that prevented the accumulation of useful scientific data. After all, Kepler's laws were based on naked eye observations. We know from the Chinese Chronicles that many comets and novae as well as variable stars were missed in antiquity and the Middle Ages in Europe. And so when GALILEO turned his telescope to the moon and discovered according to Milton (*Paradise Lost*, **I**, 290) "new lands, rivers or mountains on her spotty globe" it was a considerable shock to most of his contemporaries and the beginning of a new era in astronomy.

REFERENCES

ARGENTIERI, D., 1956, *Leonardo's Optics*, pp. 405-436 in *Leonardo da Vinci* (Reynal Co., New York).

BURIDAN, J., 1942, *Quaestiones super libris quattuor de Caelo et Mundo*, (E.A. Moody, ed. Medieval Ac. of America, Cambridge, Mass.).

DUHEM, P., 1906-1913, *Études sur Léonard de Vinci*, 3 vol., Paris.

DUHEM, P., 1954, *Le Système du Monde*, vol. 1-10, Paris.

FLAMMARION, C., 1900, *Bull. Soc. Astr. de France*, 14, 45-50; 93-98; 140-145; 183-188; 227-233; 275-283; 298-306. (Gauthier-Villars, Paris).

GAYTHORPE, S.B., 1934, *Journ. British Astr. Assoc.*, **45**, 68-72.

HARLEY, T., 1885, *Moon Lore* (London).

KOHL, K., 1925, *Über das Licht des Mondes — Eine Untersuchung von Ibn al Haitham*, *Sitzber. phys.-mediz.*, Sozietät zu Erlangen, 56-57, 305-398.

KUNICKE, H., 1927, *Zur Deutung der Mondflecken*, *Die Sterne*, 6, 46-53.

MacCURDY, E., 1938, *The Notebooks of Leonardo da Vinci*, 2 (New York).

NAU, F., 1900, *Le livre de l'Ascension de l'Esprit*, **121**, Bibl. de l'E.H.E., Paris).

PICKERING, W.H., 1915, *Report on Mars*, No. 11, *Popular Astronomy*, **23**, 569-588.

PICKERING, W.H., 1925, *Journ. British Astron. Assoc.*, **36**, 83-84.

PLASSMANN, J.P., 1924, *Studien über das aschgrause Mondlicht*, *Himmelswelt*, **34**, 95-103.

PLASSMANN, J.P., 1928, *Aus der morgenländischen Sternkunde und Sterndeuterei*, *Himmelswelt*, **38**, 20-25.

RICHTER, J.P., 1939, *The Literary Works of Leonardo da Vinci*, (2nd ed. Oxford Univ. Press, Oxford).

SAMBURSKY, S., 1956, *The Physical World of the Greeks* (New York).

SCHOY, C., 1925, Abhandlung des Schaichs... Ibn Al-Haitham: *Über die Natur der Spuren (Flecken) die man auf der Oberfläche des Mondes sieht*, Hannover.

STEIN, J.W., S.J., 1950, *Specola Vaticana Misc. Astronomica*, **3**, No. 102.

WOHLWILL, E., 1909, *Galilei und sein Kampf fur die Copernicanische Lehre*, 2 vol. (Leipzig).

Kepler's third law and radar determinations
of the astronomical unit of length in general relativity

MOGENS RUDKJØBING

Ole Rømer Observatory, Aarhus, Denmark

Abstract

Kepler's third law for planetary motion is found to be valid without relativistic corrections when the semi-major axis is measured by the value of the coordinate r of Schwarzschild's solution for the line element in a weak-field approximation, for orbits of small
eccentricity.

This result permits the calculation of relativistic corrections to the value of the astronomical unit of length as calculated according to classical formalism from radio-echo
observations of distances between the earth and Venus.

1 — Introduction

The accuracy with which distances between the earth and Venus have
recently been measured by several independent groups of observers with the
radio-echo method is of the order of one part in 10^6. However, the accuracy
obtainable with the aid of systems now under construction has been estimated by PETTENGILL [1962], in a review of observational results, to be of
the order of one part in 10^8.

For the reduction of interplanetary radar observations made with an
accuracy as high as this it would be necessary to take account of general
relativistic effects. This is due to the fact that the length that corresponds to
the solar mass, namely 1.48 km, is about the fraction 10^{-8} of the astronomical
unit of length, $1.496 \cdot 10^8$ km, which is the length of the semi-major axis
of the earth's orbit.

Even if the occurrence of plasma in varying densities in interplanetary
space may have a much larger influence on the observational results than
relativistic effects, calculations of the latter may still be of at least theoretical
interest.

The principal aim of radar observations of planets is the determination
of the astronomical unit of length in kilometers. Classically, the procedure
is the following. The interplanetary distance is calculated with the use of
ordinary plane trigonometry from the heliocentric angular distance between

the two planets and the lengths of the two planetary radii vectores, as known in astronomical units with sufficiently high accuracy. The result is then compared with the distance as found in kilometers by radio-echo observations on the assumption of rectilinear motion of the signals with a constant velocity equal to that determined in terrestrial laboratories as the velocity of light in vacuum.

A fundamental question naturally raised in this connection is that of what becomes of Kepler's third law in general relativity. The reason is that the ratio of the dimensions of the orbits dealt with is determined in practice, in the case of an inferior planet and the earth, from the ratio of the orbital periods. The trigonometric parallax method is probably less accurate in this case, due to the phases shown by Mercury and Venus as observed from the earth. The periods, however, are well determined from observations of passages of the planets across the solar disc.

In our present investigation we shall consider such general relativistic effects as are connected with the motion of each planet in the gravitational field of the Sun only and assume the mutual perturbations of the planets to be given by their classical expressions. This is allowed for our purpose, since the largest planetary mass, that of Jupiter, is of the order of 10^{-3} solar masses. It has been shown by LEVI-CIVITA [1937] that the relative motion of two bodies with finite masses is equal to that of one of vanishing mass under the influence of a fixed mass equal to the sum of the two masses, just as in classical mechanics. Since the effects of the motion of the Sun relative to the center of gravity of the solar system is included in the classical planetary perturbations, it follows that we need to study the effect of general relativity on Kepler's third law in its original form only, without the extension to include the planetary masses. The effects of the extension is quite within the field covered by classical mechanics within the limits of accuracy here considered.

In section 2 of the present paper we shall find that Schwarzschild's solution for the line element in the gravitational field of a point mass is unique in the sense that it leads to Kepler's third law in its classical form for such planetary orbits for which the square of the orbital eccentricity is negligible in the relativistic corrections to the classical planetary orbits. This is the case for the orbits of the earth and Venus, but not for Mercury's orbit.

Schwarzschild's form of the expression for the line element is therefore a natural basis for calculations of the relativistic effects on the echo times. The planetary orbits are then assumed to be known accurately with account taken of classical perturbations as well as of relativistic influences on their forms, such as the latter have been calculated by CLEMENCE [1962].

The echo-time corrections are calculated in section 3. Regard is taken of the variation of the velocity of light with the gravitational potential and of the curvature of the light rays. Numerical results are given for the case of observations of distances of Venus from the earth, tabulated as a function of the heliocentric angular distance between the two planets. A classical effect is included here, because it is of the same order of magnitude as the relativistic effects. It is that effect of the curvature of the earth's orbit that makes the distance between the planets at the mean of the times of emission and reception of the signals differ from the mean of the distances at the two moments.

2 — Kepler's third law

The following equations (MØLLER, [1952], XII (26), (27), (17), and (18)) are valid for planetary motion in the gravitational field of the Sun

$$(1) \qquad u^2 = C^2 (1-\alpha\rho) \left[\left(\frac{d\rho}{d\phi} \right)^2 + \rho^2 - \alpha\rho^3 \right]$$

$$(2) \qquad (1-\alpha\rho)^2 = E^2 \left[1 - \alpha\rho - \frac{u^2}{c^2} \right]$$

$$(3) \qquad \Gamma r^2 \dot\phi = CE$$

$$(4) \qquad \frac{r^2 \dot\phi}{1 - \dfrac{\alpha}{r}} = C$$

In the first two equations $1/r$ is denoted by ρ. Eliminating the square of the velocity, u^2, from (2) with the aid of (1) we get

$$(5) \qquad \left(\frac{d\rho}{d\phi} \right)^2 = \frac{c^2}{C^2} \left[1 - \frac{1-\alpha\rho}{E^2} \right] - \rho^2 (1-\alpha\rho)$$

Since the function Γ in (3) is equal to (MØLLER, [1952] VIII (99) and XII, (10))

$$(6) \qquad \sqrt{\left(1 - \frac{\alpha}{r} - \frac{u^2}{c^2} \right)^{-1}} = \sqrt{\left(1 + \frac{2\chi}{c^2} - \frac{u^2}{c^2} \right)^{-1}} = \frac{dt}{d\tau}$$

we may write (3) as

(7)
$$r^2 \frac{d\phi}{d\tau} = CE$$

With the use of this we get

(8)
$$\frac{d\rho}{d\phi} = -\frac{1}{r^2}\frac{dr}{d\phi} = -\frac{1}{r^2}\frac{dr}{d\tau}\frac{d\tau}{d\phi} = -\frac{1}{CE}\frac{dr}{d\tau}$$

with the aid of which we eliminate ϕ from (5). Introducing $1/r$ instead of ρ we get

(9)
$$\frac{1}{C^2 E^2}\left(\frac{dr}{d\tau}\right)^2 = \frac{c^2}{C^2}\left[1 - \frac{1-\frac{\alpha}{r}}{E^2}\right] - \frac{1}{r^2}\left(1 - \frac{\alpha}{r}\right)$$

Differentiation with respect to τ gives

(10)
$$\frac{2}{C^2 E^2}\frac{d^2 r}{d\tau^2} = -\frac{c^2}{C^2 E^2}\frac{\alpha}{r^2} + \frac{2}{r^3} - \frac{3\alpha}{r^4}$$

or, with the use of the relation $\alpha = \dfrac{2\,kM}{c^2}$

(11)
$$\frac{d^2 r}{d\tau^2} = -\frac{kM}{r^2} + C^2 E^2\left[\frac{1}{r^3} - \frac{3\,kM}{c^2\,r^4}\right] = f(r)$$

We intend to use the above equation for the determination of the period of oscillations of small amplitude around that value of r, equal to r_0, which makes $f(r) = 0$. The period of such oscillations it the so-called anomalistic period of orbits of small eccentricity, in this case as expressed in units of the planet's proper time. We intend to approximate $f(r)$ in the region considered by a linear expression

(12)
$$\frac{d^2 r}{d\tau^2} = (r - r_0)\left(\frac{df}{dr}\right)_0$$

The relations between r_0 and CE is

(13)
$$C^2 E^2 = kMr_0\left(1 + 3\frac{kM}{c^2\,r_0}\right)$$

We neglect here and in what follows everywhere terms of higher than the first order in α. We differentiate f with respect to r and find from (11)

(14)
$$\frac{df}{dr} = 2\frac{kM}{r^3} - 3\frac{C^2\,E^2}{r^4} + 12\,C^2\,E^2\,\frac{kM}{c^2\,r^5}$$

The value at the zero point for f is found from (13) and (14) as

(15)
$$\left(\frac{df}{dr}\right)_0 = \frac{2\,kM}{r_0^3} - \frac{3}{r_0^4}\,kMr_0\left(1+3\frac{kM}{c^2\,r_0}\right)\left(1-4\frac{kM}{c^2\,r_0}\right)$$

or

(16)
$$\left(\frac{df}{dr}\right)_0 = -\frac{kM}{r_0^3}\left(1-3\frac{kM}{c^2\,r_0}\right)$$

The linear approximation for (11) then is

(17)
$$\frac{d^2\,r}{d\tau^2} = -\frac{kM}{r_0^3}\left(1-3\frac{kM}{c^2\,r_0}\right)(r-r_0)$$

The oscillations are described by

(18)
$$r-r_0 = r_0\,e\,\sin(\omega\tau+\delta)$$

Then r oscillates between $r_0(1+e)$ and $r_0(1-e)$. Thus e is the eccentricity of the orbit and r_0 the semi-major axis as measured in terms of the coordinate r in Schwarzschild's solution. From (18) we get

(19)
$$\frac{d^2\,r}{d\tau^2} = -\omega^2\,(r-r_0)$$

and from a comparison with (17)

(20)
$$\omega^2 = \frac{kM}{r_0^3}\left(1-3\frac{kM}{c^2\,r_0}\right) = \left(\frac{2\,\pi}{U'}\right)^2$$

or, denoting the semi-major axis by a

(21)
$$U' = 2\,\pi\left(\frac{a^3}{kM}\right)^{\frac{1}{2}}\left(1+\frac{3}{2}\frac{kM}{c^2\,a}\right)$$

Here U' denotes the anomalistic period, equal to the time interval between successive perihelion passages, as measured in planetary proper time. In order to find the sidereal period in units of coordinate time, which is that period which we are interested in from the point of view of Kepler's third law, we first introduce coordinate time by the relation (6)

$$(22) \qquad \frac{dt}{d\tau} = \sqrt{\left(1 - \frac{4\,kM}{c^2\,r} + \frac{kM}{c^2 a}\right)^{-1}} = 1 + 2\frac{kM}{c^2\,r} - \frac{1}{2}\frac{kM}{c^2 a}$$

We have eliminated u^2 from the small term with the aid of the classical relation

$$(23) \qquad u^2 = kM\left(\frac{2}{r} - \frac{1}{a}\right)$$

The anomalistic period measured in units of coordinate time is determined by the integral of dt taken over one anomalistic period:

$$(24) \qquad U'' = \int_0^{U''} dt = \int_0^{U'} d\tau\left(1 + \frac{2\,kM}{c^2\,r} - \frac{1}{2}\frac{kM}{c^2\,a}\right)$$

Classically, the time mean value of the potential energy is given by the semimajor axis by the following relation

$$(25) \qquad \int_0^{U} \frac{dt}{r} = \frac{U}{a}$$

where we need not distinguish between the different kind of periods. We introduce this in the small terms of (24) and find

$$(26) \qquad U'' = U'\left(1 + \frac{3}{2}\frac{kM}{c^2\,a}\right)$$

or, with the use of (21)

$$(27) \qquad U'' = 2\pi\left(\frac{a^3}{kM}\right)^{\frac{1}{2}}\left(1 + 3\frac{kM}{c^2\,a}\right)$$

The relation between the anomalistic and the sidereal orbital periods is determined by the rate of the relativistic advance of perihelion. The increase in the angle ϕ between two successive perihelion passages is given as (MØLLER [1952], XII (36)):

$$(28) \qquad 2\pi\left[1 + \frac{3}{4}\alpha\,(\rho_1 + \rho_2)\right] = 2\pi\left[1 + 3\frac{kM}{c^2\,a}\right]$$

when terms of the order of e^2 are neglected. Then the (mean value of) sidereal period U as measured in coordinate time is given by the relation

(29)
$$U = 2\pi \left(\frac{a^3}{kM} \right)^{\frac{1}{2}}$$

For two planets we then have

(30)
$$\left(\frac{U_1}{U_2} \right)^2 = \left(\frac{a_1}{a_2} \right)^3$$

We have thus shown that Kepler's third law is valid without relativistic corrections in the coordinate system used, in the limit of vanishing orbital eccentricity. Implicitly, this result is also contained in the expressions derived by GEISLER [1963]. No other forms for the line element are compatible with the law, except such forms that arise through scale changes, which are without interest here, however, since we use the distance of the earth from the Sun as a unit of length and are going to measure it with the use of the known velocity of light.

The ratio of the orbital periods is uninfluenced by a change from coordinate time to terrestrial proper time, because the deviations from a mere scale factor, which cancels in the formation of the ratio of the periods, is of a purely periodic nature and therefore vanish when the mean is taken over long enough periods.

3 — General relativistic corrections to radio-echo times

In what follows we shall assume that the planets considered, namely the earth and Venus, are moving in circular orbits in a plane. The orders of magnitude of the orbital eccentricities and of the relative inclination of the orbits are such that they are vanishing in combination with the general relativistic corrections, as are planetary perturbations of the orbits, as already mentioned. The corrections to be derived in the following will therefore be valid for the actual orbits within the accuracy of measurement.

In the case of actual observations, however, the true rate of advance of the observer's proper time must be taken into account for the reduction to the rate that corresponds to circular motion.

For a light ray we have the relations (MØLLER [1952] VIII (69′) and X (94))

(31)
$$\frac{d\sigma}{dt} = w$$

and

(32)
$$w = c \sqrt{(1 + 2\chi/c^2)}$$

(We shall use Møller's notations throughout). Echo times as measured by radar correspond to (twice) an interval of coordinate time

$$(33) \qquad \int_1^2 \frac{d\sigma}{w}$$

where the integral is taken along a light ray connecting planet 1 (the earth) with planet 2. Since the ratio of dt and $d\tau$ for the earth may be treated as a constant during the few minutes of travel time of the signals, the distance calculated by the observer is equal to [compare (6)]

$$(34) \qquad c \int d\tau = c \left(1 + \frac{2\chi}{c^2} - \frac{u^2}{c^2}\right)_1^{\frac{1}{2}} \int_1^2 \frac{d\sigma}{w}$$

The three-dimensional line element $d\sigma$ is given by MØLLER [1952], XI (79) with $\lambda = 0$ as

$$(35) \qquad d\sigma^2 = \frac{dr^2}{1 - \frac{\alpha}{r}} + r^2 (d\theta^2 + \sin^2 \theta \, d\phi^2), \quad \frac{\alpha}{r} = -\frac{2\chi}{c^2}$$

We put $d\theta = 0$ and $\sin \theta = 1$ and find dt to be given by

$$(36) \qquad dt^2 = \frac{d\sigma^2}{w^2} = \frac{dr^2}{c^2 \left(1 - \frac{\alpha}{r}\right)^2} + \frac{r^2 \, d\phi^2}{c^2 \left(1 - \frac{\alpha}{r}\right)}$$

The relation between dr and $d\phi$ for a light ray is given by MØLLER [1952], XII (47)

$$(37) \qquad \left(\frac{d\rho}{d\phi}\right)^2 = \frac{1}{\Delta^2} - \rho^2 + \alpha\rho^3$$

which is transformed into

$$(38) \qquad dr^2 = d\phi^2 \left[\frac{r^4}{\Delta^2} - r^2 \left(1 - \frac{\alpha}{r}\right)\right]$$

We eliminate dr from (36) with the aid of (38) and get, after a reduction

$$(39) \qquad dt^2 = \frac{d\phi^2}{c^2} \frac{r^4}{\Delta^2 \left(1 - \frac{\alpha}{r}\right)^2} \qquad \text{or} \qquad dt = \frac{d\phi}{c} \frac{r^2}{\Delta \left(1 - \frac{\alpha}{r}\right)}$$

The sign chosen corresponds to light moving in a direction as in figure 1.

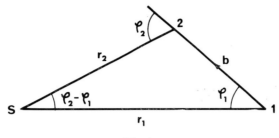

Fig. 1

We introduce a new variable instead of r by the relation (MØLLER [1952], XII (48))

(40)
$$\sigma = \Delta\rho(1-\alpha\rho)^{\frac{1}{2}}$$

Here we introduce an angle ψ, which differs from ϕ by terms of the order of α only, by

(41)
$$\sigma = \sin \psi$$

With (40) and (41) introduced into (39) we have

(42)
$$c \, dt = \Delta \frac{d\phi}{\sin^2 \psi}$$

From the relation between ϕ and ψ (MØLLER [1952] XII (50))

(43)
$$\phi = \sin^{-1} \sigma - \frac{\alpha}{\Delta}(1-\sigma^2)^{\frac{1}{2}} + \frac{\alpha}{\Delta} = \psi + \frac{\alpha}{\Delta}(1-\cos \psi)$$

We find by differentiation

(44)
$$d\phi = d\psi \left(1 + \frac{\alpha}{\Delta} \sin \psi\right)$$

Elimination of $d\phi$ from (42) with the aid of (44) leads to

(45)
$$c \, dt = \Delta \left(\frac{d\psi}{\sin^2 \psi} + \frac{\alpha \, d\psi}{\Delta \sin \psi}\right)$$

This equation is integrated directly to give

$$(46) \qquad c\,(t_2 - t_1) = \Delta\,(\cotan\,\psi_1 - \cotan\,\psi_2) + \alpha\,\ln\,\frac{\tan\,\dfrac{\psi_2}{2}}{\tan\,\dfrac{\psi_1}{2}}$$

From (40), written as

$$(47) \qquad \sigma = \Delta\rho\left(1 - \frac{\alpha\rho}{2}\right)$$

we derive, using (41)

$$(48) \qquad \left(r + \frac{\alpha}{2}\right)\sin\psi = \Delta$$

We see that the light ray is a straight line in the $(r + \alpha/2,\ \psi)$ plane. The first term on the right-hand side of (46) is the distance between the planets as measured in this plane. We shall denote this distance by a and find its relation to the corresponding distance b in the $(r,\ \phi)$ plane. The latter is the classically calculated distance between the two planets. The square of a is given by

$$(49) \quad a^2 = \left(r_1 + \frac{\alpha}{2}\right)^2 + \left(r_2 + \frac{\alpha}{2}\right)^2 - 2\left(r_1 + \frac{\alpha}{2}\right)\left(r_2 + \frac{\alpha}{2}\right)\cos\,(\psi_2 - \psi_1)$$

With the aid of (43) we find after some reduction

$$(50) \qquad a^2 = b^2 - 2\,\alpha\,(r_1 + r_2)\,\sin^2\frac{\phi_2 - \phi_1}{2}$$

We eliminate $(r_1 + r_2)$ from the small term with the aid of a relation from ordinary plane trigonometry (cf. fig. 1)

$$(51) \qquad r_1 + r_2 = b\,\frac{\sin\,\dfrac{\phi_2 + \phi_1}{2}}{\sin\,\dfrac{\phi_2 - \phi_1}{2}}$$

and get

$$(52) \qquad a = b - \alpha\,\sin\frac{\phi_2 + \phi_1}{2}\,\sin\frac{\phi_2 - \phi_1}{2}$$

or, from (46)

$$(53) \qquad c\,(t_2-t_1) = b - \alpha \sin \frac{\phi_2+\phi_1}{2} \sin \frac{\phi_2-\phi_1}{2} + \alpha ln \frac{\tan \dfrac{\phi_2}{2}}{\tan \dfrac{\phi_1}{2}}$$

What is observed is however the terrestrial proper time interval $\tau_2-\tau_1$. Assuming circular motion for the earth we get

$$(54) \qquad \tau_2-\tau_1 = \left(1 - \frac{2\,kM}{c^2\,r_1} - \frac{u_1^2}{c^2}\right)^{\frac{1}{2}} (t_2-t_1)$$

which in this case reduces to

$$(55) \qquad \tau_2-\tau_1 = \left(1 - 3\,\frac{kM}{c^2\,r_1}\right)^{\frac{1}{2}} (t_2-t_1) = \left(1 - \frac{3}{4}\,\frac{\alpha}{r_1}\right)(t_2-t_1)$$

The interplanetary distance is then measured as

$$(56) \qquad c\,(\tau_2-\tau_1) = b - \frac{3}{4}\,\alpha\,\frac{b}{r_1} - \alpha \sin \frac{\phi_2-\phi_1}{2} \sin\frac{\phi_2+\phi_1}{2} + \alpha ln \frac{\tan \dfrac{\phi_2}{2}}{\tan \dfrac{\phi_1}{2}}$$

where

$$(57) \qquad \frac{b}{r_1} = \frac{\sin (\phi_2-\phi_1)}{\sin \phi_2}$$

The angles ϕ_1 and ϕ_2 are found from r_1, r_2, and $(\phi_2-\phi_1)$ with the use of ordinary plane trigonometry.

The effect of the curvature of the orbit of the earth may naturally be included here. The time variation of b is given by

$$(58) \qquad b^2 = r_1^2 + r_2^2 - 2\,r_1\,r_2 \cos (\phi_2-\phi_1)$$

Here r_1 and r_2 are constants. The rate of change of the heliocentric angular distance between the planets is given by

$$(59) \qquad \frac{d}{dt}\,(\phi_2-\phi_1) = (kM)^{\frac{1}{2}} \left(\frac{1}{r_2^{\frac{3}{2}}} - \frac{1}{r_1^{\frac{3}{2}}}\right)$$

since the planets revolve in the same direction around the Sun. We find by straightforward calculations

$$(60) \qquad \frac{d^2 b}{d t^2} = \frac{r_1 r_2}{b} kM \left(\frac{1}{r_2^{\frac{3}{2}}} - \frac{1}{r_1^{\frac{3}{2}}} \right)^2 \cos \phi_1 \cos \phi_2$$

If we denote the light time that corresponds to the interplanetary distance b by Δt, then the deviation of $b(t)$ from a linear function makes the mean of the actual travel distances of the signals deviate from the distance at the mean of the times of emission and reception by the quantity

$$(61) \tfrac{1}{2} \frac{d^2 b}{d t^2} (\Delta t)^2 = \tfrac{1}{2} \frac{d^2 b}{d t^2} \left(\frac{b}{c} \right)^2 = \tfrac{1}{4} r_1 r_2 \, b\alpha \left(\frac{1}{r_2^{\frac{3}{2}}} - \frac{1}{r_1^{\frac{3}{2}}} \right)^2 \cos \phi_1 \cos \phi_2$$

We add this to (56). Then what would be found as the astronomical unit of length by a naïve user of classical theory is derived by multiplication with r_1/b:

$$(62) \qquad r_1 - \tfrac{3}{4} \alpha - \frac{r_1}{b} \alpha \sin \frac{\phi_2 + \phi_1}{2} \sin \frac{\phi_2 - \phi_1}{2} +$$

$$+ \frac{r_1}{b} \alpha ln \frac{\tan \dfrac{\phi_2}{2}}{\tan \dfrac{\phi_1}{2}} + \frac{\alpha}{4} \left[\frac{n_1}{r_2} - \left(\frac{n_2}{n_1} \right)^{\frac{1}{2}} \right]^2 \cos \phi_1 \cos \phi_2$$

Table I contains r_1 minus (62) calculated in kilometers as a function of the heliocentric distance between Venus and the earth with

$$r_2/r_1 = 0.7233, \quad \alpha = 2.954 \text{ km}$$

The function tabulated should be added to the classically determined astronomical unit in order to give the value corresponding to Schwarzschild's r.

The length of the astronomical unit changes with the form for the line element used. Thus the change to "isotropic" coordinates is equivalent to a reduction of r by the quantity

$$m = \frac{\alpha}{2} = 1.48 \text{ km}$$

in the weak-field region considered. This may be seen from the relation between Schwarzschild's r and the "isotropic" r' (MØLLER [1952] XI (85))

$$(63) \qquad r = r' \left(1 + \frac{m}{2 \, r'} \right)^2$$

TABLE I

$\phi_2-\phi_1$	Corr. (km)	$\phi_2-\phi_1$	Corr. (km)
0°	− 1.45	40°	+ 0.04
2°	− 1.43	50°	+ 0.07
4°	− 1.37	60°	+ 0.04
6°	− 1.27	70°	− 0.03
8°	− 1.15	80°	− 0.15
10°	− 1.02	90°	− 0.32
12°	− 0.89	100°	− 0.54
14°	− 0.76	110°	− 0.82
16°	− 0.64	120°	− 1.18
18°	− 0.53	130°	− 1.65
20°	− 0.43	140°	− 2.26
24°	− 0.27	150°	− 3.12
28°	− 0.15	160°	− 4.39
32°	− 0.06	170°	− 6.87
36°	0.00	180°	− ∞

REFERENCES

CLEMENCE, G. M., 1962, *A. J.*, **67**, 379.
GEISLER, P. A., 1963, *A. J.*, **68**, 715.
LEVI-CIVITA, T., 1937, *Am. J. of Math.*, **59**, 225.
MØLLER, C., 1952, *The Theory of Relativity* (Oxford University Press, Oxford).
PETTENGILL, G. H. *et al.*, 1962, *A. J.*, **67**, 181.

Solar activity and efflux of gases from the sun

E. R. MUSTEL

Astronomical Council, USSR Academy of Sciences

1 — Introduction

The efflux of gases from the Sun is one of the most fundamental properties inherent to some extent to the majority of stars.

Particles, which leave the Sun may be quite conventionally divided into two groups. To the first group belong particles (ions, electrons, neutral atoms) the kinetic energy of translational motion of which is relatively low. In this case we speak about those comparatively dense streams of solar gas, which are characterized by mass velocity of the order of a few hundred km/sec or maximum two-three thousands km/sec. To the second group belong particles of solar origin (ions and electrons), which are characterized by considerably higher energy and which are named solar cosmic rays.

In the present paper we shall consider mainly particles, which refer to the first group. These particles constitute practically all the mass of gases ejected from the Sun. But at the same time we shall use some information on cosmic rays, because it allows us to obtain some additional data on the physical properties of solar corpuscular streams.

Corpuscular streams, proceeding from the active regions of the Sun are the most interesting components of the solar corpuscular emission. However in order to understand a number of properties of these streams it is necessary to take into consideration their interaction with the practically continuous efflux of gases from the Sun, which is called the "solar wind".

2 — "Solar wind" from the undisturbed regions of the Sun

A large number of independent facts shows that the interplanetary space is filled with gases moving approximately radially from the Sun and even in the days when geomagnetic disturbances are practically absent (planetary geomagnetic index $K_p \approx 0$). This is considered as a confirmation of the hypothesis that even the *undisturbed* parts of the outer atmosphere of the Sun, i.e., the solar corona are practically a continuous source of corpuscular

Gauthier-Villars, Paris - Modern Astrophysics - 1967

emission which is called the "solar wind". We shall use further the term "solar wind" only when we speak about the outflow of gases from the undisturbed regions of the Sun. Let us discuss briefly the above mentioned facts. Many of them have been discussed in details by the author in his review papers [1964a, 1964b].

(a) Already the first direct measurements of the properties of the interplanetary plasma carried out by means of the Soviet space probes, (GRINGAUZ et al., 1960), pointed to the presence of a practically continuous efflux of the plasma moving from the Sun. The presence of a practically continuous outflow of the solar plasma (both in space and time), even during geomagnetically quiet days (when K_p is very small) was confirmed by measurements carried out by the American space probe Mariner 2 (SNYDER and NEUGEBAUER, 1963); and for other investigations see MUSTEL [1964a].

The velocity of gases composing the "solar wind" is within 250-400 km/sec (data from space probes), and the concentration of protons (which are the principal component of the "solar wind") is within $1 \, \text{cm}^{-3} - 10 \, \text{cm}^{-3}$.

(b) The fact of the presence of a practically continuous "solar wind" with the intensity, which almost does not change with the phase of the solar cycle, results from an analysis of the variations of the magnetic field recorded at the magnetic polar "caps" of the Earth during the periods when $K_p \approx 0$, (BOBROV et al., 1964) and figure 6 of the paper by MUSTEL [1964b].

(c) The same conclusion about the continuity of the "solar wind" results from an analysis of the rapid variations of the magnetic field of Earth (VINOGRADOV 1964). Rapid variations of Pc4 type are most characteristic for the geomagnetically quiet periods of time ($K_p \approx 0$). These variations can be observed mostly on that side of the Earth which is directed to the Sun (maximum at) (about 12^h of local geomagnetic time) and they possess periods from 45 to 150 sec.[1] All data available confirm the hypothesis that these rapid variations are only due to the "solar wind" (TROITSKAYA, 1964). The amplitude of rapid variations Pc 4, which is a direct indicator of the intensity of the "solar wind", does not also depend on the phase of solar activity, (BOLSHAKOVA, 1965).

(d) Cometary tails of type I which are always directed from the Sun also speak in favour of the continuous "solar wind" (BIERMANN, 1951, and ANTRACK et al., 1964).

Direct measurements of the interplanetary magnetic fields show, that the gaseous formations, of which the "solar wind" is composed, carry away

---

[1] *Most often these periods vary (for $K_p \approx 0$) between 60 and 90 sec.*

from the Sun the frozen-in magnetic fields, the strength of which at the Earth orbit is of the order of a few gammas (1 gamma $= 10^{-5}$ œrsteds), (MUSTEL, 1964a).

The configuration of magnetic fields, which characterize the "solar wind", is not quite clear yet. Some authors consider that the "solar wind" is composed of spirals arising in the space due to the rotation of the Sun. However an analysis of the data (for the angles ϕ, NESS, SEARCE et al. 1964) shows that the vectors of the strength of the interplanetary magnetic field for small K_p are most often directed from the Sun ($\phi \approx 180°$). It seems that this fact corresponds to the conception (MUSTEL, 1964a, page 168) according to which the "solar wind" is composed of comparatively isolated gaseous condensations (with frozen-in magnetic fields) which are elongated along the line Sun-Earth, see for instance figure 4 in the paper by DE JAGER [1962] and also the component (β) on figure 9 of MUSTEL [1964a]. Additional considerations are in favour of the same conclusion (the end of the present paper).

The most accepted hypothesis on the origin of the continuous "solar wind" is the hypothesis of the thermal dissipation of gases from the solar corona. The temperature of the solar corona is so high (of the order of 1 million degrees) that the corona cannot be in the state of hydrostatic equilibrium. It must be in the state of a dynamic continuous expansion. A rather brief description of this hypothesis is given by MUSTEL [1964a]; a systematic presentation of the hypothesis of the dynamic corona is given by PARKER [1963]. However it seems that not only processes of thermal dissipation of coronal gases must be taken into consideration here but other possible sources of continuous efflux of gases from the Sun may also play a certain role, see the next part of the paper and also MUSTEL (1964a, 1965a).

3 — Quasistationary corpuscular streams of gases proceeding from the active regions of the Sun

The analysis of geomagnetic data shows that geomagnetic disturbances reveal very often a recurrency with a 27-days period. These data show that there are some relatively stable sources of efflux of gases in the Sun. The efflux of gases from such a source we shall call "quasistationary corpuscular stream."

In 1942 the author came to the conclusion, (MUSTEL, 1944) that the sources of quasistationary streams are the *active regions* and that these streams are nearly radial,[2] at least on the declining branch of the cycle of solar

---

[2] For a more detailed discussion of radiality see MUSTEL, 1964a, page 184.

activity. In 1951-1953 the velocities of gaseous condensations composing these streams were estimated for the first time (MUSTEL, 1957); (MUSTEL and MITROPOLSKAYA, 1958) and were shown to be rather small (on the average 400 km/sec). At last in 1960 a conclusion was drawn (MUSTEL, 1960), that each quasistationary corpuscular stream proceeding from an active region (with its local magnetic fields) is an assembly of comparatively continuous magnetic "tubes"—rather extended coronal rays—which are very curved in space due to solar rotation and small plasma velocities.

It may be suggested that for comparatively small distances from the Sun the density of the kinetic energy E_k of the translational motion of gases in the tubes is less than the magnetic energy density E_h of the fields frozen in the tubes and in this case the "tubes" can be considered as "elastic". As for the larger distances, the curvature of the "magnetic" spirals depends mostly on the velocity of solar plasma ($E_k \gg E_h$).

Further development of the problem and particularly the investigation of the solar plasma by means of space probes confirmed all the above-mentioned conclusions. For instance, it was shown (MUSTEL, 1964a; 1965b), that a critical analysis of solar-geomagnetic relations as well as of extra-atmospheric data on the variation of cosmic rays of solar origin, completely confirms the hypothesis according to which the principal source of quasistationary corpuscular streams are the active regions. Then the above-mentioned small velocities of solar plasma of the order of 400 km/sec at the *commencement* of the geomagnetic disturbance were confirmed by means of space probes measurements (SNYDER and NEUGEBAUER, 1963; MUSTEL, 1964a). And at last, measurements of the interplanetary magnetic fields of solar origin (NESS, SEARCE and SEEK, 1964; NESS and WILCOX, 1964) confirmed directly the presence of magnetic spirals in the space. This fact as well as other ones discussed (MUSTEL, 1965b), speak in favour of the hypothesis (MUSTEL, 1960) according to which every quasistationary corpuscular stream is actually composed of rather curved coronal structures—"tubes" or "hoses", the magnetic field of which is characterized by a spiral structure.

In figure 1 we give a model of a quasistationary corpuscular stream taken from MUSTEL [1965b], which shows what form the tubes can have in different points of the section of the stream and how the velocities of the plasma are distributed inside the stream (from the leading front ff to the terminal boundary of the stream).

A very interesting fact resulting directly from measurements of the solar plasma (fig. 16 from SNYDER and NEUGEBAUER [1963] is that the commencement of the disturbance t_0 (the leading front ff of the stream) corresponds

to a relatively low velocity of the solar plasma comparable to the velocity
of gases of the solar "wind". Then, with the development of the disturbance
the velocity grows and in one to three days after the moment t_0 it reaches a
certain maximum. As it was shown by the author [1964a, 1964b], all this is

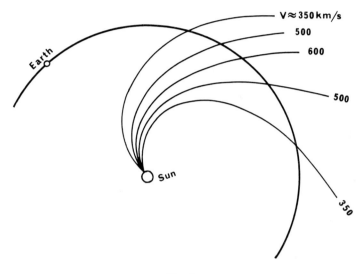

Fig. 1

due to the interaction of gases of a quasistationary stream with the gases
of solar "wind". As a result, a more dense leading front of the stream arises
which may produce in a number of cases a sudden commencement of
recurrent disturbances (MUSTEL, 1964b). We may point out that just this
fact was observed in October 7, 1962 (NEUGEBAUER and SNYDER, 1962) and
in December 2, 1964 (NESS, SEARCE and SEEK, 1964).

Our knowledge on the fine structure of quasistationary corpuscular streams
is rather poor. Some quantitative data on the fine structure (irregularities)
of interplanetary plasma are obtained by HEWISH, SCOTT and WILLS [1964].
However, the division of the plasma into streams and solar "wind" was not
done in this work. A model of a quasistationary stream, in which the force-
free magnetic fields play a noticeable part, is considered by MOGILEVSKY
[1962]. This problem waits for a detailed study.

The question about the origin of quasistationary corpuscular streams is a very important one. There are two possibilities here:

(a) The enhanced efflux of gases from the active regions is the process of a "dynamic dissipation of gases from these regions[3] and it may be connected with an increased temperature of the solar corona above the active region, see for details (MUSTEL, 1964a, pages 218-220).

(b) The efflux of gases from the active regions takes place as a result of the action (partially or wholly) of a certain comparatively continuous non-thermal process of electro-magnetic nature (MUSTEL, 1964a, 1965a, 1965b). In this connection we should like to indicate the intense turbulent motions of non-thermal character in the solar corona discovered quite recently (CHISHOLM and JAMES, 1964).

For the solution of this problem we should proceed from the fact that the principal factor, upon which the majority of physical processes depend in the active regions are their local magnetic fields. The process of the quasistationary efflux of gases from the active regions is connected also with the above mentioned processes. Indeed, a number of facts shows that a rather intense process of the efflux of gases from the active regions may continue for a rather long time, even after the moment, when the enhanced chromospheric (lines H and K, Ca^+ and H α) and coronal (lines 5303 and 6374 Å) emission from an active region disappears and only local magnetic fields are present in the latter. During this phase of existence of an active region ("magnetic tail") the temperature of coronal gases above it is the same as above the undisturbed regions of the Sun. But in spite of this, an active region may continue to create strong and sometimes even very strong geomagnetic recurrent disturbances during several rotations of the Sun, see corresponding examples in MUSTEL [1964a, 1965a, 1965b]. It must be stressed that we deal here with *continuous* efflux of gases from active regions. This is confirmed by the fact that the above mentioned geomagnetic disturbances are characterized as a rule by rather intense *rapid variations* of the magnetic field of Pc3 type, the very presence of which speaks in favour of a direct injections of condensations of solar plasma into the uppermost layers of the magnetosphere. This forces us to suggest that processes of the continuous efflux of gases of non-thermal character may also play an important part in the solar "wind".

---

[3] As well as in the case of the solar "wind".

4 — Ejection of gases from chromospheric flares

As it is known, a certain number of chromospheric flares is followed by the ejection of comparatively dense gases, moving from the Sun with the average velocities of the order of 1 000 km/sec. These *non-stationary* corpuscular streams give rise to sporadic geomagnetic disturbances. Regretfully it is not yet clear which chromospheric flares give rise to sporadic disturbances. Some authors consider that the probability of the rise of a sporadic disturbance depends on the fact whether the chromospheric flare is accompanied by the radio event of type IV or not. However if we relate chromospheric flares to sporadic disturbances, using quite objectively *all* phenomena connected with the flare, then the role of the radio event of type IV appears to be considerably smaller (MUSTEL and EGOROVA, 1965). At any rate, there are many quite clear cases, when chromospheric flares not followed by radio events of type IV created nevertheless sporadic geomagnetic disturbances.

In connection with this question we must not exclude the possibility that sometimes chromospheric flares do not create geomagnetic disturbances simply because ejected gases miss the Earth. In general the question of the solid angle Ω inside which gases are ejected is not clear yet (MUSTEL and EGOROVA, 1965). The phenomena of propagation of gases (from a chromo-chromospheric flare), which produce the H_α-line (ATHAY and MORETON, 1961), confirm the hypothesis that sometimes gases ejected from chromospheric flares may be ejected inside a rather wide solid angle Ω and even almost along the surface of the Sun. However, it seems that these cases are comparatively rare.

It may be suggested that the more intense a chromospheric flare is, the bigger the angle Ω is. And indeed gases ejected from a strong chromospheric flare possess enough energy to overcome the resistance of those gases (of the solar corona and of the interplanetary medium) which are on their way and thus to move inside a comparatively wide solid angle. At the same time there are reasons to think (MUSTEL, 1964c) that gases ejected from weak chromospheric flares can move along the spirals—"tubes"— of a quasistationary stream proceeding from an active region, which had created the chromospheric flare.

The problem of the thickness ΔR of the considered corpuscular streams, where the thickness is measured in the radial direction, is very interesting. The initial fact is that even rather strong chromospheric flares continue to exist for one or two hours while a mean duration of a sporadic geomagnetic disturbance amounts to about $1^d.5$. It seems that the most natural explanation of this fact is that a corpuscular stream created by a chromospheric flare is rather inhomogeneous, and that gaseous condensations composing it are moving from the Sun with somewhat different velocities. Taking into account the general trend of the development of an "average" chromospheric flare it is tempting to say that gases ejected at the beginning of the flare are characterized by the highest velocities and at the end of it—by the lowest ones. In this connection we expect that the thickness of the corpuscular stream ΔR must grow with time, while the stream recedes from the Sun. From this point of view the commencement of a sporadic disturbance is produced by the fastest gases of the stream and the end of the disturbance—by the slowest gases.

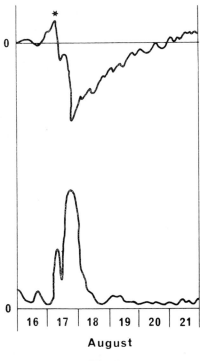

August

Fig. 2

The moment t_1 when the Earth enters a corpuscular stream can be found quite easily. It corresponds nearly to a sudden commencement of a sporadic disturbance. On the contrary the moment t_2 of the Earth's exit from the stream cannot be so definitely determined. A special investigation (MAISU-RADZE and MUSTEL, 1965) shows that this moment is fixed not by the end of the storm-time variation of a geomagnetic disturbance[4] but by the end of the geomagnetic disturbance recorded at high geomagnetic latitudes. The upper curve on figure 2 taken from the quoted paper is a storm-time variation of a sporadic geomagnetic disturbance observed in August 17-18, 1958 and the lower one gives variation of geomagnetic indices a_p at the polar cap.

Having the moments t_1 and t_2 as well as the mean moment of the chromospheric flare and supposing that the velocity of comparatively dense gases on their way from the Sun to the Earth's orbit is nearly constant, it is possible to calculate the velocities v_1 and v_2 corresponding to the "leading" and the "back" boundaries of the stream, and in this way to calculate the difference $\Delta V = v_1 - v_2$. It is found that for the above mentioned disturbance we have: $\Delta v \approx 860$ km/sec and $v_1 \approx 1660$ km/sec.

A model of a corpuscular stream given in figure 3 is constructed on the basis of these data. The magnitude of Ω is taken arbitrarily. Inhomogeneities

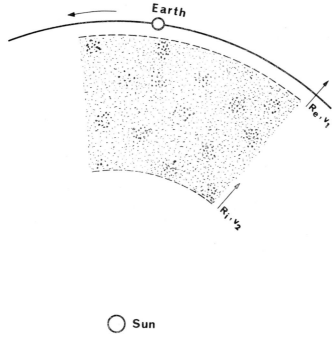

Fig. 3

[4] A storm-time variation is recorded at comparatively low geomagnetic latitudes and its "tail" part is probably a certain "inertial" effect of the Earth magnetosphere (MAISURADZE and MUSTEL, 1965).

in the structure of a corpuscular stream from a chromospheric flare are shown on this figure. The presence of such inhomogeneities results from the fact of the presence of synphase geomagnetic disturbances superimposed on the storm-time variation, (BOBROV 1961).

In conclusion we give a comparative analysis of some physical characteristics of plasma streams from the undisturbed regions of the Sun, of quasistationary plasma streams from the active regions and of non-stationary plasma streams from the chromospheric flares. In this connection it is necessary to note that the general property of gases composing these streams is that they are in the state of strong ionization.

Velocity

Gases of solar "wind" have the lowest velocity, ranging from 250 to 400 km/sec. The velocity of the radial motion of gases composing the quasistationary corpuscular streams amounts to 600-700 km/sec (SNYDER and NEUGEBAUER, 1963); the average velocity of gases ejected from chromospheric flares is about 1 000 km/sec, but can amount up to 2 000-3 000 km/sec (MUSTEL and EGOROVA, 1965).

Density of gases

Data on densities of gases composing the solar wind and quasistationary corpuscular streams speak in favour of the fact that these densities (on the Earth orbit) are of the same order, on the average a few protons in 1 cm^3; see values N for different velocities in figure 13 of SNYDER and NEUGEBAUER [1963].

Data on the densities of gases in the corpuscular streams from chromospheric flares are not available yet.

Magnetic fields

The strength of magnetic fields frozen-in the gases of the solar wind is the lowest, of the order of a few gammas, see, for instance, NESS, SEARCE and SEEK (1964). The strength of the magnetic field frozen-in quasistationary corpuscular streams is somewhat higher, up to 10-15 gammas. The strength of the magnetic field frozen-in the streams, ejected from chromospheric flares are on the average noticeably higher. According to COLEMAN et al. (1960) the magnetic field strength of the stream proceeding from a strong chromospheric flare was on April 1, 1960 about 50 gammas; the distance of gases from the Sun for which this field strength was measured was comparable to the Sun-Earth distance.

Differences among the three types of the streams are very essential in the frozen-in magnetic fields. As it was already said (analysis of angles ϕ) there are some reasons to consider that the solar "wind" is composed of comparatively isolated gaseous condensations with the frozen-in magnetic fields. This is confirmed also by an analysis of the rapid variations of the magnetic field of the Earth. It appears that the diurnal variation of those rapid variations, which are the most characteristic ones for the quiet periods of time (Pc4) and for sporadic disturbances (Pc1, Pc2), has approximately a noon maximum. At the same time the maximum in the diurnal variation of rapid variations Pc3, which are most characteristic for recurrent disturbances, is displaced to the earlier hours (BOLSHAKOVA, 1966). Such a displacement may arise only in the case when the interplanetary field has a spiral structure (WALTERS, 1964). Thus it can be expected that the solar "wind" has no spiral structure.

As to quasistationary streams from the active regions, they possess according to all data available (including those mentioned above) a clearly expressed spiral structure of magnetic fields, (MUSTEL 1964a, 1965b).

Finally, judging from all data the magnetic field frozen in corpuscular streams proceeding from chromospheric flares is of a comparatively chaotic character and in any case does not have a spiral structure (MUSTEL, 1964b).

5 — Presence of high energy particles (cosmic rays) in corpuscular streams

The presence of high energy particles trapped into the plasma streams (at the moment when they leave the Sun) and retained by the magnetic fields frozen in this plasma is one of the most characteristic properties of corpuscular streams. The conservation of such high energy particles is the most specific property of gases ejected from chromospheric flares. The presence of rapid variations of "pearl" type (Pc1) during and even a short interval before the geomagnetic disturbances confirms this. According to a number of considerations (TROITSKAYA, 1961, TROITSKAYA et al., 1962) the "pearls" are frequently connected with the presence of high-energy particles inside the stream. As to the quasistationary streams high-energy particles are present in these streams in a reduced amount (BRYANT et al., 1963, GREGORY and NEWDICK, 1964).

Here we have compared a few physical characteristics of the streams of three types. Additional data on this problem are given by MUSTEL [1964b].

REFERENCES

ANTRACK, D., BIERMANN, L. and LÜST, Rh., 1964, *Ann. Rev. of Astron. and Astr.*, **2**, 327.
ATHAY, R.C. and MORETON, G.E., 1961, *Ap. J.*, **133**, 935.
BIERMANN, L., 1951, *Zs. f. Ap.*, **29**, 274.
BOBROV, M.S., 1961, *Results of IGY, Ser. Solar Activity*, No. 1, 36.
BOBROV, M.S., KOROLEVA, N.F., NOVIKOVA, R.M., 1964, *Geomagnetism and Aeronomy*, **4**, 333.
BOLSHAKOVA, O.V., 1965, *Astr. Zh.*, **42**, no. 4, *Sov. Astron.*, **9**.
BOLSHAKOVA, O.V., 1966, *Geomagnetism and aeronomy*.
BRYANT, D.A., CLINE, T.L., DESAI, U.D., and McDONALD, F.B., 1963, *Phys. Rev. Lett.*, **11**, 144.
CHISHOLM, J.H. and JAMES, J.C., 1964, *Ap. J.*, **140**, 377.
COLEMAN, P.J., DAVIS, L. and SONETT, C.P., 1960, *Phys. Rev. Lett.*, **5**, 43.
DE JAGER, C., 1962, *Space Sc. Reviews*, **1**, 485.
GREGORY, J.B. and NEWDICK, R.E., 1964, *J. Geoph. Res.*, **69**, 2383.
GRINGAUZ, K.I., BEZRUKIKH, V.V., OZEROV, V.D., and RYBCHINSKY, R.E., 1960, *Doklady AN SSSR*, **131**, 1301.
HEWISH, A., SCOTT, P.F., and WILLS, D., 1964, *Nature*, **203**, 1214.
MAISURADZE, P.A. and MUSTEL, E.R., 1966, *Geomagn. and Aeron.* **6**, N6.
MOGILEVSKY, E.I., 1962, *Geomag. and Aeron.*, **2**, 48.
MUSTEL, E.R., 1944, *Doklady AN SSSR*, **42**, 117.
MUSTEL, E.R., 1957, *Astr. Zh.*, **34**, 120, *Sov. Astron.*, **1**, 124.
MUSTEL, E.R., 1960, *Astr. Zh.*, **37**, 403, *Sov. Astron.*, **4**, 386.
MUSTEL, E.R., 1964a, *Space Sci. Rev.*, **3**, 139.
MUSTEL, E.R., 1964b, *Astr. Zh.*, **41**, 777, *Sov. Astron.*, **8**, 619.
MUSTEL, E.R., 1964c, *Space Research*, **4**, 77.
MUSTEL, E.R., 1965a, *Astr. Zh.*, **42**, 276, *Sov. Astron.*, **9**, 215.
MUSTEL, E.R., 1965b, *Astr. Zh.*, **42**, 473, *Sov. Astron.*, **9**, 375.
MUSTEL, E.R. and EGOROVA, N.B., 1965, *Results of IGY, Ser. Solar Activity*, No. 2.
MUSTEL, E.R. and MITROPOLSKAYA, O.N., 1958, *Izvestia of the Crimean Astroph. Obs.*, **18**, 162.
NESS, N.F., SEARCE, C.S., SEEK, J.B., 1964, *J. Geoph. Res.*, **69**, 3531.
NESS, N.F., WILCOX, J.M., 1964, *Phys. Rev. Lett.*, **13**, 461.
NEUGEBAUER, M. and SNYDER, C.W., 1962, *Science*, **138**, 1095.
PARKER, E.N., 1963, *Interplanetary Dynamical Processes*, Intersc. Publ.
SNYDER, C.W. and NEUGEBAUER, M.N., 1963, *Space Research*, **4**, 89.
TROITSKAYA, V.A., 1961, *J. Geoph. Res.*, **66**, 5.
TROITSKAYA, V.A., 1964, *Proceedings of the Los Angeles IGY Symposium*, Part I, 485.
TROITSKAYA, V.A., BULATOVA, G.N., ALPEROVITCH, L.B., and MELNIKOVA, M.V., 1962, *Conf. J. Phys. Soc.*, **17**, *Suppl.* A-2, Kyoto, Japan.
VINOGRADOV, P.A., 1964, *Results of Investigations according to IGY Program, Ser. Geomag. Invest.* No. 6, 42.
WALTERS, G.K., 1964, *J. Geoph. Res.*, **69**, 1769.

Motion of zodiacal light particles

D. CLARKE*, MARK DAEHLER**, J. E. MACK†**, J. RING*, J. O. STONER, Jr.**

1 — Introduction

Although a considerable body of data on the zodiacal light has been collected during 280 years of critical observations, the phenomenon cannot be said to be well understood. The present state of knowledge of the subject, especially concerning the composition, sizes, and distributions of the scattering particles, has recently been summarized by ELSÄSSER [1963], INGHAM [1962-63], and BEGGS et al. [1964a, 1964b]. It is now thought that most of the light is scattered by solid particles rather than by electrons (BEGGS et al., 1964); particle density distributions (GIESE, 1962-63; BEARD, 1959) and mechanisms for producing and maintaining them (WHIPPLE, 1955) have been suggested.

Little direct experimental information is available on the orbits or modes of loss and replenishment of the particles responsible for the zodiacal light. A preliminary experiment (RING et al., 1964) has suggested that the orbits may not be Keplerian. Calculations of spatial distributions of particles in the solar system are usually made under the assumption that most of the zodiacal light is scattered from particles orbiting the sun rather than the earth, even though it is known that there is a dust blanket around the earth perhaps sufficiently dense to cause the gegenschein and to contribute a small part of the observed zodiacal light (INGHAM, 1962-63; GIESE, 1962-63; INGHAM, 1962; SONETT, 1963). Perturbations which may significantly influence the motions of small particles orbiting the sun include light pressure and the Poynting-Robertson effect, photo-electric charging with consequent electric and magnetic alignment and deflection, evaporation of the particles caused by solar electromagnetic and particle radiation, collisions among particles, and planetary gravitational perturbations (BEST and PATTERSON, 1962; DOLE, 1962; JENNISON and McDONNELL, 1964; INGHAM, 1964; PARKER, 1964). In the absence of definite information on particle orbits, the relative importances of these perturbations cannot be determined.

* University of Hull.
** University of Wisconsin.
Prof. Mack† is deceased on April 14, 1966.

Gauthier-Villars, Paris - Modern Astrophysics - 1967.

Several phenomena associated with the zodiacal light have only very tentative explanations at this time. The polarization appears to be too high to be explained by solid particle scattering (BEGGS, 1964b; WEINBERG, 1964). Occasional pulsations in the brightness of the zodiacal light have been observed (WEINBERG, 1964; BLACKWELL and INGHAM, 1961b; JONES 1854-1855). The deviation of the line of maximum brightness of the zodiacal light from the ecliptic may depend upon the observer's position (JONES, 1854-1855; DIVARI, 1959; PETERSON 1961; BLACKWELL and INGHAM, 1961a). It is possible that the particles responsible for the zodiacal light and part of the corona may luminesce under photon or corpuscular bombardment from the sun, filling in the absorption lines, and causing the zodiacal light brightness to vary.

Some of the advantages of observing from Mount Chacaltaya, Bolivia, have been listed by BLACKWELL and INGHAM [1961a]. In June, July, and August, 1964, an expedition from the University of Hull and the University of Wisconsin to Mount Chacaltaya made interferometric measurements on the profile of the Hβ absorption line in the morning and evening zodiacal light spectrum at a variety of elongations. We hoped to obtain data with sufficient photometric and wavelength precision to allow the determination of the velocity distributions of the dust particles. Given these distributions, one might be able to determine not only which perturbations are most important in the motion of the particles, but also the relative number of co-and contra-revolving particles and the most important processes involved in the production of the particles.

2 — The experiment

The following requirements were imposed upon the spectrometer: high luminosity, resolution of about 3 000, lightness, compactness, and simplicity of operation. The latter three considerations arose because of the remote location (part of the trip to the summit had to be made on foot), and because a crude hut and an erratic power supply were the only laboratory conveniences available at the summit.

The resulting spectrometer had as its resolving elements a Fabry-Perot interferometer and an interference filter. Scanning was accomplished by changing the gas pressure in the chamber containing the interferometer. The signal was detected by a photomultiplier; for the faintest signals (zodiacal light scans) individual photo-electron pulses were detected and counted electronically.

The optical system is shown in figure 1. An altazimuth-mounted mirror directed sky light from the desired direction directly into a Fabry-Perot étalon having 40 mm diameter free aperture. A diverging lens permitted the interference filter to be placed in a parallel beam; the lens following refocused the Fabry-Perot fringes in the plane of the 8 mm diameter aperture, where only 1/30 of the area of the central order was admitted to the photomultiplier.

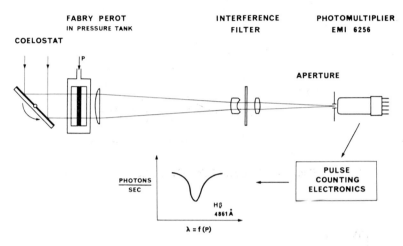

Fig. 1 — Schematic of the optical system used. The coelostat mirror was used in an altazimuth mounting.

The use of mica spacers about 40 microns thick provided Fabry-Perot transmission peaks spaced by about 30 Å; of these peaks only one was transmitted by the 6.5 Å passband of the interference filter. We achieved a finesse of about 20, thus using a spectrometer having a resolution of about 3 300, i.e. with a passband about 1.5 Å wide (see figure 2).

Sulfur hexafluoride was selected as the scanning gas because of its inertness, high refractive index, and low condensation temperature. A pressure range of 0 to 80 psi gauge (where 1 psi gauge = 51.7 torr pressure difference) provided a wavelength scanning range of 20 Å.

The photomultiplier was an especially selected EMI 6256 S, cooled with crushed CO_2.

With the apparatus described, a series of observations was made on the Hβ line in the morning and evening zodiacal light at various elongations. The usual procedure involved aligning the étalon while it was illuminated by a mercury germicidal lamp, then scanning the (narrow) Hβ line from a low-pressure discharge tube containing either dry hydrogen or water

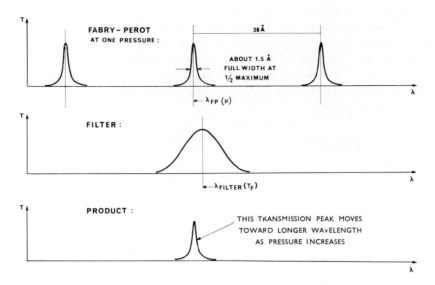

Fig. 2 — Characteristics of the spectrometer.

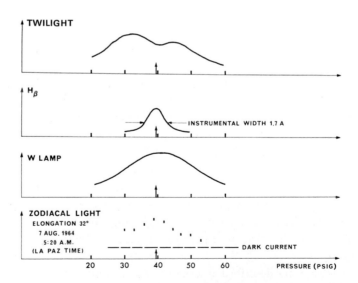

Fig. 3 — Results of typical scans taken. The rms noise on the continuous traces is of the order of the trace thickness. The fourth graph shows a sample of the raw data taken of the zodiacal light, uncorrected for the effects of filter profile and instrumental width. Uncertainties shown on the zodiacal light points are 2 statistical standard deviations estimated on the basis of number of pulse counts only. La Paz standard time is referred to longitude 60° W.

An estim

An exa
that their
that the
was foun
vicinity c
contained
region of

Re

Elvey a		
Dir		
Rev		
Henyey		
Elsässer		
Dir		
Rev		
Roach a		
Mean (r		
Integrate		
Ratio $\overline{G}$		
$\overline{G} + s$		
Ratio: $\overline{G}$		

vapor to determine the instrumental profile. A scan was made of the continuum from a tungsten lamp in order to check the position of peak transmission of the thermally sensitive filter profile; occasionally profiles would be taken of the Hβ region in twilight. All these scans were made with d.c. amplification of the photomultiplier output and continuous pressure-scanning. When the zodiacal light was allowed to enter the instrument, the d.c. amplifying circuit was replaced by pulse-counting equipment and counts were taken for 50- or 100-second intervals at fixed pressures. Typically, signals of 2000 pulses and dark counts of 650 pulses were recorded during 50-second counting periods. Because of the severe temperature fluctuations on the mountain top during the observations, it was necessary to bracket all zodiacal light scans with Hβ and tungsten light scans to enable corrections to be made for thermal drifts of the etalon and the filter. Figure 3 shows typical spectra obtained. About fifty such sets of scans were obtained of the morning and fifty of the evening zodiacal light during July and August, 1964.

3 — Results thus far

The analysis of the data obtained has not proved to be a simple task. The apparent difficulties lie in the fact that the instrumental width was comparable with or greater than the widths of interesting details and that the nature of these details varied. The following can be stated definitely now on the basis of the raw data alone: The Hβ line (or a line very close to it) appeared in emission in many of the scans made, in the direction of brightest part of the zodiacal light at an altitude of about ten degrees above the horizon. This was probably from the geocorona. (It is interesting to note here the study of the Hα emission of the night sky by SHCHEGLOV [1964].) The intensity of the emission in a 1.5 Å region centered at Hβ was comparable with that of the zodiacal light at an elongation of 30° in that region (cf. figure 3). The width of the emission was apparently not more than about 1 Å wide and the emission line was not shifted by more than about $\frac{1}{4}$ Å relative to the laboratory line; we hope to put more precise limits on the position, width and intensity after further analysis. Until the effects of Hβ emission have been isolated from the data, it will not be possible to obtain the desired information on the effects of scattering by the zodiacal light solid particles.

This work was supported in part by the U.S. National Science Foundation and in part by the research committee of the Graduate School of the

TABLE II *(continued)*

Sid. Time (deg.)	O	ZSA	G	Sid. Time (deg.)	O	ZSA	G
121	301	285	16	151	251	240	11
122	298	282	16	152	249	239	10
123	296	279	17	153	247	238	9
124	294	277	17	154	218	238	8
125	291	275	16	155	244	237	7
126	288	274	14	156	242	236	6
127	286	274	12	157	242	236	6
128	283	271	12	158	241	234	7
129	280	270	10	159	240	234	6
130	278	268	10	160	239	234	5
131	276	267	9	161	239	231	8
132	273	265	8	162	238	231	7
133	272	263	9	163	237	231	5
134	271	262	9	164	236	230	6
135	270	261	9	165	236	230	6
136	269	259	10	166	235	227	8
137	268	259	9	167	234	227	7
138	267	256	11	168	234	227	7
139	266	254	12	169	234	226	8
140	265	252	13	170	233	226	7
141	263	251	12	171	232	226	6
142	263	250	13	172	232	226	6
143	262	248	14	173	231	227	4
144	261	246	15	174	230	226	4
145	259	246	13	175	229	226	3
146	258	244	14	176	228	226	2
147	259	244	15	177	227	225	2
148	256	243	13	178	226	225	1
149	254	241	13	179	225	225	0
150	252	240	12	180	225	225	0

TABLE II *(continued)*

Sid. Time (deg.)	O	ZSA	G	Sid. Time (deg.)	O	ZSA	G
181	224	225	−1	211	218	215	3
182	223	224	−1	212	218	215	3
183	223	224	−1	213	218	214	4
184	222	224	2	214	218	215	3
185	222	223	1	215	218	215	3
186	222	223	−1	216	218	214	4
187	221	222	−1	217	218	214	4
188	220	222	−2	218	218	214	4
189	220	221	−1	219	218	214	4
190	220	221	−1	220	218	214	4
191	219	221	−2	221	217	213	4
192	218	220	−2	222	217	213	4
193	218	220	−2	223	217	214	3
194	218	220	−2	224	217	212	5
195	217	219	−2	225	217	212	5
196	217	219	−2	226	217	213	4
197	217	218	−1	227	217	211	6
198	216	218	−2	228	217	212	5
199	216	218	−2	229	217	212	5
200	216	218	−2	230	218	210	8
201	216	218	−2	231	218	210	8
202	216	217	−1	232	219	211	8
203	216	218	−2	233	220	211	9
204	217	218	−1	234	221	209	12
205	217	217	0	235	222	209	13
206	217	217	0	236	223	210	13
207	217	215	2	237	224	211	13
208	216	215	1	238	226	210	16
209	217	215	2	239	227	212	15
210	217	215	2	240	228	213	15

TABLE II *(continued)*

Sid. Time (deg.)	O	ZSA	G	Sid. Time (deg.)	O	ZSA	G
241	229	216	13	271	334	308	26
242	230	218	12	272	338	313	25
243	231	220	11	273	340	318	22
244	232	222	10	274	340	318	22
245	232	224	8	275	344	318	26
246	233	226	7	276	351	318	33
247	234	229	5	277	365	318	47
248	234	231	3	278	379	318	61
249	235	234	1	279	394	318	76
250	236	236	0	280	398	318	80
251	238	239	−1	281	389	318	71
252	239	242	−3	282	398	318	80
253	240	244	−4	283	391	317	74
254	242	246	−4	284	392	317	75
255	244	248	−4	285	377	317	60
256	246	250	−4	286	374	317	57
257	248	252	−4	287	375	347	58
258	253	256	−3	288	384	367	17
259	256	259	−3	289	387	377	10
260	260	263	−3	290	391	386	5
261	265	265	0	291	405	396	9
262	269	268	1	292	425	406	19
263	276	272	4	293	461	416	45
264	283	277	6	294	515	426	89
265	289	282	7	295	539	424	105
266	296	286	10	296	545	416	129
267	301	291	10	297	531	411	120
268	307	295	12	298	498	403	95
269	322	299	23	299	477	396	81
270	330	303	27	300	457	387	70

TABLE II *(continued)*

Sid. Time (deg.)	O	ZSA	G	Sid. Time (deg.)	O	ZSA	G
301	440	380	60	331	273	247	26
302	428	374	54	332	272	244	28
303	416	367	49	333	270	243	27
304	411	363	48	334	268	244	24
305	404	357	47	335	267	244	23
306	396	351	45	336	266	244	22
307	380	346	34	337	264	244	20
308	354	340	24	338	263	243	20
309	340	334	6	339	262	244	18
310	327	327	0	340	262	244	18
311	320	323	−3	341	261	244	17
312	315	314	1	342	260	244	16
313	307	307	0	343	260	243	17
314	300	300	0	344	260	244	16
315	298	292	6	345	259	243	16
316	296	284	12	346	259	244	15
317	295	277	18	347	258	243	15
318	294	274	20	348	258	243	15
319	292	272	20	349	257	244	13
320	290	271	19	350	257	243	14
321	288	269	19	351	256	244	12
322	287	266	21	352	255	243	12
323	285	265	20	353	255	243	12
324	283	262	21	354	255	243	12
325	282	259	23	355	255	243	12
326	280	258	22	356	255	243	12
327	279	255	24	357	256	244	12
328	277	253	24	358	256	244	12
329	276	251	25	359	257	245	12
330	274	248	26	360	259	245	14

Some comments are in order regarding the original data. First of all, one year of *zenith* observations enters into the analysis. Corrections for lower atmospheric extinction and scattering are minimized for zenith observations compared with those made at significant zenith distances. The interference filter used (wavelength of peak transmission 5 300 A) was selected to avoid bright airglow features, thus reducing the uncertainty due to airglow[4]. Individual bright stars traversing the zenith could be individually identified and "underdrawn".

The entries in Column 2 of Table II labelled "O", due to 153 nights of observations of the Haleakala[5] zenith, are ordered according to sidereal time in degrees. Between 15 and 30 separate readings enter into the mean values of O as listed.

In the third column, the quantity ZSA is based on the following studies. The zodiacal light, Z, is from a recent paper by SMITH, ROACH and OWEN [1965]. The integrated starlight term, S, is from Groningen 43 as reported by ROACH and MEGILL [1961]. The airglow term, A, is based on a graphical solution: in Table II, it has been assumed to be 37 S_{10}(vis) units. Corrections (-2 and -8) were applied to refined solutions in the latter part of the paper. The residual, G, is listed in the fourth column.

In figure 1 is shown a plot of O, ZSA and G versus sidereal time from Table II. The two Milky Way traversals are obvious at sidereal times 89° and 292°[6]. With regard to the galactic light, G, it is noted that (a) it tends to increase in the general vicinity of the Milky Way, (b) it has a physically impossible negative value near the center of the 89° Milky Way crossing, and (c) it is sensibly zero between the Milky Way traversals near sidereal time 200° when the Haleakala zenith is near the galactic pole, but positive near sidereal time 0° for which the galactic latitude is about 40°. This last point suggests the desirability of rearranging the data for G as a function of galactic latitude. In figure 2 we show, as a function of galactic latitude, the results of the present study together with those (a) of HENYEY and GREENSTEIN [1940] for the Taurus-Auriga (galactic longitude, $l^I = 140°$) and the Cygnus (galactic longitude $= 40°$) regions and (b) of ELVEY and ROACH [1937] based on a reading of their figure 11 for the galactic positions

---

4 Even with selected filters, there is an airglow component due to a so-called "continuum".

5 Mount Haleakala on the Hawaiian island of Maui is at an elevation of 10,026 feet above sea-level (3 056 meters). Its latitude is N 20°.7; its longitude W 156°.2.

6 The galactic longitudes (old system) of the two Milky Way crossings are, respectively, 156° and 23°.

of the Haleakala readings. The portions of the Milky Way which go through the Haleakala zenith are within 17° of the two regions measured by HENYEY and GREENSTEIN [1940]. All three investigations suggest the reality of a galactic light component in the general vicinity of galactic latitude zero.

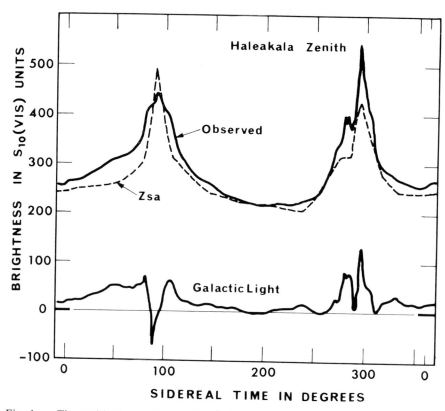

Fig. 1 — The zenith observations at Haleakala as a function of sidereal time, including (a) the observed brightness, (b) the adopted brightness of the zodiacal light, plus integrated starlight plus airglow and (c) the differential interpreted as galactic light.

The data of the present study have been averaged in groups of 10° of galactic latitude[7] (Table III and figure 3). An interesting feature of figure 3 is the evidence for a *maximum* in the ratio, galactic light/integrated starlight, at a galactic latitude of 35°. A reexamination of the data based on the use of the MW 301 star counts, as shown in figure 4, suggests a more or less

---

[7] The mean airglow was assumed to be 35 S_{10}(vis) units, 2 units lower than in the entries of Table 2. This makes the deduced galactic light systematically higher by 2 units.

Yerkes Observatory to assume the position of astronomer-in-charge of the
McDonald Observatory under the directorship of Professor STRUVE in 1935.
Dr. ELVEY and I spent the ensuing year (1935-1936) in the detailed analysis
of the accumulated photometric records which resulted in our paper in 1937
on the general subject of the light of the night sky with particular reference
to the galactic light.

Throughout the period during which Dr. ELVEY and I were working on the
paper, we were encouraged by Professor STRUVE who was, at the time,
himself actively studying the problem of diffuse scattering of light in the
galaxy. It should be noted that the last several pages of the ELVEY-ROACH
[1937] paper were contributed by Professor STRUVE.

REFERENCES

DE VAUCOULEURS, G., 1949, *Ann. d'Ap.*, **12**, 162.

DUFAY, J., 1957 (translated into English by A.J. Pomerans), *Galactic Nebulae and Interstellar Matter* (Philosophical Library Inc., New York).

ELVEY, C.T. and F.E. ROACH, 1937, *Ap. J.*, **85**, 213.

ELSÄSSER, H. and U. HAUG, 1960, *Zs. f. Ap.*, **50**, 121.

HENYEY, L.G. and J.L. GREENSTEIN, 1940, *Ann. d'Ap.*, **3**, 117 also, 1941, *Ap. J.* **93**, 70.

HOUTEN, C.J. VAN, 1961, *B.A.N.*, **16**, 1.

RHIJN, P.J. VAN, 1925, *Publ. Ast. Lab. Groningen*, No. 43.

ROACH, F.E., and L.R. MEGILL, 1961, *Ap. J.*, **133**, 228-242.

ROACH, F.E., HELEN B. PETTIT, and E. TANDBERG-HANSSEN, DOROTHY N. DAVIS, 1954,
Ap. J., **119**, 253.

ROACH, F.E. and M.H., REES, 1956, The Absolute Photometry of the Gegenschein,
The Airglow and the Aurorae (Pergamon Press, London,).

ROACH, F.E. and L.L., SMITH 1964, Absolute Photometry of the Light of the Night Sky,
NBS Technical Note 214.

SEARES, F.H., P.J. VAN RHIJN,, M.C., JOYNER, and M.L., RICHMOND, 1925, *Ap. J.*, **62**,
320, Mt. *Wilson Contribution* No. 301.

SMITH, L.L., F.E., ROACH and R.W., OWEN, 1965, *The Absolute Brightness of the Zodiacal
Light, Planetary and Space Science*, **13**, 207-217.

WANG SHIH-KY, 1936, *Pub. Obs. Lyon*, **1**, fasc. 19.

WEINBERG, J.L., 1963, *Photoelectric Polarimetry of the Zodiacal Light at* λ 5300, PhD.
dissertation, University of Colorado.

The surface brightness of dark nebulae

BEVERLY T. LYNDS

Steward Observatory, University of Arizona

In 1919 E. E. BARNARD wrote that the object B 92, one of the dark markings in his catalogue, appeared visually to be feebly luminous. He suggested that the obscuring nebulae seen projected against the rich star fields of the Milky Way appeared black only by contrast and may not necessarily be devoid of light.

This problem of the surface brightnesses of dark nebulae was extensively studied by Struve and his associates at the Yerkes Observatory from the period 1936-1940. An attempt was made by STRUVE and ELVEY [1936] to measure the magnitude difference between the surface brightness of a dark nebula and that of the sky background. The resulting fact that the magnitude difference was quite small led the authors to suggest the existence of scattered starlight produced by the particles in interstellar space. The following year Struve continued this analysis and pointed out that many of the Barnard objects had very dark cores with rims which appeared to be brighter, although they were still opaque to any background starlight. From a comparison of the variation in the surface brightness across an opaque cloud, STRUVE [1937] concluded that the albedo of the grains comprising the nebula must be relatively high, ranging from 0.5 to 1.0, and that the particles must scatter radiation preferentially in the forward direction.

In order to interpret the observations properly it is necessary to have some quantitative measure of the luminosity of the night sky. The analysis of ELVEY and ROACH, [1937] provided an estimate of this datum, and indicated further evidence for the presence of one component of this luminosity due to starlight scattered by the interstellar medium. This latter component was studied in more detail by HENYEY and GREENSTEIN [1941], who used the Fabry photometer constructed by STRUVE and ELVEY for their observations of the dark nebulae.

The basic approach to the problem of scattering in a diffuse nebula was outlined by SCHOENBERG [1929]. Consider an idealized nebula to be a uniform plane-parallel slab of scattering particles (Fig.1). Let: R = thickness of nebula; σ = scattering cross-section of the particles; n = no. of scattering particles/cm^3.

Gauthier-Villars, Paris - Modern Astrophysics - 1967.

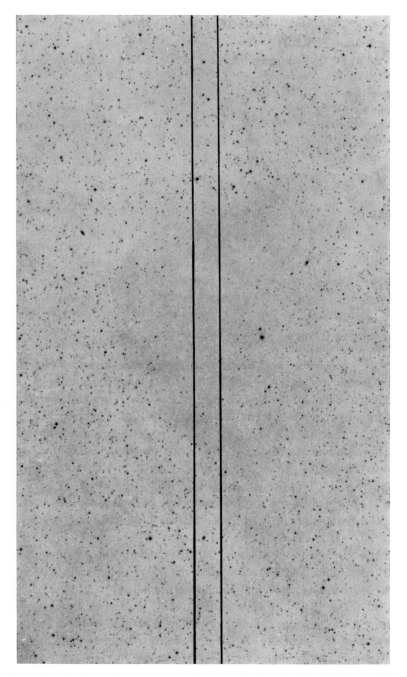

Fig. 3 — (a) The dark nebula # 1780 as photographed by the 48-inch Palomar Schmidt telescope in red light.

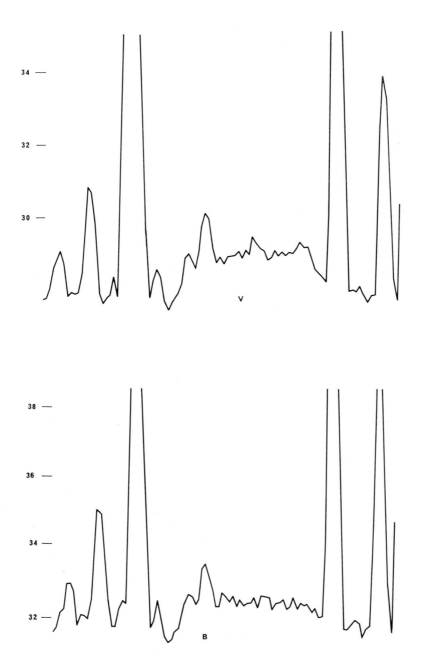

Fig. 3 — (b) and (c) Brightness of # 1780 as measured with pulse counting equipment at Kitt Peak National Observatory; (b) through the V filter and (c) through the B filter. The diaphragm covered the region of the nebula marked on Figure 4(a) as the object was allowed to drift across the field of view.

to drift across the field of view. B and V measures were made using integration times of 4 seconds. Figures 3 (*b*) + (*c*) shows the results of the mean of five such scans. The nebula was found to have a surface brightness 0.050 mag. greater than the sky in V and 0.026 mag. in blue. The values are:

$$V_{neb} = 21.85 \ mag/\square'', (B-V)_{neb} = +0.93$$

$$V_{sky} = 21.90 \ mag/\square'' \ (B-V)_{sky} = +0.91$$

A single scan across the object was made by Dr. Frank Low and the author, using the 21-inch telescope of the Catalina station of the Lunar and Planetary Laboratory. Preliminary results indicate that the nebula is approximately 10% brighter than the sky in the R color, and slightly less than 40% through the I filter (JOHNSON, 1963). It may well be that the nebula becomes progressively more transparent from R to I, and therefore we should subtract out the contribution of the stars shining through the nebula. No estimate of this correction was made. Obviously more data are needed in these wavelength regions.

On the basis of our simple model we would conclude that the object is a cloud illuminated by the general galactic radiation field and is at a distance of about 800 parsecs from the earth. This conclusion, however, is not consistent with the star count data, which limits the distance to about 200 parsecs. Furthermore, if the object were at a distance of 800 parsecs, then it would lie about 500 parsecs above the galactic plane and therefore our assumption of an isotropic radiation field is no longer valid.

STRUVE and ZEBERGS [1962] have discussed other possible sources of the illumination of the nebula including the possibility of the K-type stars in the vicinity of the nebula; or Antares, located some 40° from it, or the sun itself.

The author wishes to express her thanks to Drs. C. R. LYNDS and FRANK Low for their generous assistance in the observations of # 1780, and to Dr. R. J. WEYMANN for many helpful discussions. The author is greatly indebted to Dr. OTTO STRUVE for his continued interest in the study of dark nebulae and for the many years during which the author profited by his association.

REFERENCES

ALLEN, C. W., 1964, *Astrophysical Quantities*, (2nd ed.; University of London; The Athlone Press).
CHANDRASEKHAR, S. and BREEN, F. H. 1948, *Ap. J.*, **107**, 216.

ELVEY, C.T. and ROACH, F.E., 1937, *Ap. J.*, **85**, 213.

GEHRELS, A.M., 1965, *private communication.*

HENYEY, L.G., 1937, *Ap. J.*, **85**, 107.

HENYEY, L.G. and GREENSTEIN, J.L., 1941, *Ap. J.*, **93**, 70.

JOHNSON, H.L., 1963, *Basic Astronomical Data*, ed. K. Strand, (Chicago: University of Chicago Press) p. 218.

LYNDS, B.T., 1962, *Ap. J. Suppl.* **7**, 1.

LYNDS, B.T., 1965, *P.A.S.P.*, No. 455, **77**, 134.

SCHOENBERG, E., 1929, *Handbuch der Astrophysik*, **2**, (1st. ed.; Berlin: Julius Springer) p. 35.

STRUVE, 0., 1937, *Ap. J.*, **85**, 194.

STRUVE, O. and ELVEY, C.T., 1936, *Ap. J.*, **83**, 162.

STRUVE, O. and ZEBERGS, V. 1962, *Astronomy of the* 20th *Century*, (1st ed.; New York: Macmillan Company) pp. 399-401.

A note on the MK classification system

W. W. MORGAN

Yerkes Observatory, University of Chicago

The classification system of the Yerkes Atlas of Stellar Spectra rests on a group of standard stars which, in effect, define the system itself. With the subdivision of luminosity class I (supergiants) into I*a*, and I*b*, the number of luminosity classes used between spectral types B 0 and K 2 is six; for types later than K 2, luminosity class IV (subgiants) is as a rule not used.

A group of "non-peculiar" spectra assigned to one specific spectral type and luminosity class appeared to be uniform in appearance, in classifications carried out earlier; however, at the present time, due to improvements in plate quality— and to further experience—we are now able to observe a considerable range in spectroscopic appearance. This is especially true for main-sequence stars of classes B 0-B 3 inclusive.

A very interesting and spectacular example of the range in appearance among spectra of stars of the same type is shown when we compare the brighter stars of the Orion Nebula cluster with the neighboring clustering associated with the star *ι* Orionis. The latter is immediately south of the Orion Nebula cluster— and is a part of the Sword subsystem of the Orion association to which the nebula cluster itself belongs. Investigation by Dr. KERSTIN LODÉN and the writer has shown that the *ι* Orionis group exhibits a well-defined main sequence; the B 0-B 3 stars in this clustering have a "normal" spectroscopic appearance— that is, they resemble closely the standard stars illustrated in the Yerkes Spectral Atlas. On the other hand, the O 6-B 2 members of the Orion Nebula cluster have a different appearance, in respect to the hydrogen absorption lines: the latter are very strong and broad, and differ greatly from the ordinary spectral standards.

This peculiarity of the brightest members of the Orion Nebula cluster was noted many years ago at the Yerkes Observatory; however, it had been considered to be a unique phenomenon— and therefore not of particular interest in spectral classification. Recently, however, in the course of an investigation being carried out jointly with Dr. W. A. HILTNER, a number of other clusters containing this spectral peculiarity have been noted; and the situation can be described about as follows: There are a number of B stars of similar spectral type and luminosity which differ spectroscopically from

Gauthiers-Villars, Paris - Modern Astrophysics - 1967.

each other in a manner not explainable in terms of differing temperature or luminosity— or of axial rotation. The Orion Nebula cluster phenomenon is only one example of this "fuzziness" within a single spectral compartment; a similar fuzziness has been observed among main-sequence stars of classes F 8-G 2.

We seem to have arrived at a stage where the MK spectral type and luminosity class are not by themselves completely satisfactory for the precise classification of what have been considered "normal" stellar spectra; and the problem is to devise a modification which would be more satisfactory. For this purpose, we now introduce a supplementary hierarchy, which we label "coeval sequences". A coeval sequence is a series of spectra of stars belonging to a single cluster—or of a group of stars possessing similar ages.

The broad hydrogen lines observed in certain clusters cannot be interpreted in terms of the ordinary relationship between luminosity and Balmer line intensity. The actual position of such stars with respect to normal main sequences is still uncertain, because of the uncertainty in the correction of luminosities for interstellar absorption. However, it can be stated with some certainty that such stars lie either above the normal main sequence—or along it; at present, the latter possibility seems preferable, in the light of some recent very fine work on the law of interstellar absorption by H. L. JOHNSON.

It is known from the work of VYSSOTSKY and SKUMANICH that the G-band of CH is enhanced in the spectra of certain stars which we would now consider to belong to a very old population. A similar effect was noted some time ago in the case of certain G 0 V standard stars on the MK system. More recently, investigations by Hiltner and the writer indicate the possibility that such an effect is present in star clusters of differing evolutionary stages. While the relationship is not as close as some others, it seems that, on the average, the younger the cluster, the weaker the CH absorption.

Other spectroscopic characteristics have been noted which seem to be peculiar to stars or clusters of certain evolutionary stages; and the conclusion now seems definite that a considerable increase in the accuracy of spectral classification can be achieved by the inclusion of an additional stage in the classification process. This would consist in the adding of a stage in which the star being classified would be compared with a standard series of coeval sequences. Such an additional step will add to the complexity of the classification system, but the additional information thus gained would seem to justify the cost.

Critère photométrique de population stellaire, tiré de la photométrie en six couleurs de l'observatoire Lick

R. CANAVAGGIA

Observatoire de Paris

1 — Résumé

Un critère photométrique infrarouge de population stellaire, tiré des quatre couleurs les plus rouges de la photométrie en six couleurs de l'Observatoire Lick, est comparé au critère m_1 de la photométrie $uvby$ de Strömgren pour 23 étoiles de la séquence principale, de F 8 V à G 2 V.

Les indications que l'on peut tirer des couleurs les plus rouges de la photométrie en six couleurs de l'observatoire Lick, ou de couleurs équivalentes, au point de vue de la teneur en métaux des étoiles, ont fait l'objet de plusieurs publications récentes. Citons seulement : BAHNG [1958], CODE [1959], KRON [1960], PAGEL [1963], CANAVAGGIA et MIANES [1964].

Le point de vue adopté ici est le suivant:

Pour 23 naines ou sous-géantes de F 8 V à G 2 V, un critère de composition chimique basé sur les quatre couleurs les plus rouges de l'observatoire Lick est comparé au critère m_1 de Strömgren.

Rappelons les longueurs d'onde des deux systèmes de photométrie en question :

Longueurs d'onde effectives de la photométrie en six couleurs de l'observatoire Lick (bandes larges) :

U	V	B	G	R	I
3530	4220	4880	5700	7190	10300

Longueurs centrales de la photométrie $uvby$ de Strömgren (bandes de largeur moyenne) :

u	v	b	y
3500	4110	4670	5470

Les longueurs d'onde de la photométrie $uvby$ sont assez voisines des longueurs d'onde effectives les plus courtes de la photométrie en six couleurs.

Gauthier-Villars, Paris - Modern Astrophysics - 1967.

2 — Matériel

Les 23 étoiles considérées ici figurent en même temps dans la table II de Stebbins et Kron [1956][1] et dans le catalogue de Strömgren et Perry, plus exactement : ce sont les étoiles de la table II de Stebbins et Kron [1956] qui figurent dans la table I de Wilson et Skumanich [1964] avec un b-y compris entre 0,325 et 0,425, à l'exception de η Boo (écartée en tant que binaire spectroscopique). Ces étoiles sont toutes considérées par Wilson et Skumanich comme membres légitimes de la séquence principale (4071/4077 $\geqslant$ 2), à l'exception de 44 And (4071/4077 = 1,2). Parmi ces étoiles : cinq figurent dans la table III de Pagel [1963] (« old subgiants » within 25 pc); trois figurent dans le catalogue de Roman [1955]; quatre ont une émission H et K suivant Wilson et Skumanich [1964]; six sont analysées dans Wallerstein [1962] au point de vue de la composition chimique.

Les 23 étoiles sont données dans la table I où les colonnes ont la signification suivante : Numéro d'ordre. Numéro d'ordre dans le catalogue Strömgren et Perry. Numéro d'ordre du HD. Nom. Classification spectrale dans le système MK quand l'étoile figure dans le catalogue de Jaschek, Conde et de Sierra [1964]. Indice B-R et couleur I de la photométrie en six couleurs. Indice b-y et critère m_1 de la photométrie $uvby$, émission de H et K et rapport [Fe/H] dans les ouvrages cités, numéro du catalogue de Roman. Les sous-géantes de la liste de Pagel [1963] sont en italique dans les colonnes 2 et 3.

Comme l'examen annoncé plus haut se réduit à la comparaison de deux graphiques, il importe que ces graphiques soient compris, et pour cela j'ouvre une parenthèse pour introduire le diagramme en six couleurs de la figure 2.

3 — Diagramme en six couleurs dans le cas du rayonnement de Corps Noir

La figure 1 a pour but de faire comprendre par l'image, sur l'exemple du rayonnement de Corps Noir, comment ce genre de diagramme s'introduit très naturellement en photométrie multicolore.

Considérons, dans la loi du rayonnement de Corps Noir, la fonction qui seule joue un rôle en photométrie :

$$\log_{10} b_\nu = \log_{10} \left[e^{c\theta\nu} - 1 \right]^{-1}$$

---

[1] C'est dire que les six couleurs de ces étoiles sont données dans Stebbins et Whitford [1945] ou dans Stebbins et Kron [1956].

N°	Strömgren Perry= n°	HD	Nom	Sp.	B-R	I	b-y	m_1	H/K	[Fe/H]	Roman
1	1 081	199 960	11 Aqr	G 1 V	−0,04	+0,13	0,406	0,209			
2	490	72 905	π¹ UMa	G 0 V	−0,04	+0,11	0,390	0,206	3		
3	620	95 128	47 UMa	G 0 V	−0,04	+0,11	0,392	0,203			
4	293	34 411	γ Aur	G 0 Vst [1]	−0,05	+0,13	0,389	0,206	2	+0,22	
5	332	39 587	χ¹ Ori	G 0 V	−0,05	+0,12	0,380	0,193			
6	565	84 737	HR 3881	G 1 V [2]	−0,06	+0,12	0,390	0,203			
7	850	141 004	λ Ser	G 0 Vst [3]	−0,06	+0,17	0,385	0,199			
8	61	10 307	HR 483	G 2 Vst	−0,08	+0,11	0,389	0,203		+0,20	72
9	138	19 373	ι Per	G 0 Vst [4]	−0,08	+0,13	0,376	0,201		+0,14	376
10	855	142 373	χ Her	F 9 Vst [5]	−0,09	+0,13	0,381	0,151			
11	1 039	190 406	15 Sge	G 1 V	−0,10	+0,14	0,389	0,197			
12	706	109 358	β CVn	G 0 Vst	−0,10	+0,16	0,385	0,182			
13	712	110 897	10 CVn	G 0 V	−0,10	+0,09	0,375	0,150	2	−0,32	296
14	38	6 920	44 And	F 8 V	−0,11	+0,10	0,390	0,168			
15	739	115 383	59 Vir	F 8 V [6]	−0,12	+0,17	0,376	0,191			
16	1 191	221 356	HR 8931	—	−0,13	+0,20	0,350	0,162			
17	735	114 710	β Com	G 0 Vst	−0,14	+0,21	0,372	0,193	1	+0,19	
18	666	102 870	β Vir	F 8 Vst [7]	−0,15	+0,21	0,354	0,190		+0,33	
19	828	136 064	HR 5691	F 8 V	−0,15	+0,18	0,350	0,177			
20	1 072	198 084		F 8 IV	−0,15	+0,22	0,353	0,197			
21	1 030	187 691	o Aql	F 8 V v	−0,16	+0,20	0,356	0,188			
22	1 083	200 790	4 Eql		−0,16	+0,18	0,350	0,170			
23	604	90 839	36 UMa A	F 8 Vst	−0,18	+0,22	0,341	0,172			

Remarques. — Le catalogue de la Plata donne aussi : [1] G 2 IV-V, G 0 IV. — [2] G 2 V, G 3 V. — [3] G 0,5 V, G 2 V. — [4] G 4 V. — [5] F 8 V, G 0 IV. — [6] G 0 V. — [7] F 7 V.

Cette fonction est symétrique en θ et v. Sa dérivée par rapport à v (ou par rapport à θ) est sensiblement égale à $-1,24\,\theta$ (ou à $-1,24\,v$).

La première dérivée a donné lieu, pour le rayonnement des étoiles, à la considération du gradient (dans certains domaines limités de longueur d'onde) et plus généralement à des diagrammes du genre de ceux de JOHNSON [1964] ou de CODE [1959].

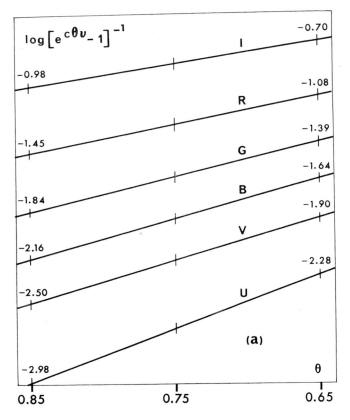

Fig. 1a — Formation du diagramme en six couleurs pour le rayonnement de Corps Noir, pour θ compris entre 0,85 et 0,65.

La variation par rapport à θ peut être utilisée à la formation de diagrammes de type différent, qui, dans certains cas, peuvent être d'un emploi plus commode.

Dans la figure 1a, $\log b_v$ est porté en fonction de θ pour six valeurs de v (inverses des longueurs d'onde effectives de la photométrie en six couleurs). Il en résulte six lignes (pratiquement six droites de pente $1,24\,v$).

Figure 1*b*. Chaque ligne est rapportée, comme origine, à la valeur de log b_v pour $\theta = 0,75$.

Figure 1*c*. Toutes les ordonnées ont été multipliées par—2,5. De plus, sur chaque verticale, elles ont été rapportées, comme origine des ordonnées, à la moyenne des trois couleurs B, G, R (moyenne qui, ici, est toujours

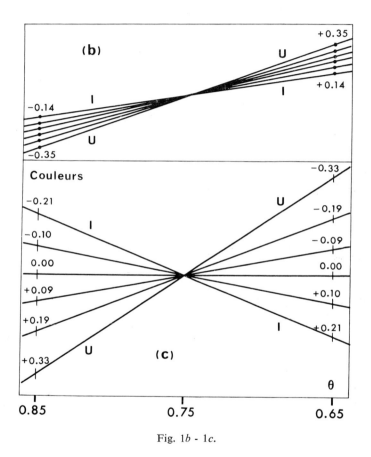

Fig. 1*b* - 1*c*.

sensiblement zéro). Les six chiffres correspondant à une valeur de θ sont alors : les « couleurs » du Corps Noir à la température considérée, rapportées au Corps Noir de température $\theta = 0,75$ comme origine.

Les six couleurs forment un graphique à six branches.

A droite (CN plus chauds que le CN de référence), tous les indices sont négatifs. A gauche (CN plus froids), tous les indices sont positifs.

4 — Diagramme en six couleurs des 23 naines ou sous-géantes considérées ici

Pour grouper les couleurs des étoiles comme on vient de grouper celles du Corps Noir, il faut convenir de porter quelque chose en abscisses. Si les étoiles formaient un groupe homogène, on pourrait espérer qu'en portant en abscisses l'indice G-I, ou B-R (avec une échelle convenable), on obtiendrait un diagramme rappelant celui de la figure 1c.

Pour les 23 étoiles considérées ici, il faut s'attendre à un résultat plus compliqué, quel que soit l'indice choisi. Nous avons choisi de porter en abscisse l'indice B-R (les diagrammes ainsi obtenus sont d'un emploi commode dans les questions de rougissement interstellaire). Ainsi le diagramme de la figure 2 représente les six couleurs des 23 étoiles de la table I, par ordre de B-R de plus en plus négatifs (du n° 1 à gauche au n° 23 à droite).

Pour l'ensemble des étoiles, les couleurs B, G, R s'alignent assez bien en trois branches. Cela vient, naturellement, de l'abscisse choisie, et aussi de ce que la configuration des couleurs R, G, B n'est pas très différente d'une étoile à l'autre.

Les couleurs U et V sont beaucoup plus dispersées (cf. paragraphe suivant).

En ce qui concerne la couleur I : une dizaine de points sont alignés suivant une ligne pointillée qui va aboutir, en bas à droite, à un petit carré qui représente la couleur I de l'étoile n° 36 des Hyades ($+18°$ 629, F 6 V), obligeamment communiquée par Mlle J. ROUSSEAU[2]. Tout les autres points (sauf λ Ser) se placent au-dessus de la ligne[3], le plus élevé étant celui qui correspond à la sous-naine 10 CVn.

Une interprétation vient tout de suite à l'esprit : à température égale (c'est-à-dire sensiblement à indice R-I égal), les étoiles déficientes en métaux ont un indice B-R plus négatif que les étoiles de composition normale (la couleur B étant moins affectée par les raies d'absorption). Elles figurent dans la diagramme à côté d'étoiles plus chaudes qu'elles. Mais leur indice R-I reste celui d'une étoile froide. Les étoiles déficientes en métaux se manifestent

---

[2] Mlle Rousseau, de l'Observatoire de Lyon, travaille en ce moment, suivant l'exemple donné par les astronomes de l'observatoire Yerkes, à constituer une séquence principale des Hyades en six couleurs, qui permettra de préciser la notion de critère infra-rouge de population stellaire.

[3] Remarquons que la ligne pointillée, prolongée vers la gauche, passe bien au-dessous de l'origine des coordonnées (marquée d'une croix). Cela n'a rien de surprenant si l'on pense que les couleurs définies par STEBBINS et WHITFORD [1945] sont rapportées, comme étoile origine, à une étoile fictive, moyenne de 10 étoiles, allant de dG 0 à dK 2, et comprenant 3 étoiles du catalogue de ROMAN [1955]. Il y a donc quelque chose d'arbitraire dans la façon dont chaque branche du diagramme est localisée en ordonnée. (Pour les trois étoiles les plus froides (à gauche), la branche B passe au-dessous de la branche G.).

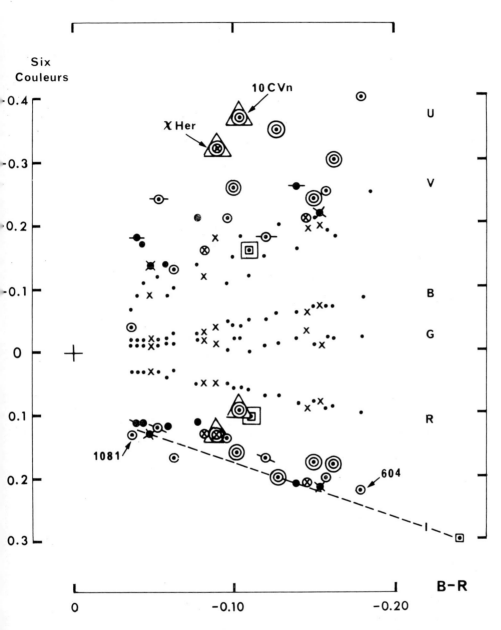

Fig. 2 — Couleurs I, R, G, B, V, U des étoiles de la table I. En abscisses, l'indice B-R. En ordonnées, de bas en haut, les couleurs de I à U. Les couleurs I et U sont représentées, pour chaque étoile, par le même signe que dans la figure 3. Pour les cinq sous-géantes, les couleurs R, G, B , U sont représentées par des croix. Pour les quatre étoiles qui ont une émission H et K de WILSON et SKUMANICH, le signe représentatif est traversé par une petite ligne.

donc, dans le diagramme, par un « excès de I », excès apparent bien entendu, puisqu'il s'agit en fait d'un excès de rayonnement dans la couleur B.

Cet « excès de rayonnement infrarouge » qui accompagne, chez les sous-naines, l'excès de rayonnement violet et ultraviolet (quand on se place, par exemple, à indice B-V égal) a été signalé et interprété par CODE, et est représenté dans la figure 1 de CODE [1959].

Mianes et moi avons signalé que, dans la photométrie en six couleurs, il est difficile de distinguer cet effet de composition chimique de l'effet de l'absorption interstellaire, qui se traduit également, à couleurs intermédiaires égales, par un excès de rayonnement rouge, violet et ultraviolet.

5 — La dispersion des points U et V selon la photométrie *uvby* de Strömgren

Les idées directrices de la photométrie *uvby* (voir, par exemple, *Stars and stellar Systems III*, p. 123) rendent compte de la dispersion que l'on rencontre dans les couleurs V et U de la figure 2.

En effet, on doit s'attendre à trouver sur ce diagramme :

1. Des naines de composition chimique normale (voisine de celle du Soleil) et non encore évoluées. Ces naines ont beaucoup d'ultraviolet parce que leur discontinuité de Balmer est petite. Ce sont, par exemple, π^1 UMa et β Com (n° 2 et 17, deux étoiles qui ont une émission Het K selon WILSON et SKUMANICH).

2. Des naines ou sous-géantes de composition chimique normale mais évoluées. Ce sont par exemple les sous-géantes λ Aur et 198 084 (N° 4 et 20).

3. Des étoiles plus ou moins déficientes en métaux.

Les étoiles 2 se distinguent des étoiles 1, dans la photométrie *uvby*, par le critère :

$$c_1 = (u\text{-}v) - (v\text{-}b)$$

qui est une mesure de la discontinuité de Balmer. Dans la figure 2, les étoiles 2 se distinguent des étoiles 1 parce que leur couleur U est moins élevée au-dessus de la couleur V.

Les étoiles 3 se distinguent des étoiles 1 et 2 par le critère

$$m_1 = (v\text{-}b) - (b\text{-}y),$$

différence de deux indices dont l'un est très affecté par les raies d'absorption et l'autre moins affecté.

Ce critère a aussi son équivalent, dans la photométrie en six couleurs, mais il est plus instructif de considérer le critère infrarouge.

6 — Correspondance entre le critère infrarouge et le critère m_1 de Strömgren

Le critère infrarouge défini au paragraphe 3 est semblable au critère m_1 de la photométrie *uvby* en ce qu'il repose sur la comparaison de deux indices dont l'un est plus affecté que l'autre par les raies d'absorption. Mais il lui est opposé, en ce sens que l'indice peu affecté de la photométrie *uvby* fait intervenir des couleurs qui, dans le critère infrarouge, sont considérées comme les plus affectées.

Les deux critères sont donc indépendants et il est intéressant de chercher à voir s'ils conduisent, en gros, à des résultats équivalents. C'est ce que nous faisons dans les figures 2 et 3.

La figure 3 représente le diagramme $m_1/(b-y)$ pour les étoiles de STRÖMGREN et PERRY citées par WILSON et SKUMANICH [1964] dans l'intervalle de $b-y$ considéré ici (on a retiré les binaires spectroscopiques et les étoiles dont le critère de luminosité selon W et SK est inférieur à 2, exception faite pour 44 And).

Les 23 étoiles de la table I ont été divisées en quatre catégories et représentées par des signes différents, suivant la position qu'elles occupent dans le diagramme :

1. Etoiles très basses (composition chimique normale).
2. Etoiles moins basses.
3. Etoiles hautes.
4. Etoiles exceptionnellement hautes.

Dans la figure 2 (qui donne les six couleurs des étoiles de la table I) les couleurs I et U sont représentées, pour chaque étoile, par le même signe que dans la figure 2.

Pour qu'il y ait accord entre les deux critères, il faut que, dans la figure 2, le point représentatif de la couleur I se place de plus en plus haut (par rapport à la ligne pointillée) à mesure qu'on va des étoiles 1 aux étoiles 4.

Le résultat se voit sur la figure.

Catégorie 1 : 6 étoiles (dont 2 sous-géantes et 2 étoiles ayant une émission H et K) se placent au voisinage de la ligne pointillée. Une anomalie cependant : l'étoile n° 8 (HD 10 307) présente un grand excès d'IR. La déficience en métaux indiquée ainsi n'est pas confirmée par WALLERSTEIN. L'hypothèse

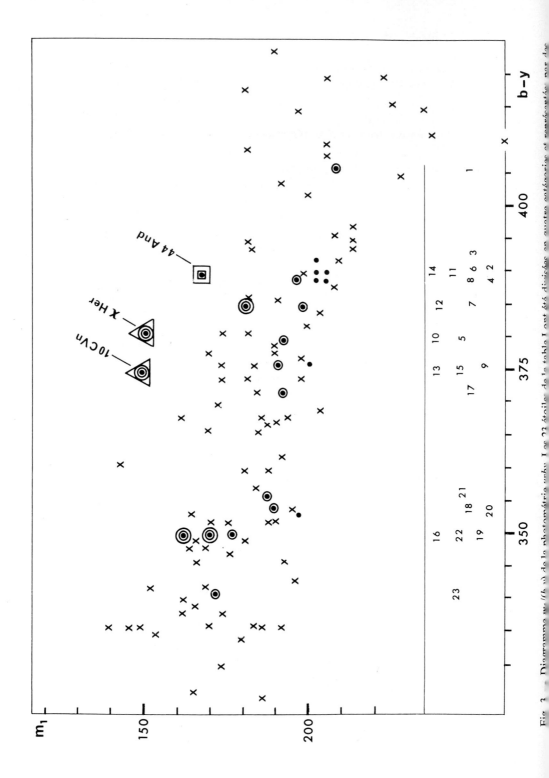

Fig. 3. — Diagramme $m_1/(b-y)$ de la photométrie uvby. Les 23 étoiles de la table I ont été divisées en quatre catégories et représentées par des

d'une erreur dans les couleurs de l'observatoire LICK semble exclue (trois observations).

Catégories 2 et 3. Les étoiles présentent généralement un excès d'IR, mais on ne peut pas dire que l'excès croisse systématiquement de la catégorie 2 à la catégorie 3.

Anomalies : λ Ser (n° 7, catégorie 2) est au-dessous de la ligne pointillée. HD 221356 (n° 16, catégorie 3) ne manifeste aucun excès d'IR. La déficience en métaux indiquée par le critère m_1 est confirmée cependant par un U et un V très élevés.

Catégorie 4. Elle comprend 3 étoiles : 34 And, la sous-géante χ Her (Roman 376) et la sous-naine 10 CVn (Roman 712).

44 And pose un problème spécial : cette étoile semble avoir, à certains points de vue, un comportement de géante ($4071/4077 = 1,2$ selon W et SK, c_1 élevé, UV peu brillant malgré la déficience en métaux indiqué par m_1 et par l'infrarouge.

χ Her et 10 CVn sont très élevés et assez voisins dans la figure 3. Mais seule 10 CVn présente un excès d'infrarouge exceptionnellement grand dans la figure 2. Dans la mesure où l'on peut faire confiance au critère infrarouge, cela pose la question : 2 étoiles de température et de composition chimique différentes peuvent-elles voisiner dans le diagramme $m_1/(b-y)$? La question peut se poser tout au moins dans la partie du diagramme étudiée ici (du côté des étoiles les plus froides).

10 CVn appelle encore une remarque. C'est une des 6 étoiles considérées ici dont la composition chimique est analysée dans WALLERSTEIN [1962]. Dans l'évaluation de la température d'ionisation de ses étoiles, WALLERSTEIN fait intervenir l'indice G-R des six couleurs (et non l'indice G-I, pour éviter de faire intervenir la couleur infrarouge du Soleil). Mais un coup d'œil jeté à la figure 2 montre que, dans le cas de 10 CVn en particulier, il n'est pas indifférent d'utiliser G-R ou G-I. Ce dernier indice aurait conduit à une température plus basse et à une déficience plus grande. Dans le cas de λ Aur, le phénomène inverse a pu se produire : la considération de l'indice G-R a pu conduire à sous-estimer l'excès de métaux.

Je signale seulement cette difficulté pour montrer qu'il y a intérêt à essayer de mieux comprendre la signification des six couleurs.

7 — Conclusion

Pour les 23 étoiles étudiées ici, le critère infrarouge défini au paragraphe III donne des résultats qui sont en assez bon accord avec le critère m_1 de la photométrie *uvby*, sans toutefois que l'accord soit aussi précis qu'on aurait pu l'attendre. La comparaison des critères demanderait à être appuyée par des analyses de composition chimique plus nombreuses et indépendantes des résultats de la photométrie en six couleurs.

BIBLIOGRAPHIE

BAHNG, J.D.R., 1958, *Ap. J.* **128**, p. 572.

CANAVAGGIA, R. et MIANES, P., 1964, *C.R. Acad. Sc. Paris*, **258**, p. 5808.

CODE, A.D., 1959, *Ap. J.*, **130**, p. 473.

JASCHEK, C., CONDE, H., et DE SIERRA, A.C., 1964, *Catalogue of stellar Spectra classified in the Morgan-Keenan System*.

JOHNSON, H.L., 1964, *Ap. J.* **141**, p. 170.

KRON, G.E., 1960, *Vistas in Astronomy*, (ed. A. Beer Pergamon Press, London) **3**, p. 171.

PAGEL, B.E.J., 1963, *Observatory*, **83**, p. 133.

ROMAN, N.G., 1955, *Ap. J. Suppl.*, **2**, 195.

STEBBINS, J. et WHITFORD, A.E., 1945, *Ap. J.*, **102**, p. 318.

STEBBINS, J. et KRON, G.E., 1956, *Ap. J.* **123**, p. 440.

STRÖMGREN, B., *Stars and stellar Systems III*, p. 123 (ed. K. AA. Strand, University of Chicago Press).

STRÖMGREN, B. et PERRY, C., *Photoelectric uvby photometry for* 1217 *stars* (en préparation).

WALLERSTEIN, G., 1962, *Ap. J. Suppl.*, **6**, p. 407.

WILSON, O.C. et SKUMANICH, A., 1964, *Ap. J.*, **140**, p. 1401.

Note ajoutée au moment de la correction des épreuves : Sur la question soulevée ici, on peut consulter : « Nécessité d'un paramètre de température pour l'étude photométrique des étoiles froides », R. CANAVAGGIA, ESO Colloquium on photometry, 1966, Kapteyn Observatory *(sous presse).*

The peculiar a stars and the oblique rotator hypothesis

Erika Bőhm-Vitense

Institut für Theoretische Physik, Kiel, Germany

1 — Abstract

After a brief review of the observations on the Ap stars the oblique rotator hypothesis is discussed in detail. A magnetic field (called H 3) is found which does reproduce the observed mean periodic variations of the magnetic α variables. The inclination between the axis of rotation and the magnetic axis is about 70°. The properties of the field H 3 are discussed. Connections with the solar activity are shown. The spectroscopic variations are connected with the magnetic observations. It is found that the Eu II lines are mainly formed in both polar regions while the Cr II lines originate in an equatorial belt.— The Ap stars appear to be more slowly rotating than normal A stars. The relatively slow rotation and the absence of an effective hydrogen convection zone in the A stars is used as an argument in favour of the fossil hypothesis for the magnetic fields.

Introduction

As BABCOCK [1947] discovered all sharplined peculiar A stars have strong, variable magnetic fields. According to their variability they can be classified in 4 groups designated by α, β, γ, δ (BABCOCK, 1960). The stars of the α group show periodically varying magnetic fields—with some irregular variations superimposed—accompanied by periodic spectrum variations. The β variables show irregular variations with changing polarity while the γ variables are also irregular but keep their polarity. This article shall be mainly concerned with the α group. The periodic variations give evidence of an organized field which may possibly be understood easiest. From the correlations between the magnetic and the spectral changes we may hope to get information about the interaction of magnetic fields with the matter in stellar atmospheres.

2 — Short Review of Observations

(a) The magnetic fields

In his review article BABCOCK [1960] gives several examples for the periodic variations of the magnetic fields. They are usually unharmonic with a broad minimum, sometimes with a shallow secondary maximum imbedded, and a

Gauthier-Villars, Paris - Modern-Astrophysics - 1967.

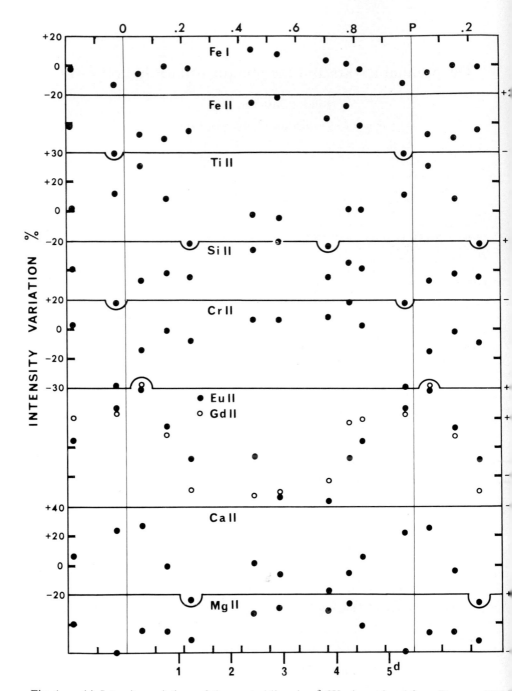

Fig. 1 — (a) Intensity variations of the spectral lines in α^2 CVn (reproduced from DEUTSCH [1956

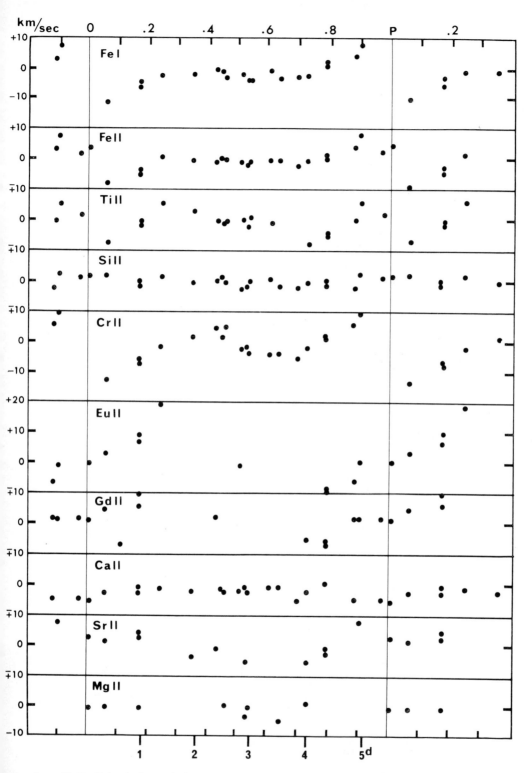

Fig. 1 — (b) Radial velocity variations in the spectrum of α^2 CVn (reproduced from DEUTSCH [1956]).

narrower maximum (or with opposite sign). In the figures 12-18 the observations for several stars are reproduced as given by Babcock [1960].

(b) The spectrum variations

In the spectra of the α variables some of the lines, especially those with abnormal line strengths show periodic variations correlated with the magnetic variations. In figure 1a and 1b the observations for the star α^2 CVn are reproduced as collected by Deutsch [1956]. The periods of the spectrum variations agree with or are half as long (HeI 4026 in 56 Ari) as the magnetic periods. The Eu II lines on one side and the Cr I and Cr II lines on the other side vary always in antiphase. For some stars the maximum intensity of Cr I and Cr II occur for maximum positive field strength (α^2 CVn) and for others for the maximum negative field (HD 125248). Eu II is always strongest during the broad extremum. There are also changes of the radial velocities observed which are different for different lines and which are correlated with the changes in equivalent width.

(c) The crossover effect

The crossover effect occurs quite often when the magnetic field changes sign. At this time several lines are conspicuously broader in the spectrum

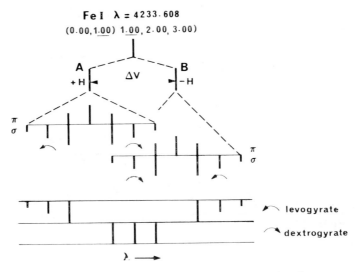

Fig. 2 — Schematic representation of Babcock's hypothesis for the crossover effect. (Adapted from H. W Babcock [1956]).

with one direction of circular polarization than in the spectrum with opposite polarization.

A simple explanation was given by BABCOCK [1951]. It is reproduced in figure 2 for the Fe I line $\lambda = 4233.608$ Å as an example. Parts of the stellar surface which have opposite polarity of H have also velocities in opposite directions. The lines originating at these surface regions are split by the velocity difference ΔV and in addition by the Zeemansplitting. If ΔV and H happen to have a certain ratio (resonance-ratio) the components of the line with one direction of polarization will fall on top of each other, while the components with opposite polarization will be separated by the Doppler plus Zeeman splitting. This spectrum will therefore have broad lines.

(d) Light variations

For some of the α variables periodic variations of the luminosities have been observed (STIBBS [1950], THIESSEN [1962]). The amplitude is a few

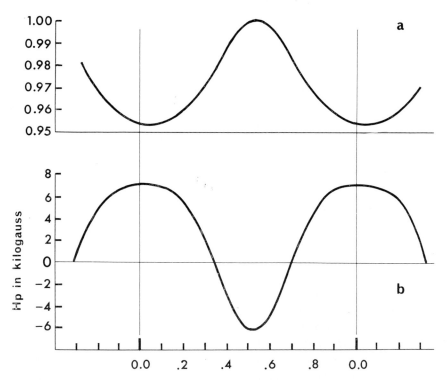

Fig. 3 — Luminosity (*a*) and magnetic field (*b*) variations in HD 125248 according to Stibbs [1950]. (Adapted from LEDOUX and WALRAVEN [1958]).

hundredths of a magnitude. The period agrees with the magnetic period. In figure 3 a comparison of the light and magnetic variations for the star HD 125248 is reproduced as given by LEDOUX and WALRAVEN [1958].

(e) Rotational velocities

Magnetic fields are only observable for sharplined stars, so naturally $v \cdot \sin i$ is small for the observed magnetic stars, but we do not know whether v or $\sin i$ or both are small. Since all sharplined A_p stars have strong magnetic fields we may assume that all A_p stars are magnetic stars. In general the A_p stars have line widths which are about a factor 3 smaller than in normal A stars, (BABCOCK, 1960).

(f) Period—linewidth relation

In 1947 DEUTSCH discovered a roughly linear relation between the period of the spectral variations of the A_p stars and their inverse linewidths. This may easily be understood on theoretical grounds, since rapid changes of the magnetic field can only be achieved by rapid motions.

3 — The magnetic variations on the oblique rotator hypothesis

Three basically different explanations for the observations have been discussed so far : (a) the oscillator model (BABCOCK and COWLING, 1955), (b) the solar cycle model (BABCOCK, 1960) and (c) the oblique rotator (DEUTSCH, 1947).

Since in the author's mind the last one encounters the least difficulties we shall discuss this one in detail.

(a) General discussion

It is assumed that the magnetic axis m is inclined to the axis of rotation $\vec{\omega}$ by an angle β. If the line of sight b does not coincide with the axis of rotation the angle α between $\vec{m}$ and $\vec{b}$ will change periodically and the observer of the integrated light will see a periodically varying magnetic field. This model provides the easiest way to explain the rapid reversals of the magnetic field. It also provides an explanation for the crossover effect. It is supported by the observations of the close binary system HD 98088, whose stars have a distance of only 10 stellar radii. We therefore expect the rotation period to agree with the period of revolution. For this star the magnetic period is observed to agree with the period of revolution.

These large advantages of the oblique rotator hypothesis seem to justify a more careful investigation.

So far the only general investigation of the magnetic variations to be expected on this hypothesis has been done by STIBBS [1950]. For a spherically symmetric star with a dipole field he obtained harmonic variations of the observed magnetic field, where the amplitude and the zeropoint depend on β and on the angle i between $\vec{\omega}$ and $\vec{b}$. Since the observed variations are not all harmonic this result has often been used as an argument against the oblique rotator hypothesis. However we do not know what we may expect for non-spherically symmetric stars or other than dipole fields. In the discussion of these possibilities we shall follow the procedure used by STIBBS.

(b) The computational procedure

For a given field the observable mean longitudinal field H_{eff} is first computed as a function of the angle α between the magnetic axis m and the line of sight b. The field component in the direction of the line of sight H_b

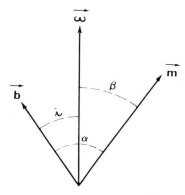

Fig. 4 — Schematic representation of the line of sight $\vec{b}$, the magnetic axis $\vec{m}$ and the axis of rotation $\vec{\omega}$ with the angles of inclination.

is computed for each surface element $d\sigma$ and a weighted mean is taken over the visible hemisphere with $I(\vartheta) \cdot \cos \vartheta$ as a weighting function (STIBBS, 1950)

(1)
$$H_{eff}(\alpha) = \frac{\int H_b(\alpha, z, \rho, \varphi) I(\vartheta) \cos \vartheta \, d\sigma}{\int I(\vartheta) \cos \vartheta \, d\sigma}$$

where ϑ is the angle between the normal on $d\sigma$ and the line of sight. For the limb darkening it was assumed

(2) $$I(\vartheta) = I \cdot (1 - u + u \cos \vartheta)$$

with $u = 0.45$.

After $H_{eff}(\alpha)$ is known, the angle α is computed as a function of phase. With $\theta = 2\pi$. phase the angle α is given by Stibbs [1950]

(3) $$\cos \alpha = \cos i \cdot \cos \beta + \sin i \sin \beta \cdot \cos \theta$$

Since θ depends symmetrically on i and β we can always interchange these two.

(c) Nonspherical stars

For a star with a strong magnetic field we cannot be quite sure that the observed layer of the star, corresponding to $\tau \approx 2/3$, is actually spherical. Therefore $H_{eff}(\alpha)$ is computed for a surface which is a rotational ellipsoid around the magnetic axis. In the figure 5a and b we show the curves $H_{eff}(\alpha)$ for different ellipticities of the star for a dipole field and also for another field called H 3 to be discussed in section g. Since the polar fieldstrength is unknown we may multiply the curves by an arbitrary factor. With this in mind it is obvious, that the shape of the curves is not much altered by a possible ellipticity of the star.

(d) Nonspherically symmetric brightness distribution

Since $H_{eff}(\alpha)$ depends on the weighting function $I(\vartheta)$ this may influence $H_{eff}(\alpha)$.

Cylindrically symmetric brightness distributions around the magnetic axis were investigated. The following forms of distributions were considered :

(4) $$I \sim 1 + e \cdot \sin \psi^\gamma$$

(5) $$I \sim 1 + e \,|\cos \psi|^\gamma$$

(6) $$I \sim 1 + e \,|\cos \psi \cdot \sin \psi|^\gamma$$

with $e = 0.1$ or 2, and $\gamma = 2.1$ or 0.5 . ψ stands for the colatitude $0 \leqslant \psi \leqslant \pi$.

The influence of these brightness distributions on the observed magnetic field is shown in figure 6a, b, and c again for the field H 3, (also used in Fig. 5b). Again it is noticed that the influence is of minor importance. The $H_{eff}(\alpha)$ curve is mainly determined by the distribution of the field on the star's surface.

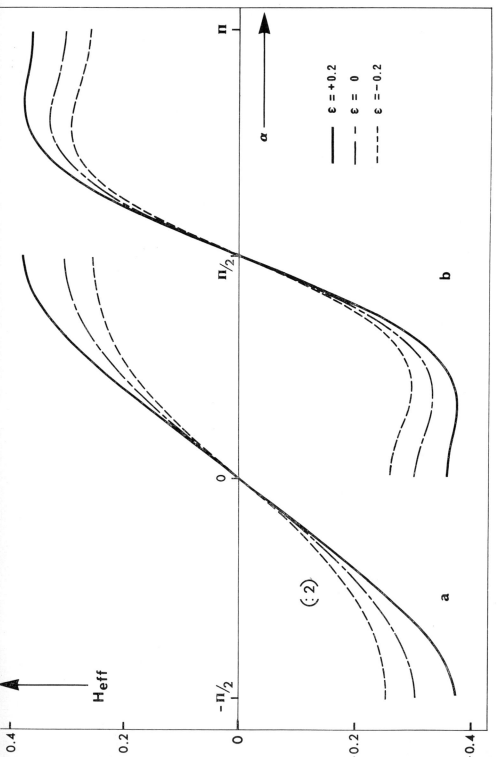

Fig. 5 — The measurable longitudinal field H_{eff} as a function of α, —the inclination between the line of sight b and the magnetic axis $\overline{m}$—for different ellipticities of the star. — a. for a dipole field. — b. for the field H 3 to be discussed in section Bg.

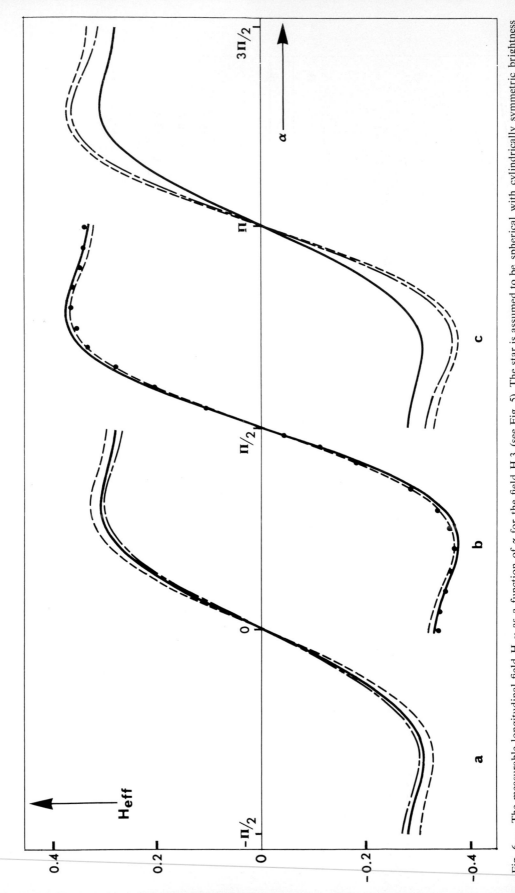

Fig. 6 — The measurable longitudinal field H$_{eff}$ as a function of α for the field H 3 (see Fig. 5). The star is assumed to be spherical with cylindrically symmetric brightness distribution around the magnetic axis. — a. The latitude dependence of the brightness is given by (4), e being 0 (— — —), 1 (————) and 2 (—·—·—). γ is one. — b. The

(e) Nondipolar fields

1. Types of fields investigated.

Only cylindrically symmetric fields are considered. A magnetic field can always be written as the sum of a toroidal field $\vec{t}$ and a poloidal field $\vec{p}$. Toroidal fields around the magnetic axis cannot be observed because the eastern and western hemisphere cancel out against each other. Therefore we consider only poloidal fields.

Generally a divergencefree cylindrically symmetric field can be described by LUST and SCHLUTER [1954].

$$(7) \qquad \vec{p} = \mathrm{curl}\left(p\,(\rho, z)\, \frac{[\vec{r}, \vec{m}]}{r} \right)$$

where $\vec{m}$ is a vector in the direction of the magnetic axis. In cylindrical coordinates the components are then

$$\vec{p} = \begin{bmatrix} p_t \\ p_\rho \\ p_\varphi \end{bmatrix} = \begin{bmatrix} -\left(\dfrac{\partial p}{\partial \rho} + \dfrac{p}{\rho}\right) \\ +\dfrac{\partial p}{\partial z} \\ 0 \end{bmatrix}$$

where p can now be *any* function of the cylinder coordinates ρ and z.

For a dipole field

$$(9) \qquad p = \frac{m\rho}{r^3} = \frac{m \cdot \rho}{(z^2 + \rho^2)}\, 3/2$$

For the fields investigated here p was chosen of the form

$$(10) \qquad p = \frac{\rho}{(az^2 + \rho^2)\, \rho/2}$$

where a and δ are varied arbitrarily.

In figures 7a and b the lines of force for some of the fields are shown in comparison with a dipole field ($a = 1$, $\delta = 3$). Figure 7a shows the influence of a on the shape of the lines of force and figure 7b the influence of δ.

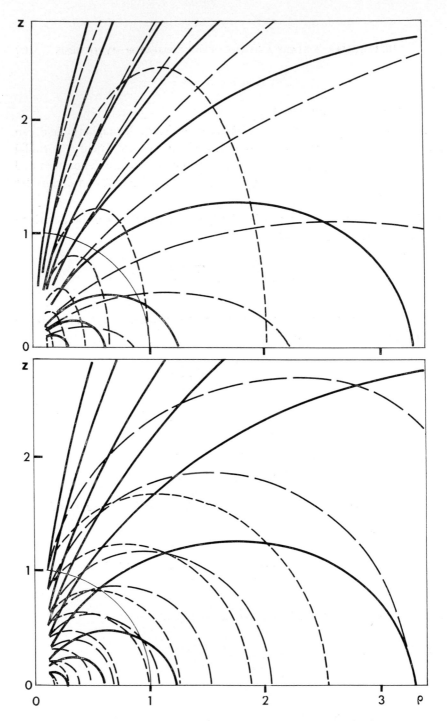

Fig. 7 — The lines of force for magnetic fields given by (8) and (10) in the plane of the cylindercoordinates ρ and z.

a. With $\delta = 3$, for the dipole field with $a = 1$ (———), for $a = 0,1$ (-----), and for the field H 3 with $a = 3$ (— — —).

b. With $a = 1$, for the dipole field $\delta = 3$ (———), for $\delta = 5$ (— — —), and $\delta = 7$ (-----).

2. The observable mean longitudinal field $H_{eff}(\alpha)$.

In figure 8 the dependence of $H_{eff}(\alpha)$ on the value of the parameter a is shown for $\delta = 3$. The observations suggest a steep increase of H_{eff} with α and also a secondary maximum as appears for $a \geqslant 3$.

In figure 9 the dependence of $H_{eff}(\alpha)$ on the parameter δ is shown for $a = 3$. The curves change sign for $\delta \geqslant 3$. Otherwise the general shape of the curves is not altered much except that the secondary extremum becomes more pronounced for larger values of δ.

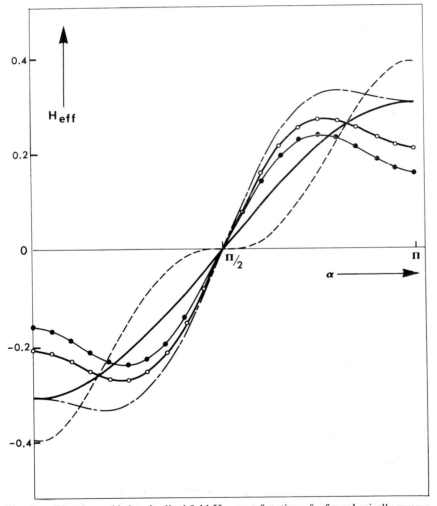

Fig. 8 — The observable longitudinal field H_{eff} as a function of α for spherically symmetric stars and for fields given by (8) and (10). $\delta = 3$ and $a = 0,1$ ($---$), $a = 1$ (———), $a = 3$ ($-----$), $a = 5$ ($-$o$-$o$-$, $a = 7$ ($-\cdot-\cdot-$). (Arbitrary units).

(f) Time variations of magnetic fields

If we want to investigate the time variations of magnetic fields as a function of phase θ we have to compute $\alpha(\theta)$ according to (3) for a given pair i and β. From figures 8 and 9 (or corresponding ones for other fields) we can then read $H_{eff}(\alpha(\theta)) = H_{eff}(\theta)$.

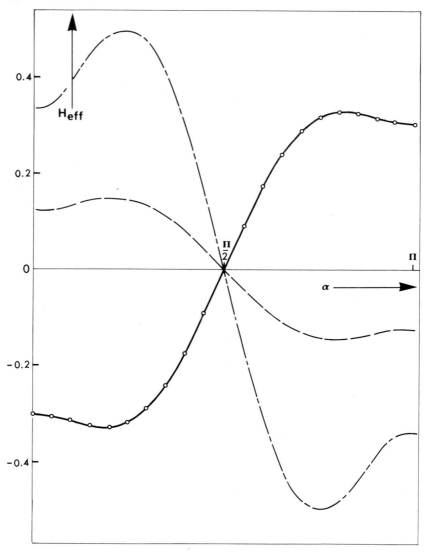

Fig. 9 — The observable longitudinal field H_{eff} as a function of α (see Fig. 4), for spherically symmetric stars and for fields given by (8) and (16). $a = 3$, and $\delta = 3$ (—o—o—o), $\delta = 5$ (———), $\delta = 7$ (—————), (Arbitrary units).

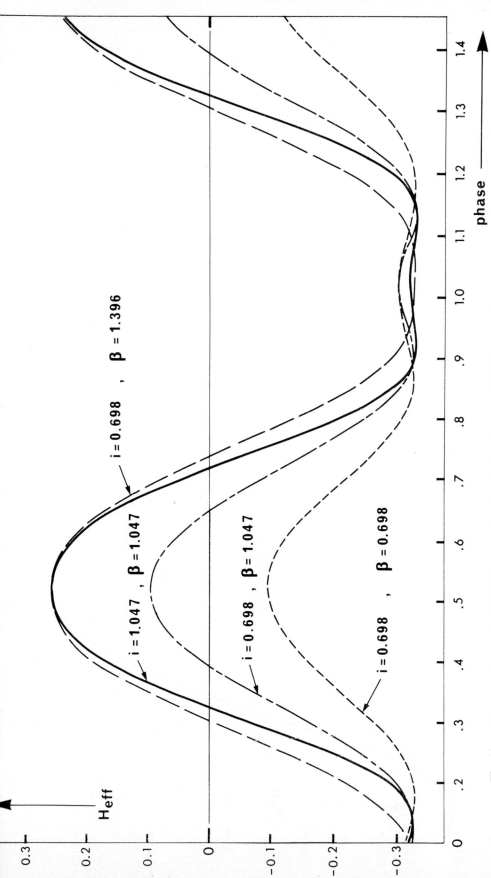

Fig. 10 — The mean longitudinal field H_{eff} as a function of phase for the field H 3 ($a = 3$, $\delta = 3$) for different pairs i and β (see Fig. 4).

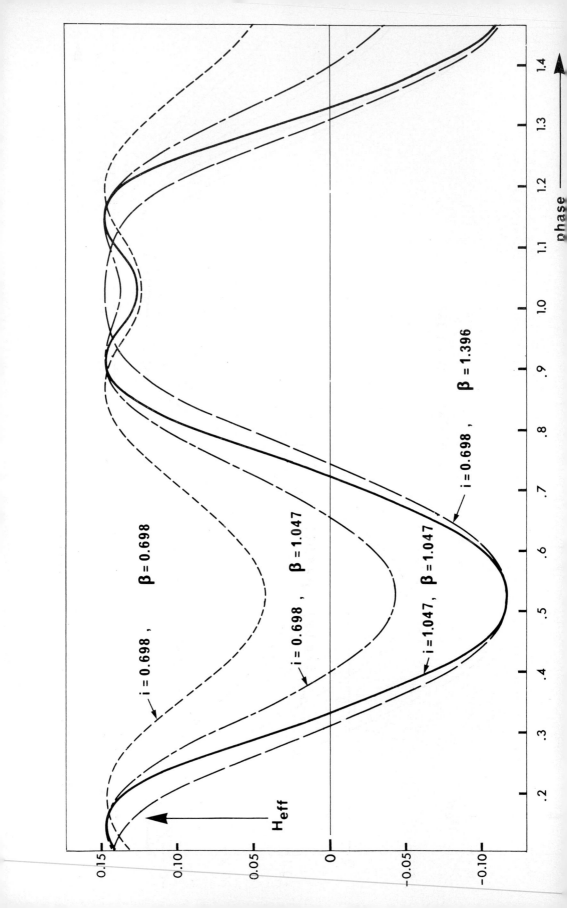

In figure 10 and 11 we show several possibilities for a number of pairs i and β and for the fields $a = 3\ \delta = 3$ and $a = 5\ \delta = 5$ respectively. Fields with $a < 1$ were not considered because $d\,H_{eff}/d\alpha$ in the neighborhood of $\alpha = \pi/2$ is too small in comparison with the observations.

(g) Comparison with Observations

When trying to fit certain curves $H_{eff}(\theta)$ to the observed curves as given by BABCOCK [1960] we find that there are usually several types of fields which will represent the observations almost equally well. In figure 12 α^2 CVn is shown as an example. We have to take into account other observations to select the best field. BABCOCK states that the observed line widths for lines influenced by the Zeeman effect indicate that the actual maximum fields H(max) present on the star's surface are not much different from the observed maximum mean field H_{eff}(max). For the different types of field the ratios of $H(max)/H_{eff}(max) = R$ are quite different.

In table I these values are given for some of the fields.

TABLE I

$H(max)/H_{eff}(max = R$ *for different fields*

δ	3	3	3	3	5	5	5	5
a	1	3	5	7	1	3	5	7
R	3,30	5,25	6,47	8,44	9,26	20,4	29,5	37,9

For the non dipole fields R is closest to 1 for $a = 3$, $\delta = 3$.

We therefore think that this field represents the observations best. We called it H 3.

There may of course be slight differences between the shape of the fields for various stars. For the following discussion we concentrate on the field H 3. (This field was also used in Figures : 5b and 6).

In figures 13 to 18 we show a comparison of the observed values $H_{eff}(\theta)$ as given by BABCOCK [1960] for the α variables and the theoretical curves obtained for certain values of i and β, chosen to give good agreement. It appears that the observed regular variations can be represented rather well.

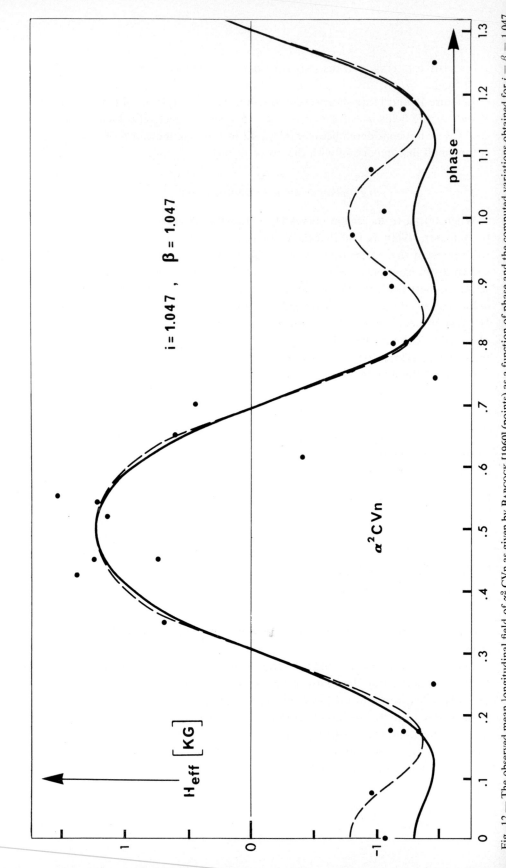

Fig. 12 — The observed mean longitudinal field of α^2 CVn as given by Babcock [1960] (points) as a function of phase and the computed variations obtained for $i = \beta = 1,047$

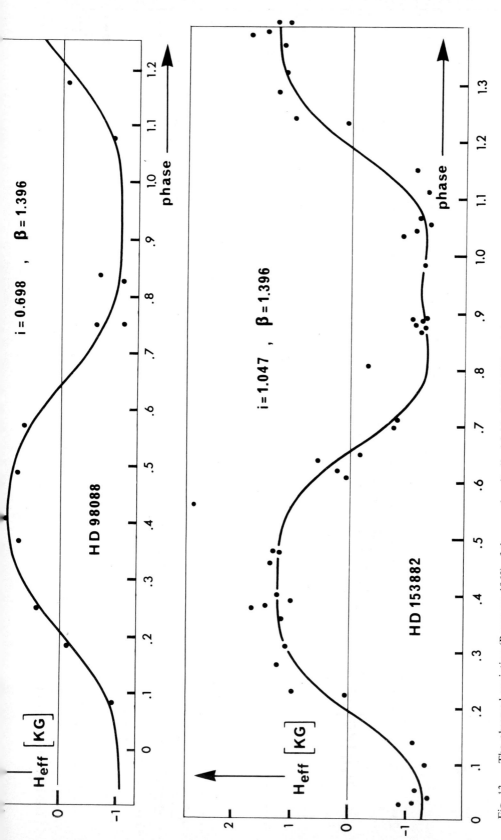

Fig. 13 — The observed variation (BABCOCK, 1960) of the mean longitudinal field of HD 98088 and the one computed with the field H 3 for $i = 0,698$ and $\beta = 1,396$.

Fig. 14 — The observed variation (BABCOCK, 1960) of the mean longitudinal field of HD 153882 and the computed one with the field H 3 for $i = 1,047$ and $\beta = 1,396$.

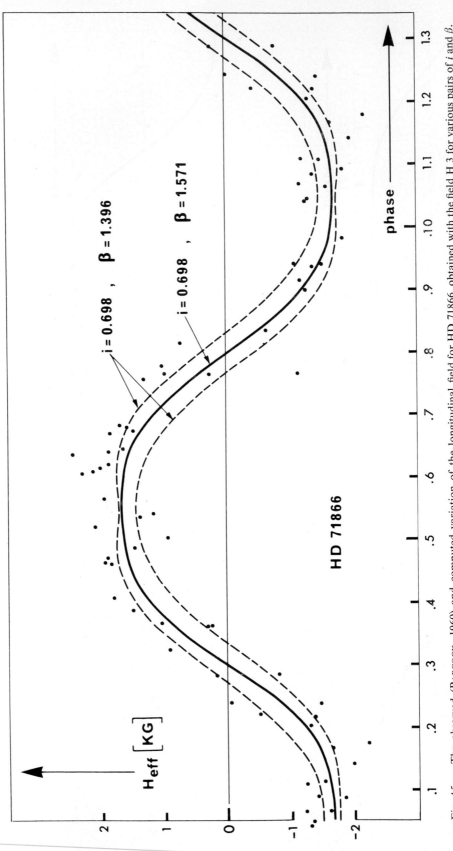

Fig. 15 — The observed (Babcock, 1960) and computed variation of the longitudinal field for HD 71866, obtained with the field H 3 for various pairs of i and β.

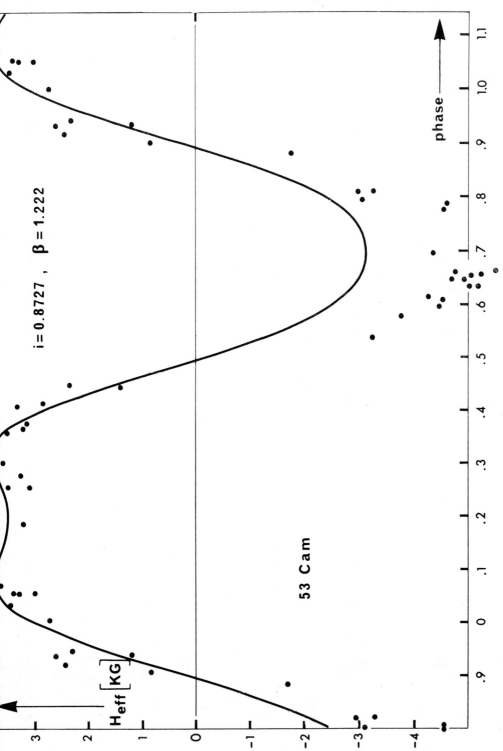

Fig. 16 — The observed (Babcock, 1960) and computed variation of the longitudinal field for 53 Cam, obtained with the field H 3 for $i = 0{,}8727$ and $\beta = 1{,}222$.

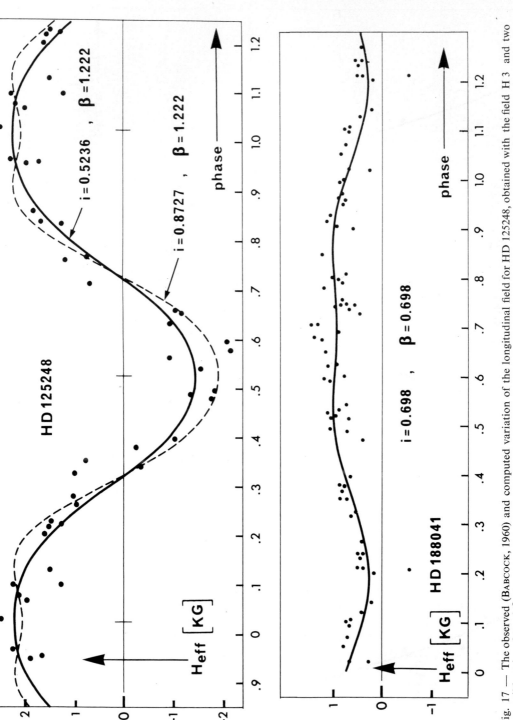

Fig. 17 — The observed (Babcock, 1960) and computed variation of the longitudinal field for HD 125248, obtained with the field H 3 and two possible pairs of i and β.

Fig. 18 — The observed (Babcock, 1960) and computed variation of the longitudinal field for HD 188041 obtained for the field H 3 with

The superimposed irregular variations will have to be explained by some irregular distortions of the lines of force possibly due to some activity. It is interesting to note, that i and β are usually rather large. For i we would expect a statistical distribution ($\sim \sin i$), so that possibly always $\beta = \beta_0 = 1.2 \pm 0.1$. This large inclination between $\vec{m}$ and $\vec{\omega}$ is rather surprising but may perhaps be understood as was pointed out by MESTEL [1965].

4 — Discussion of the Field which fits the Observations best

(a) Latitude dependence of field strength

In the figure 19 I have plotted the absolute field strength as a function of latitude for the field H 3 ($a = 3, \delta = 3$) which was used in the figure 12 to 18. For comparison I have also plotted the field strength for a dipole field ($a = 1, \delta = 3$) and for the field with $a = 0.1, \delta = 3$. While the dipole field and the latter field have their maximum field strength at the poles, the type of field which fits the observations has it maximum field strength close to the equator at $\psi_m = 1.257$, or latitudes of about $\pm 20°$. The agreement of ψ_m and β_0 is rather interesting to note. The sharp maximum of the field strength in the regions close to the equator makes it understandable that the largest irregularities are observed when we view the stars mainly perpendicular to $\vec{m}$: Small distortions in the lines of force due to some activity will change the longitudinal component of the field remarkably.

(b) Comparison with solar phenomena

In figure 19 I have noted the region of latitudes where the sunspots occur mainly on the sun by horizontal lines on the curve $|H|(\psi)$. They obviously inclose the region where we find the maximum field strength on the A_p stars.

The similarity between the solar activity and the field ditribution found for the A_p stars is also demonstrated in figure 20, where again $|H|$ is drawn as a function of latitude but in a polar diagram. I have plotted in the same diagram the frequency of eruptive prominences on the sun as given by KIEPENHEUER [1953] as a measure of solar activity as a function of latitude. The agreement is amazing. Does this indicate that a magnetic field similar to the one in A_p stars is present in the sun probably below the hydrogen convection zone ?

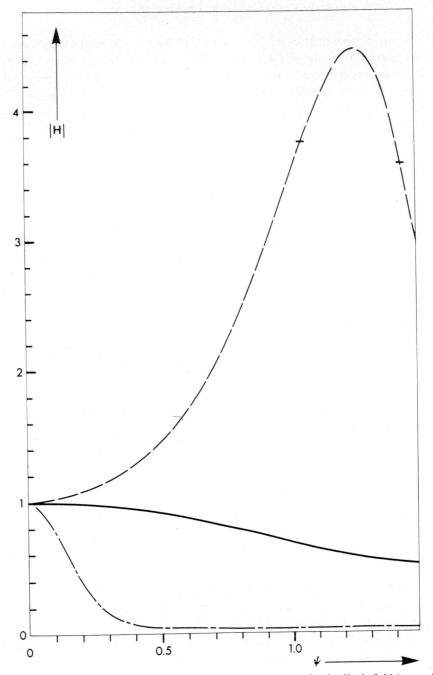

Fig. 19 — The magnetic field strength as a function of latitude for the dipole field (———)
for the fields given by (8) and (10) with $\delta = 3$ and $a = 0,1$ (—·—·—) and for $a = 3$,
the field called H 3 (———). The crosses on the latter curve mark the region of latitudes
where the sunspots occur on the sun.

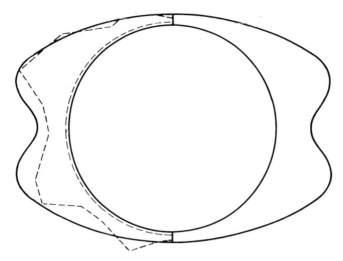

Fig. 20 — The magnetic field strength for the field H 3 shown in a polar diagram (———).
For comparison the frequency of eruptive prominences on the sun is also shown as
given by KIEPENHEUER, [1953] (— — —). (The solar surfaces are also given for the two
representations).

(c) The current densities

From the comparison with the observed time variations of the magnetic
field we can only determine the field distribution at the surface of the star
which means in the layer where the observed lines are formed. Actually
we cannot say anything about the field in the interior of the star. Nevertheless it might be interesting which currents are derived from the formulas
that represent the field at the surface. The current densities multiplied by
ρ^2 are shown in the figure 21. The current densities are not zero at the surface
but they are 8 powers of ten smaller than at $r = 0.01$ R$_*$. The density at the
surface layers is about 10^{-10} times the density at $r = 0.01$ R$_*$.

The question whether a toroidal field could be found to make the field
force free, remains to be investigated. The observed low electron pressures
in the A$_p$ stars (SEARLE and SARGENT 1964) seem to suggest that the field is
not force free.

5 — Qualitative discussion of spectroscopic observations

(a) Line intensity variations

The computation of the expected time variation of the magnetic field
shows that we observe a broad flat maximum when we look at the polar

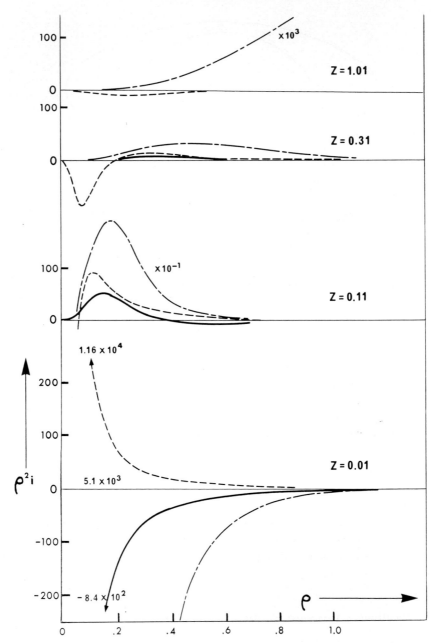

Fig. 21 — The current densities $\cdot \rho^2$ for different fields as a function of the distance from the magnetic axis ρ for different values of z, measured from the center of the star. (The stars radius being unity). The curves are plotted for the fields H 3 (———), for the field with $a = 0.1$, $\delta = 3$ (— — —), and for a field with $a = 5$, $\delta = 5$ (—·—·—). For the latter field the current densities for $z = 1.01$ have been multiplied by 10^3.

region of the magnetic field. Since the Eu II lines are always associated with the broad maximum regardless of polarity—see for instance α^2 CVn and HD 125248—we may infer that the Eu II lines are preferentially formed in *both* polar regions. During the narrow and rather pointed maximum we do not view the other pole but a region just beyond the equator, therefore we usually do not see another Eu II intensity maximum. Only for $i \sim \pi/2$, when we obtain a nearly symmetric curve for $H_{eff}(\theta)$ we expect to see another maximum in the line intensities of the Eu II lines. In α^2 CVn the Eu II and Ca II lines show a suggestion of this. Since the Cr II lines are strongest during this narrow maximum they must be mainly formed in the equatorial region. Since the equatorial region is in view during a large fraction of the period the Cr II lines appear strong over long time intervals with only minor variations. They only decrease during a short period when we view the pole.

If on the other hand for the lines originating at latitudes around 45° or over large fractions of the stellar surface we expect little variation of the line intensities.

With the magnetic field H 3 with its maximum field strength close to the magnetic equator we may therefore restore complete symmetry between the magnetic poles also for the spectroscopic properties of the star.

(b) Radial velocity variations

We now know that during the broad maximum of the magnetic field strength one pole is in front and the Eu II lines originate mainly at the pole. The difference between the radial velocity v_r of the star and the v_r of the Eu II lines therefore ought to be zero at this time as is indeed observed. From there on the pole should move away from us and the Eu II lines ought to show increasing and positive v_r. If the Eu II lines are strongly concentrated toward the pole it should reach almost the total rotational velocity of the poles. If we assume a stellar radius 2.3 times the radius of the sun the equatorial velocity (equatorial with respect to ω) for α^2 CVn comes out to be 21.4 km/sec. The observed maximum radial velocity of the Eu II lines in α^2 CVn is between 15 and 20 km/sec, indicating a strong concentration of the Eu II lines toward the poles. Therefore the Eu II lines also appear fairly sharp. The observed large enhancement of the lines becomes even more puzzling then. The Cr II lines on the other hand are week when the pole is in front because the equatorial (with respect to $\bar{m}$) belt is barely visible at the edges of the star. Afterwards this belt turns into the visible part moving towards us with negative radial velocities while the intensity is increasing. When the equatorial belt moves across the visible hemisphere there are minor changes in the radial velocity, the lines are fairly broad because the equatorial ($\bar{m}$) belt includes more different radial velocities than do the polar regions. While the intensities decline when the belt moves out of the visible hemisphere the v_r become > 0 but remain well below the equatorial ($\vec{\omega}$) velocity. Lines which are not so much concentrated in certain regions or originate around latitude of 45° will show little variations in radial velocity.

For α^2 CVn (Babcock, 1960) gives a mean line width of 0.3 Å. The rotational velocity of 21.4 km/sec would yield a total line width of 0.61 Å at $\lambda = 4300$ Å. The difference confirms that most of the lines do not originate all over the star but are concentrated in certain regions with a narrower range in v_r. Babcock states that the systematic variations in linewidth are most extreme when the magnetic variations are extreme as in 53 Cam and α^2 CVn. Obviously the concentration of the lines in the polar or equatorial ($\bar{m}$) region increases with increasing field strength.

(c) The crossover effect

The explanation given by Babcock requires that the regions with opposite polarity have opposite radial velocities. On the oblique rotator hypothesis this is naturally achieved.

Using the magnetic field H 3 we can study the crossover effect quantitatively. According to Deutsch [1958], the maximum crossover effect for a field of 4,4 KG is obtained for $\Delta v_r \sim 5$ km/sec (mean for sensitive lines). According to our table 1 the ratio of the observed H_{eff}(max) and the maximum field strength H(max) occuring at the stellar surface is 5.58. In α^2 CVn H_{eff}(max) ≈ 1.45 KG, indicating H(max) ~ 8 KG. For this field strength the resonance Δv_r should be 9.1 km/sec. The largest component of |H| in the line of sight occurs at colatitudes (with respect to $\bar{m}$) $\psi = 1,257$. During the crossover phase [$\alpha = \pi/2$] the velocity component in the line of sight at this point comes out to be 4.9 km/sec, so that $\Delta v_r = 9,8$ km/sec. Obviously other points of the stellar surface will also contribute to the light. But nevertheless it appears that for α^2 CVn Δv_r and H are fairly close to resonance. If the maximum field strength would occur at the poles Δv_r would be much too large (Deutsch, 1958).

(d) The rotational velocities

As was emphasized by Babcock [1960] the periods of the A_p stars are in general about a factor 3 longer than the mean rotational periods for

A stars. Could the A_p stars actually be more slowly rotating than normal A stars?

BABCOCK investigated this problem statistically. According to him we should see about ten narrow line ($v . \sin i \leqslant 16.8$ km/sec) stars with appearent magnitude $m \leqslant 6$ and with an equatorial $v_r \geqslant 100$ km. There are actually 43 narrow line stars observed, $33 A_p$ stars and ten normal stars. It then appears that the bulk of the A_p stars must have $v_r < 100$ km/sec. So we find that in any case the A_p stars in the mean are more slowly rotating than normal A stars. This may easily be understood by magnetic braking (BABCOCK, 1960).
This may easily be understood by magnetic braking (BABCOCK, 1960).

The period-line width relation also indicates slow rotation. If the A_p stars would be rapidly rotating stars, seen pole on, the line width would be mainly determined by the angle i of inclination, which could hardly be correlated with the period. If the linewidth would be determined by other than rotational velocities we would have to conclude that the rotational velocities are still smaller.

(e) The origin of the magnetic field

There are two possibilities, either they are fossil or they are generated within the star. The correct explanation should also explain why the large fields are observed only in A stars. (If there are fields observed in other stars, they are much smaller according to BABCOCK's catalog [1958]).

All dynamic theories make use of rotational and turbulent velocities. While the A stars in general are rapid rotators we have just concluded that the A_p stars rotate much more slowly than normal A stars. In addition we know that just the A stars do not have an effective hydrogen convection zone and have only a very small convective core.

Since the diffusive decay times for stellar magnetic fields is of the order of 10^{10} years, there are no difficulties with a fossil magnetic field. The question is rather why did the other stars loose their magnetic fields? The author is inclined to connect the disappearance of the magnetic field with the presence of a hydrogen convection zone in the cooler stars. In the deeper layers this may twist the lines of force thereby reducing the scale of the magnetic fields. The diffusion time may then be much reduced in the convection zone (BABCOCK and COWLING, 1953).

126   E. BÖHM-VITENSE

REFERENCES

BABCOCK, H.W., 1947, *Ap. J.*, **105**, 105.
BABCOCK, H.W., 1951, *Ap. J.* **114**, 1.
BABCOCK, H.W. and COWLING, T.G., 1953, *M.N.R.A.S.*, **113**, 357.
BABCOCK, H.W., 1956, *Ap. J.* **124**, 489.
BABCOCK, H.W., 1960, *"Stellar Atmospheres"* (ed. J.L. Greenstein, p. 282 University of Chicago Press).
DEUTSCH, A.J., 1947, *Ap. J.* **105**, 283.
DEUTSCH, A.J., 1956, *P.A.S.P.*, **68**, 92.
DEUTSCH, A.J., 1958, *Handbuch der Physik*, **51**, 689.
KIEPENHEUER, K.O., 1953, *"The Sun"* (ed. G.P. Kuiper, p. 322 University of Chicago Press).
LEDOUX, P. and WALRAVEN, Th., 1958, *Handbuch der Physik*, **51**, 428.
LÜST, R. and SCHLÜTER, A., 1954, *Z. Astrophys.* **34**, 263.
MESTEL, L., 1965, *Nato Institute, Newcastle*.
SEARLE, L. and SARGENT, W., 1964, *Ap. J.*, **139**, 793.
STIBBS, D.W.N., 1950, *M.N.R.A.S.*, **110**, 395.
THIESSEN, G., 1962, *Astr. Abh. Hamburger Sternwarte*, **5**, 273.

The luminosities of the Beta Cephei variable stars

D. H. McNamara and G. E. Matthews

Physics Department, Brigham Young University

1 — Abstract

Luminosities of the β Cephei stars are determined from measurements of the β index and equivalent widths of the Hγ and Hδ lines of hydrogen. The period-color, and period-luminosity relations are derived from all existing data, and the position of the β Cephei variables in the H-R diagram is compared with the "zero-age" main sequence.

Otto Struve's interest in the β Cephei variable stars (called β C Ma variables by Struve) dates back to his early years at the Yerkes Observatory when he was actively engaged in observing β Cephei. His first published paper on the subject was a joint investigation with Swings [1941] in which they described some of the complexities in the spectrum and radial velocity-curve of β Canis Majoris. When he assumed the chairmanship of the Berkeley Astronomical Department in 1950, he undertook an extensive observational program aimed at improving our knowledge of these interesting variable stars. With the characteristic vigor that was the mark of his character, he secured hundreds of spectrograms of the various variable stars of this group and analysed their spectra for radial velocities and spectral changes. Although he had many other research interests at the time, his main scientific efforts in the years 1950-1954 were devoted to the β Cephei stars. There is little doubt that our knowledge of the properties of these stars was greatly improved over this four year period as a consequence of his efforts.

In this paper, we describe some new observational results secured from high-dispersion spectrograms and narrow-band photometric observations of some of the β Cephei variables.

In table I, a number of the β Cephei variables are arranged according to increasing period. In columns 2 and 4, we present some new photometric observations obtained in the (U-B)$_0$-β system. (U-B)$_0$ is the U-B color index freed from the effects of interstellar reddening and β is a measure of the strength of the Hβ line of hydrogen (Crawford, 1958). The number of observations secured in forming the mean values of (U-B)$_0$ and β is given in column 6. The average internal error in the mean (U-B)$_0$ color index (column 2) is ± 0.006 mag. (p.e.) and ± 0.004 mag. (p.e.) is the error in the

Gauthier-Villars, Paris - Modern Astrophysics - 1967.

mean β values given in column 4. For comparison purposes we list $(U\text{-}B)_0$ values and β indices for some of these stars determined elsewhere in columns 3 and 5. The sources of these $(U\text{-}B)_0$ values and β indices are given at the bottom of the table. With the exception of the $(U\text{-}B)_0$ value of σ Sco, the present observations are in excellent agreement with previous determinations of β and $(U\text{-}B)_0$ values.

TABLE I

Star	$(U\text{-}B)_0$	$(U\text{-}B)_0$	β	β	Number	W_γ	W_δ	$W_{\gamma\delta}$	W_γ Petrie
θ Oph	-0.88	-0.91^g	2.631	2.632^g	10				
γ Peg	-0.88	-0.86^a	2.618	2.628^g	12	4.4	3.9	4.15	4.2
		-0.88^c							
δ Cet	-0.90	-0.875^a	2.610		10	4.3	3.7	4.0	4.7
16 Lac	-0.91	-0.935^a	2.613	2.605^f	9	3.5	3.5	3.5	4.1
		-0.92^d							
		-0.90^f							
ν Eri	-0.94	-0.905^a	2.600		9	3.6	3.2	3.4	
15 C Ma	-0.99		2.594		4				
β Cep	-0.965	-0.98^a	2.591		9	3.4	2.9	3.15	3.4
12 Lac	-0.945	-0.955^a	2.597	2.615^f	10	3.5	3.0	3.25	3.7
		-0.96^d							
		-0.95^f							
HD 21803	-0.91		2.607		7				
BW Vul	-0.975	-0.97^a	2.598		9	3.3	3.1	3.2	3.3
ξ' C Ma	-0.99	-1.01	2.577		5	3.0	2.8	2.9	
σ Sco	-1.045	-0.94^b	2.616	2.600^e	10	2.6	2.4	2.5	
		-0.97^e							
β C Ma	-0.995	-1.00^a	2.583		5	2.8	2.6	2.7	2.0

[a] MCNAMARA and WILLIAMS, *Ap. J.*, **121**, 53 (1955).
[b] HOGG, *Monthly Notices of the Royal Astronomical Society*, **117**, 102 (1957).
[c] JOHNSON and HARRIS, *Ap. J.*, **121**, 196 (1954).
[d] HARRIS, *Ap. J.*, **121**, 555 (1955).
[e] HARDIE and CRAWFORD, *Ap. J.*, **133**, 847 (1961).
[f] CRAWFORD, *Ap. J.*, **133**, 860 (1961).
[g] CRAWFORD, *Ap. J.*, **128**, 195 (1958).

The position of the β Cephei variables in the β-(U-B)$_0$ diagram is depicted in figure 1. For comparison purposes, the luminosity class V stars of the Orion association (CRAWFORD, 1958) are also plotted in the figure. BORGMAN and BLAAUW [1964] in a recent study of the luminosities of early-type stars point out that the stars in the Orion association are among the youngest in the sky and we may, therefore, conclude that the line drawn through the Orion stars in figure 1 must approximate very closely the zero-age main

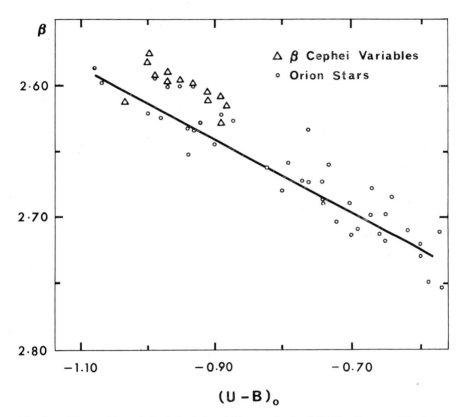

Fig. 1 — The position of the β Cephei variable stars in the β-(U-B)$_0$ diagram. The Orion stars plotted in the figure are luminosity class V only.

sequence line. The β Cephei variables form a very compact group lying on the average about 0.03 in β above the mean of the Orion stars. Since luminosity increases with decreasing β values, the position of the β Cephei variables in the β-(U-B)$_0$ diagram is consistant with the IV and III luminosity classes assigned to these variables. σ Scorpii is the only star that appears to have a discordant value. However, this star is known to be a spectroscopic binary with a period of 34 days (STRUVE, MCNAMARA and ZEBERG, 1955), and consequently the fainter component (probably a B star later in spectral type than σ Sco) probably influences the measurements.

The relationship between the $(U-B)_0$ values and periods of the β Cephei variables is exhibited in figure 2. The $(U-B)_0$ values plotted are those adopted in column 3 of table II. These values are based principally on the new $(U-B)_0$ color indices of high weight given in column 2 of table I. In some cases, a small adjustment in these $(U-B)_0$ values has been made in view of the additional values listed in column 3 of table I. Although a period-color relationship is clearly indicated, there appears to be a greater scatter around the mean line,

$$(1) \qquad\qquad (U-B)_0 = -0.540 \log P - 1.34$$

than can be accounted for by the errors of observations. For example, β Cephei and HD 21803 have nearly identical periods, yet differ by 0.06 in $(U-B)_0$. β C Ma and ξ' C Ma have periods that differ by one hour and yet these stars have essentially identical color indices. We conclude that the observational evidence indicates real scatter in the period-color relation—a result that is not unexpected if the β Cephei stars are evolving through an instability strip of definite width in the H-R diagram.

The β values listed in column 4 of table I have been used to calculate the absolute magnitudes, $Mv(\beta)$, of the β Cephei variables appearing in column 4 of table II. The mean of the author's calibration (MCNAMARA, 1965) and that given by HARDIE and CRAWFORD [1961] was used to derive these absolute magnitudes.

Equivalent widths of the $H\gamma$ and $H\delta$ lines of hydrogen have also been measured from high dispersion spectrograms for several stars in table I. The equivalent widths are the means of about four independent measurements on different spectrograms (dispersion 10 Å/mm). The $H\gamma$ equivalent widths are systematically smaller by 0.16 Å than PETRIE's [1965] equivalent widths. This correction has been applied to the equivalent widths of column 7 and absolute magnitudes, $Mv(H\gamma)$, derived from PETRIE's [1965] new calibration between absolute magnitude and the equivalent width of the $H\gamma$ line. These absolute magnitudes appear in column 5 of table II. In addition, the mean equivalent width of the $H\gamma$ and $H\delta$ lines (column 9, table I) has been utilized to derive absolute magnitudes from SINNERSTAD's [1961] calibration. A systematic correction of $+0.4$ magnitude was added to the values in column 9, to reduce them to SINNERSTAD's system before the absolute magnitudes were derived from the mean equivalent widths. The absolute magnitudes derived from SINNERSTAD's calibration are listed in column 6 of table II.

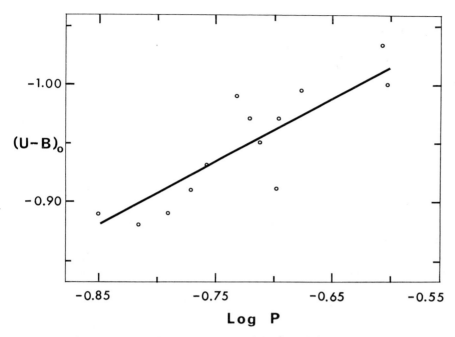

Fig. 2 — The period-color relation of the β Cephei variable stars.

TABLE II

Star	log P	$(U-B)_0$	$Mv(\beta)$	$Mv(H\gamma)$	Mv $(H\gamma, \delta)$	Mv Kopylov	Mv Assoc.	Mv
θ Oph	-0.8508	-0.89	-2.7			-3.2	-3.0	-2.9
γ Peg	-0.8182	-0.88	-3.0	-3.0	-3.3	-3.0		-3.0
δ Cet	-0.7932	-0.89	-3.3	-3.1	-3.5	-3.5		-3.4
16 Lac	-0.7721	-0.91	-3.3	-3.9	-4.0	-3.9	-3.6	-3.7
ν Eri	-0.7592	-0.93	-3.8	-3.8	-4.1	-4.1		-3.9
15 C Ma	-0.7328	-0.99	-4.1					-4.2
β Cep	-0.7212	-0.97	-4.3	-4.0	-4.0	-4.3		-4.2
12 Lac	-0.7144	-0.95	-3.9	-3.9	-3.9	-4.1	-4.0	-4.0
HD 21803	-0.6990	-0.91	-3.5					-3.6
BW Vul	-0.6968	-0.97	-3.9	-4.0	-4.0	-4.4		-4.1
ξ' C Ma	-0.6778	-0.995	-5.0	-4.3	-4.4	-4.4		-4.6
σ Sco	-0.6073	-1.035	-3.1	-4.7	-5.2	-4.8	-4.4	(-4.4)
β C Ma	-0.6021	-1.00	-4.7	-4.5	-4.7	-4.8		-4.7

They are slightly more luminous than the absolute magnitudes obtained with the Petrie calibration.

KOPYLOV [1959] has also recently determined the absolute magnitudes of the β Cephei stars utilizing equivalent widths of selected absorption lines as luminosity criterion. His results are given in column 7 of table II. Apparently, each of the four determinations lead to a well defined period-luminosity relation with only slight differences in zero point. An average absolute magnitude of each star has been calculated as listed in the last column of table II. In forming the average values, the absolute magnitudes determined from the hydrogen lines, $Mv(H\gamma)$ and $Mv(H\gamma,\delta)$, have been given half weight since both were determined from essentially the same observational data. Small corrections were also applied to the absolute magnitudes of those stars determined only from the β index since the β index gives absolute magnitudes slightly smaller than the other determinations. The average Mv values of three stars may be compared with the absolute magnitudes (column 8) determined from association memberships. The agreement

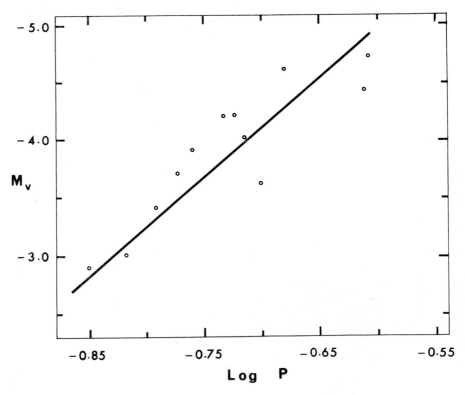

Fig. 3 — The period-luminosity relation of the β Cephei stars.

is excellent. The absolute magnitude of σ Sco in the Mv column is the association value rather than the mean. This value was adopted rather than the mean because of the binary nature of the system and the possible influence of the secondary component on the β index. The results given in table II (column 9) are depicted in figure 3. The mean line drawn by eye is given by the equation :

$$(2) \qquad\qquad Mv = -9.9 - 8.4 \log P.$$

If we now assume the β Cephei variables are homologous pulsating stars, the well known period-density law

$$(3) \qquad\qquad P\sqrt{\rho} = Q$$

must hold. Expressing the density in terms of the mass and the radius, and expressing the radius in turn in terms of the effective temperature and luminosity, one can easily show (SANDAGE and GRATTON, 1963) that equation (3) becomes:

$$(4) \qquad \log P + 1/2 \log \frac{\mathfrak{M}}{\mathfrak{M}_\odot} + 0.3\,(M_{Bol} - M_{Bol\odot}) + 3 \log \frac{Te}{Te_\odot} = \log Q$$

For the β Cephei variables we adopt:

$$(5) \qquad\qquad M_{Bol} = Mv + 2.20 + 5.00\,(U-B)_0$$

$$(6) \qquad\qquad \log \frac{\mathfrak{M}}{\mathfrak{M}_\odot} = 0.22\,Mv + 0.22$$

$$(7) \qquad\qquad \log Te = -0.947\,(U-B)_0 + 3.545.$$

Equation (5) is based on the bolometric correction data given by HARRIS [1963] while equations (6) and (7) are based on new data obtained from accurate $(U\text{-}B)_0$-β photometry of eclipsing binary stars (MCNAMARA, 1965). A small systematic correction of -0.10 has been applied to the equation

$$(8) \qquad\qquad \log \mathfrak{M}/\mathfrak{M}_\odot = -0.22\,Mv + 0.33$$

which actually gives the best fit to the eclipsing binary data to obtain equation (6). This correction was based on the evolutionary tracks computed by HENYEY, LELEVIER and LEVEE [1959] — that is the masses of the β Cephei variables are assumed to be their "zero age" main sequence values. Substituting equations (5), (6) and (7) into equation (4), and adopting $M_{Bol\odot} = +4.62$ and $Te\odot = 5784\,°K$, we obtain from equation (4)

$$(9) \qquad\qquad \log Q = \log P + 0.19\,Mv - 1.341\,(U\text{-}B)_0 - 1.267.$$

Substitution of the relevant observed data found in table II, into equation (9), leads to an average Q value for the β Cephei variables of Q = 0.035. This value differs from the values of 0.021 found by HITOTUYANAGI and TAKEUTI [1963] and 0.027 found by LEDOUX and WALRAVEN [1958]. The differences can be attributed principally to higher effective temperatures used in this investigation. STOTHER's [1965] evolutionary models have a Q value of 0.045 close to the standard model value of 0.044. If we adopt masses for the β Cephei variables consistant with their luminosities, instead of extrapolating backwards along evolutionary tracks to the main sequence, we obtain Q = 0.040. In view of the observational uncertainties of some of the observed quantities substituted into equation (4) (in particular bolometric corrections), it is not alltogether impossible that Q could be consistant with the value obtained from stellar model calculations.

Equation (1) relating $(U-B)_0$ to log P has been substituted into equation (9) along with the observed Q value of 0.035. The period-luminosity relation resulting from these substitutions is

(10) $Mv = - 10.48 - 9.07 \log P.$

This equation, based on the $P\sqrt{\rho} = Q$ relation, may be compared with equation (2) derived directly from the observational data. The agreement is quite satisfactory in view of the uncertainties involved in each equation. Equations (9) and (10) have been used to plot the position of the β Cephei variables in the H-R diagram shown in figure 4. The mean line runs diagonally up from the "zero age" main sequence, and the lines of constant periods run approximately parallel to the main sequence. The β Cephei variables are also plotted in figure 4 for comparison. It is evident that the β Cephei variables occupy a very narrow strip in the H-R diagram. If the B stars evolve upward and to the right as indicated by the current stellar models, it is evident that the periods of the β Cep variables must increase if they continue to the right through the β Cephei instability strip as Struve was the first to point out. As he has also suggested, prolonged studies of the periods of these stars offer one of the most promising areas of investigation where the detection of evolutionary changes may actually be observed. It is of interest to note here that some of these stars do show evidence of increasing period, and as yet, none have been found that show any evidence of decreasing period.

As we have already suggested, the finite width of the instability strip can also easily account for stars with widely differing periods having essentially the same colors and absolute magnitudes. A case in point is the stars β C Ma, ξ' C Ma, and 15 C Ma which have almost identical colors and yet differ widely in their period characteristics. These stars are all located in the same part of the sky and color index determinations were made on the same nights under identical conditions so there can be no doubt about observational errors affecting one star differently from the others. We conclude that there is intrinsic dispersion in the period-color relation and probably in the period-luminosity relation as well.

We are indebted to the National Science Foundation for partial support in securing some of the observational data reported in this paper.

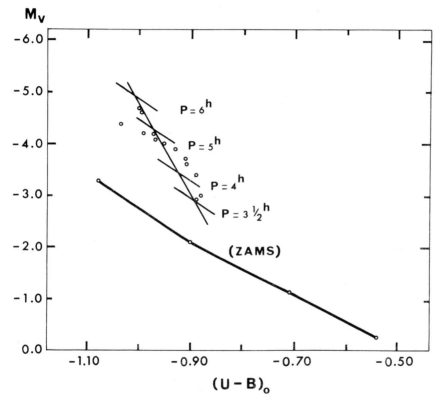

Fig. 4 — The position of the β Cephei variables in the H-R diagram. The "zero-age" main sequence is shown for comparison.

REFERENCES

BORGMAN, J. and BLAAUW, A., 1963, *B.A.N.*, **17**, 358.
CRAWFORD, D.L., 1958, *Ap. J.*, **128**, 185.
HARDIE, R.H. and CRAWFORD, D.L., 1961, *Ap. J.*, **133**, 843.

HARRIS, D.L., 1963, *Basic Astronomical Data*, (ed. K.A. Strand, Chicago Press of Chicago University) p. 269.

HENYEY, L.G., LELEVIER, R., and LEVEE, R.D. 1959, *Ap. J.*, **129**, 2.

HITOTUYANAGI, Z. and TAKEUTI, M., 1963, *Science Reports*, (Tohoku University,) **47**, 159.

KOPYLOV, L.M., 1959, *Pub. Crimean, Ap. Obs.*, **21**, 71.

LEDOUX, P. and WALRAVEN, T., 1958, *Handbuch der Physik* **51**, 581.

MCNAMARA, D.H., 1965, *I.A.U. Symposium* No. 24 190.

PETRIE, R.M., *D.A.O. Victoria* **12**, 317).

SANDAGE, A.R. and GRATTON, L., 1963, *Star Evolution* (Academic Press, New York), L. Gratton editor, p. 45.

SINNERSTAD, U., 1961, *Stockholm Ann.* **21**, No. 6.

STRUVE O., MCNAMARA, D.H., and ZEBERGS, V., 1955, *Ap. J.*, **122**, 122.

STOTHERS, R., 1965, *Ap. J.*, **141**, 671.

Slow or rapid rotation in the β CMa stars ?

A. van Hoof

University of Louvain, Belgium

Fifteen years after W. F. Meyer's discovery [1934] that the radial velocity changes of β CMa do not simply follow a six hours period, but that they show "beats" with a period of 49 days, an intrigued Struve started work with his collaborators to find out whether the other members of the β Cep group show similar phenomena. The result of his investigations was that about 50% of these stars could be said to show the beats, as well in their light as in their radial velocity variations. As β Cep itself appeared to miss this peculiarity, it gradually lost its title of prototype in favour of the more representative β CMa.

Beats reveal the presence of two variations with nearly equal periods. In the case of the β C Ma stars the two variations appear to have, despite their almost equal periods, a quite different origin and character, for one of them (called the P_2 variation by Struve) [1952a] is found back in the changing widths of the spectral lines, while the other (Struve's P_1 variation) has no apparent bearing on these widths. When faced with the challenge to explain the occurence of these two periods, most astronomers pointed to stellar rotation as the agent behind at last one of them.

Meyer himself, and for a while Struve [1952b] also, saw β CMa as a big B star around which revolves a very small but very dense companion. In their minds one of the observed periods corresponded to the time of revolution of this satellite, the other period being that of an oscillation mode of the B star which happened to be near resonance with the revolution. The mode was thought to be excited by the periodic disturbance which the star's surface had to suffer from the passing of the satellite.

When considerations on the real sizes of the B stars, and on the possible time of revolution of a satellite, proved fatal to this interpretation Struve dropped the satellite, but, firm in his believe that rotation plays a major role, replaced it by a "turbulent spot" [1950] on the surface of the now single B star. This spot was supposed to produce sharp lines in the spectrum, the rest of the stellar disk producing broad ones. The axial rotation of the star would then explain, through different and changing Doppler shifts, the observed periodic changes in the compound line profiles. With this picture

Gauthier-Villars, Paris - Modern Astrophysics - 1967.

P_2 represents the period of rotation, P_1 that of the pulsation of the star.

In connexion with the question which we want to answer in this article the relevant point in the turbulent spot hypothesis is that it implies an improbably high velocity of rotation. The hypothesis did not survive this and other objections.

In the early fifties, M. F. WALKER [1954], then one of STRUVE's students, also thought of rotation as the probable cause for the intricate behaviour of the β CMa stars. After the assumption of radial pulsations and the application of the Baade test had lead him to a negative value for the radius of 16 Lac, he expressed the opinion that non radial oscillations might perhaps provide a clue.

The same idea was fostered by P. LEDOUX [1951] who had investigated the free oscillations of a rotating gaseous star. LEDOUX had come to the conclusion that each oscillation of frequency $\sigma_{k,0}$ (k = the order of the mode) which a star suffers in the absence of rotation, gets accompanied in the case of rotation by non radial oscillations of frequency

$$\sigma_{k,0} \pm m . C_k . \Omega$$

where $m = 1, 2, 3, ...$, C_k is a constant for each mode and Ω is the angular velocity. LEDOUX paid attention only to the fundamental mode and considered that only the secondary oscillations for $m = 2$ would be of importance. He demonstrated moreover that in case the star is seen with its polar axis at right angles, each of these secondary oscillations will reflect itself in the line widths.

The point in which we are presently interested is that when Ledoux confronted his theoretical results with the observations of β CMa, he found a very *low* velocity of rotation (8-10 km/sec at the equator). But Ledoux could not explain why one of the predicted oscillations had been left unexcited, nor why there was a 180° phase difference between the predicted and the observed line widenings. And for these reasons this interpretation too met only a moderate success and left us without certitude about the real value of the rotational speed.

The present author, working with Struve in 1952, suggested that the two puzzling periods might correspond to the oscillation times along the polar radius and in the equator respectively, the difference between the two coming from the polar flattening, itself due to the *rapid* rotation of the star. According to STRUVE [1950], D. H. MENZEL had already proposed a similar interpretation, but with a magnetic field as the cause of the inequality between the polar and the equatorial periods of pulsation. The idea was dropped, apart from other reasons, because the line doubling that was observed in some stars of the group, always occurred at the time of largest amplitude in the beat cycle, thus being 180° out of phase with the prediction from the model.

In 1961, D. H. MCNAMARA and K. HANSEN [1961] pointed out that the β CMa stars all have $V_{rot} < 60$ km/sec, and that beats or irregularities in the light and velocity variations are the apanage of the group members with the highest projected rotational velocities. From these facts they concluded that, of the B stars which in the course of their evolution pass through the β CMa region of the H-R diagram, only those become variable that have rotational velocities below a well defined limit. For the smallest rotational speeds the light and radial velocity variations would obey a single period, be symmetrical and of constant amplitude; with increasing rotational speed the variations become more intricate and two periods appear. For still faster rotation ($V_{rot} > 50$ km/sec) the pulsations get completely damped. It is enough for our purpose, to retain the general conclusion from this statistical investigation: the β CMa stars have *low* to *moderate* rotational speeds.

One is forced to the opposite conclusion if he adhers to CHANDRASEKHAR and LEBOVITZ' interpretation [1963] of the beat phenomenon. Investigating the theoretically possible oscillations in distorted rotating polytropes these authors found that two different kinds of pulsation are possible: a radial pulsation R and a non radial pulsation S with

$$(\xi_{eq})_S < |(\xi_{pol})_S|$$

[$\xi = (dr)/r$] and opposite signs for the two ξ's. In the particular case $\Gamma_1 = 1.6$ however these two pulsation modes get coupled: R loses its purely radial character with $(\xi_{eq})_R > (\xi_{pol})_R$, the two periods become nearly equal with however $P_R > P_S$, and the difference $P_R - P_S$ becomes a function of Ω^2 (Ω the angular velocity). Without coupling only the R oscillations imply pressure variations through which they can affect the line widths; after coupling with the S oscillations this distinction is only partly washed out and one must still expect the R pulsations to have a heavier bearing on the line profiles than have the S oscillations. These theoretical results induced Chandrasekhar and Lebovitz to see the solution of the beat enigma in the identifications

$$P_1 \text{ (STRUVE's notation)} = P_S$$
$$P_2 \text{ (STRUVE's notation)} = P_R$$

with

$$\Gamma_1 = 1.6 \qquad \text{and} \qquad \Delta P/P = \text{const} \cdot \Omega^2$$

where the const. is a function of the polytropic index and of the central density.

The important point for us to mention is that Chandrasekhar and Lebovitz' formulae require *very high equatorial velocities* (> 100 km/sec.) to account for the observed $\Delta P/P$, which are of the order of 0.02 on the average.

An *equally rapid rotation* (V_{rot} > 90 km/sec) had to be admitted by E. BÖHM-VITENSE [1963] who, taking up an old idea and working it out to some extent, saw in polar flattening and the subsequent inequality between the pulsation periods along the polar and the equatorial radii the origin of the beats.

Both the foregoing interpretations were criticized by the present author 1964] on the ground that in the two cases where they could be checked (σ Sco and 16 Lac), they showed serious discrepancies between the required and the probable equatorial velocities of rotation.

The two stars quoted are indeed single lined spectroscopic binaries. If we postulate

$$i_{equat} = i_{orbit}$$

we find the latter from the equation

$$\sin i \,^{(1)} = \frac{(V_{rot})_{obs}}{V_{rot}}$$

where the numerator is found from the line profiles and the denominator from the ΔP's and the theories under discusssion. By then dividing the *observed* velocity in the orbit by this sin i we find the *hypothetical* velocity in the orbit itself. The latter is then compared with the *most probable* velocity in the orbit, which is derived from the formula

$$K_1 = C.P^{\frac{1}{3}}.\ \mathfrak{M}_2^{\frac{1}{3}}.\ (\alpha + 1)^{\frac{2}{3}}.\ (1 - e^2)^{-\frac{1}{2}}$$

by introducing the most probable values for $\mathfrak{M}_2$ and α.

In this way the required equatorial velocities were found to exceed the most probable ones by a factor 7 to 8.

No role is left for axial rotation in the "ejected shell" hypothesis first formulated by STRUVE [1955] and later worked out by G.J. ODGERS [1956].

Here one of the P's is identified with the free pulsation time of the variable and the other is seen as the "flight time" of a shell or superficial layer that is blown off the star at each expansion, rises to a certain height and then

---

(1) $i = 90^\circ - i_{orb}$

falls back. According as to whether the flight time is longer than the pulsation period or not, the falling shell will interfere with the nextcoming rising shell or not. Only in the first eventuality will beats ensue.

The main argument against this interpretation was that the observed widening and even doubling of the spectral lines always leave the equivalent widths of the lines unaffected (HUANG, 1955) thus bringing the proof that the component lines have their origin in regions that are *next* each other, and *not* the one *above* the other.

In the author's opinion too, rotation had nothing to do with the phenomena observed in the β CMa stars. It was even tacitly postulated that, if there was any rotation at all, it would be *so slow* that it did not affect in the least the character of the oscillations. The latter were supposed to be purely radial, the P_2 corresponding to the vibration in the fundamental mode, the P_1 representing the difference pulsation between the fundamental mode and an, at the time not yet discovered, overtone oscillation with a period about half the fundamental one (VAN HOOF, 1957).

Intensive photoelectric observations of the southern β CMa, made with the 60″ Rockefeller telescope of the Boyden Observatory, have given strong support to this interpretation, but have at the same time shown the great incompleteness of the original picture. Not only did the lightcurves of ν Eri (VAN HOOF, 1961a), β Cru (VAN HOOF, 1962a) and θ Oph (VAN HOOF, 1962b) show clearly the predicted overtone around the time of minimum amplitude in the beat cycle (i.e. whenever the two main oscillations more or less neutralized each other, thus giving the weaker overtone an opportunity to manifest its presence), but they also disclosed important differences in the lengths and the amplitudes of the successive beat cycles. In fact these irregularities are so pronounced that one cannot strictly speak of a periodic phenomenon and that any explanation has to account for the presence of many more than three incommensurable periods. The full periodogram analysis of the observations finally yielded the following results for the stars quoted:

(1) the successive lower modes are present and, despite their decreasing amplitudes can be followed up to the fourth; their frequencies stand to the frequency of the fundamental mode in the following ratios:

$$\text{fundam. mode } \sigma_0 = 1.0$$

$$\text{1st overtone } \sigma_1 = 1.5 - \varepsilon_1 \, (\varepsilon_1 \text{ small}, 0.01 - 0.02)$$

$$\text{2d overtone } \sigma_2 = 2.0 - \varepsilon_2 \, (\varepsilon_2 \text{ small}, 0.01 - 0.04)$$

3d overtone $\sigma_3 = 2.5 - \varepsilon_3$ (ε_3 small, $0.01 - 0.04$)

4th overtone $\sigma_4 = 3.0 - \varepsilon_4$ (ε_4 small, $0.01 - 0.04$)

etc.

(2) the existing ratios favour the excitation of the difference oscillations, with frequencies

$$\sigma_{0,2} = \sigma_2 - \sigma_0 = \sigma_0 - \varepsilon_2$$

$$\sigma_{1,3} = \sigma_3 - \sigma_1 = \sigma_0 - \varepsilon_3 + \varepsilon_1$$

$$\sigma_{2,4} = \sigma_4 - \sigma_2 = \sigma_0 - \varepsilon_4 + \varepsilon_2$$

etc.

which are all near perfect resonance with σ_0.

(3) furthermore are excited the difference oscillations

$$\sigma_{0,3} = \sigma_3 - \sigma_0 = \sigma_0 - \varepsilon_3$$

$$\sigma_{1,4} = \sigma_4 - \sigma_1 = \sigma_0 - \varepsilon_4 + \varepsilon_1$$

$$\sigma_{2,5} = \ \cdots\cdots$$

etc.

all near resonance with σ_1, and the difference oscillations

$$\sigma_{0,4} = \sigma_4 - \sigma_0 = \sigma_0 - \varepsilon_4$$

etc.

In brief, the free oscillation in each mode is accompanied by a number of forced oscillations of practically the same periods. In most cases it is found that $\sigma_{2,4} = \sigma_0$ and this perfect resonance probably makes the fundamental oscillation P_0 (Struve's P_2) to be the predominant one; in β CMa $\sigma_{2,4} \neq \sigma_0$ and there the free fundamental oscillation stays well behind $\sigma_{2,4}$ in strength. The difference oscillation (0,2) usually corresponds to Struve's secondary period P_1. In β Cru the first overtone is almost as strong as the fundamental oscillation and this abnormal strength can again be accounted for by the complete resonance with σ_1 of one of the difference oscillations $\sigma_{i, i+3}$

(4) the ratios of the successive free overtone frequencies to the free fundamental frequency reproduce precisely the theoretical ratios that are computed for the standard model with Γ_1 values between 1.51 and 1.53. A small run in the Γ_1's parallels the run in the periods.

The above results seemed to provide a satisfactory, physically acceptable explanation for the various features of the light and radial velocity changes (the line widening and doubling is still left out of consideration) and, with regard to the question that we try to answer in this paper, they seemed to reveal *no trace* of any effect on these changes *of either slow or rapid rotation*.

This point of view was also R. STOTHERS', whom a theoretical discussion on the radial pulsations of hydrogen burning giants lead to the conclusion that the effect of rotation on the observed phenomena in the β CMa stars is probably small.

But σ Sco and 16 Lac must rotate, for they are the bright members of spectroscopic binaries. Cannot we expect then the close investigation of their light and radial velocity changes to give information on *their* rotational speeds, thereby providing us with some test to probe further the various interpretations of the beat phenomenon that we have reviewed?

With this possibility in mind, we made intensive observations on σ Sco at Boyden in 1962-'63-'64. In all the star was observed in 70 nights. The U and Y lightcurves and their analysis disclosed the following:

(1) the average beat period is $8^d.25$ with a strong dispersion both in the lengths and the intensities of the beats;

(2) the secondary period (STRUVE's P_1) this time is shorter than the main period (STRUVE's P_2): $0.^d2396868$ against $0.^d24684063$;

(3) the colour variation in P_1 is practically zero, contrarily to what is the case in the β CMa stars investigated previously. This circumstance, together with the one sub (2), seemed to favour CHANDRASEKHAR and LEBOVITZ' interpretation, since their R and S oscillations show these peculiarities, but

(4) there is a complete set of frequencies in which one recognizes again the various lower modes, with ratios that reproduce the theoretical values for the polytrope of index 3 and $\Gamma_1 = 1.51$. Each of these frequencies is now framed by evenly spaced frequencies of the kind predicted by COWLING and NEWING [1949] and by LEDOUX [1951]. Their spacing discloses an angular velocity such that it assures synchronism between the rotation and the revolution in the orbit. With an assumed radius $R_\sigma = 10 R_\odot$ this corresponds to an equatorial speed of

$$V_{rot} = 15 \text{ km/sec.}$$

It is hard to see nothing but pure chance behind the equality P_{beat} $= 1/4 P_{orbit}$, the more so that the amplitude in the beat cycle is maximum precisely at the times that the star is nearest to us, farthest from us and midway in between. One starts thinking that the beats might simply represent the effect of changing perspective on the apparent strength of the distorsions which one of the non-radial oscillations impresses on the star, something e.g. like would occur if the deformations were as in figure 1.

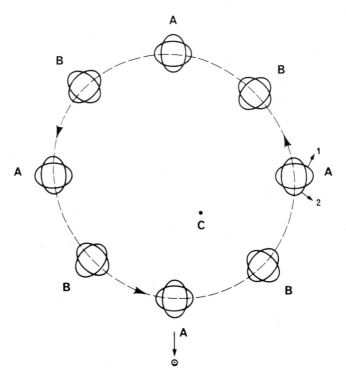

Fig. 1 — The figure represents eight positions of σ Sco in its orbit. They correspond to the epochs of maximum (positions A) and of minimum (positions B) amplitude in the beat cycle. For each position the equator is shown at the phases of maximum deformation (ellipses 1 and 2). The deformations have been enormously exaggerated, actually no radius changes its average length by more than a few hundredths. The main (radial pseudo-radial) oscillation and secondary phenomena are not represented.

But this model too is hard to reconcile with some details of both the photometric and the spectroscopic observational results. We refrain from further discussing this point since it is beyond the scope of this article.

For our present problem it is enough to state that one β CMa star at least gave good evidence that it is *rotating slowly*.

Intrigued by the discovery of non radial oscillations in σ Sco[2] we examined again the periodogram, reproduced in figure 2, which we had constructed earlier for v Eri. It shows distinctively a number of evenly spaced peaks to the left and right of P_0, which we had neglected as non significant at the time of our first investigation. If we accept them now as the sign of the star's rotation, they indicate through their spacing a rotational speed at the equator of v Eri of

$$V_{rot} = 9\text{-}12 \text{ km/sec}$$

for an assumed radius $R_v = 8 \text{ R}_\odot$ (VAN HOOF, 1961*b*) so teaching us that a second β CMa star is *rotating slowly*.

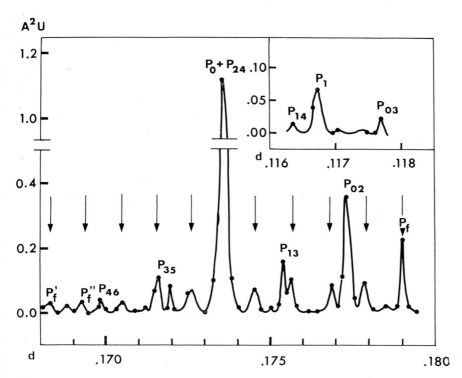

Fig. 2 — Periodogram of v Eri (*Zeit. f. Astroph.*), **53**, 106, 1961). The arrows point towards evenly spaced peaks. Their spacing suggests an equatorial velocity of rotation of 9-12 km/sec.

---

[2] The implications of this discovery on our previous interpretation of the β CMa stars will be examined elsewhere.

The same can be said of 16 Lac. A detailed search for the frequencies that shape its light and velocity curves has not yet been made, but in its absence, strong arguments can be derived from its orbital elements, the mass-function and its "observed" rotational velocity, in favour of the thesis that its equatorial velocity

$$V_{rot} \leqslant 30 \text{ km/sec.}$$

The objection could be made that our velocities have a tendency to be smaller than the "observed" or "projected" rotational speeds determined from spectral lines. The answer is that these "observed" speeds are usually derived under the assumption that the deviations of the line profiles from their normal shape are entirely due to rotation, while it is evident that non radial oscillations—implying different velocities of expansion or of contraction over the stellar disk,—may broaden the lines as well. In the case of β CMa itself, e.g., for which a $V_{rot} \sin i$ of 30 km/sec is given in the litterature, the author found that about half the line width came from what is usually called "turbulence". The published $V_{rot} \sin i$'s should therefore be considered (in the case of the β CMa stars!) as representing absolute maxima, which the real projected rotational velocities can be far from attaining.

The above remark still accentuates the smallness—evidenced by the narrow spectral lines—of the projected rotational velocities of the β CMa stars. That this smallness is not due to the projection angle, but that it is caused by intrinsic slow rotation seems now well established in the three cases where a check was possible. This undeniably raises a strong presumption that *slow rotation* is the rule among the other members of the group also.

REFERENCES

BÖHM-VITENSE, E., 1963, *P. A. S. P.*, **75**, 154.
CHANDRASEKHAR, S. and LEBOVITZ, N. R., 1963, *Ap. J.* **136**, 1082 and 1105.
COWLING, T. G. and NEWING, R. A., 1949, *Ap. J.* **109**, 149.
HUANG, S. S., 1955, *P. A. S. P.*, **67**, 22.
LEDOUX, P., 1951, *Ap. J.* **114**, 373.
McNAMARA, D. H. and HANSSEN, K., 1961, *Ap. J.* **134**, 207.
MEYER, W. F., 1934, *P. A. S. P.*, **46**, 202.
ODGERS, G. J., 1956, *Publ. D. A. O. Victoria* **10**, 215.
STOTHERS, R., *private communication*.
STRUVE, O., 1950, *Ap. J.* **112**, 520.
STRUVE, O., 1952a, *P. A. S. P.* **64**, 20.'
STRUVE, O., 1952b, *Ann. d'Ap.* **15**, 157.
STRUVE, O., 1955, *P. A. S. P.*, **67**, 135.
VAN HOOF, A., 1957, *P. A. S. P.*, **69**, 308.

VAN HOOF, A., 1961a, *Zs. f. Ap.* **53**, 106.
VAN HOOF, A., 1961b, *Zs. f. Ap.* **53**, 124.
VAN HOOF, A., 1962a, *Zs. f. Ap.* **54**, 244.
VAN HOOF, A., 1962b, *Zs. f. Ap.* **54**, 255.
VAN HOOF, A., 1964, *Zs. f. Ap.* **60**, 184.
WALKER, M. F., 1954, *Ap. J.* **120** 58.

The stars of low luminosity

WILLEM J. LUYTEN

University of Minnesota

One of the principal aims of the proper motion survey on 48″ Schmidt plates was to determine the frequency and the kinematic properties of the stars of low luminosity and, from it, to make a new determination of the luminosity function. While the survey has been operating only two years enough material has accumulated to make possible at least a preliminary analysis, especially for the stars of *very* low luminosity, almost unknown before. First of all, however, it is necessary to define what we mean by "very low" luminosity. This should be done in such a way as to obtain a sizeable number of individual objects to treat statistically, and yet not involve such enormous numbers as to become almost unworkable. Arbitrarily I have selected as the upper limit for such very low luminosity stars a bolometric luminosity of one thousandth of that of the sun, or $M_{bolo} = +12.2$. Since the vast majority of stars with these luminosities will be red dwarfs the correction from bolometric to visual absolute magnitude — which, at $M_{bolo} = +8.6$ amounts to $+1.9$ (HARRIS, 1963)—may be estimated to be at least $+2.5$, hence our limiting visual absolute magnitude is $+14.7$. With red stars of this kind, the colorindex will probably be at least around $+1.8$ hence the photographic absolute magnitudes we are interested in will be those larger than $+16.5$ pg. We are, however, dealing with a proper motion survey of stars for which few, if any, parallaxes are known. The objects we want must therefore be selected statistically according to large values of $H = m + 5 + 5 \log \mu$. Arbitrarily assuming an average tangential velocity of 75 km/sec for these large proper motion stars—which corresponds to the value $H - M = 6$,—we thus finally arrive at the lower limit $H = 22.5$ for the selection of stars of very low luminosity. While admittedly the assumptions made here are tentative I do think that one can be reasonably certain that stars for which $H = m + 5 + \log \mu \geqslant 22.5$ will, on the average, have luminosities smaller than 1/30,000 of that of the sun, photographically, or smaller than 1/1,000 bolometrically.

In terms of apparent magnitude and proper motion this means we are looking for stars with $m = 14$ pg and proper motion larger than 5″ annually, or $m = 17.5$, $\mu = 1″$ down to $m = 21$, $\mu = 0″20$. Before the present survey

Gauthier-Villars, Paris - Modern Astrophysics ▪ 1967.

began only twelve such stars were known, and six of these are faint components of wide binaries, the faintest being van Biesbroeck's star ($+4$:
40 48 B, 19.4, $1''46$). Only a few percent of the sky have been examined on the
48″ SCHMIDT plates and although only about two thirds of the plates blinked
have been completely measured, another 205 stars of this kind have been
added- eloquent testimony for the power of this unique telescope.

The plates blinked have purposely been selected so as to give reasonably
representative coverage of the northern hemisphere for the purpose of a
solar motion determination. In order to facilitate the actual calculations
straight averages were first obtained for each area and adjacent areas were
further averaged together. While this resulted in rather widely different
numbers of stars, ranging from 4 to 31, being represented by each area, I
believe that this way is preferable to treating all stars individually, and at
any rate the final result will not be very different. The averages finally accepted
for the solution are shown in table I.

TABLE I

Area	Center 1950		No. of Stars	$\overline{m}_{pg}$	$\overline{\mu}_\alpha \cos\delta$	$\overline{\mu}_\delta$
I	0:00	$+90$	8	20.6	$+''27$	$+''06$
II	1 33	$+18.5$	21	20.6	$+''23$	$-''20$
III	1 41	-17.5	18	20.9	$+''05$	$-''16$
IV	2 19	$+17.4$	10	20.6	$+''14$	$-''11$
V*	4 18	$+20.2$	25	21.0	$+''18$	$-''23$
VI	7 30	$+65.0$	5	20.3	$-''10$	$-''38$
VII	8 29	$+17.7$	7	20.9	$-''11$	$-''26$
VIII	10 24	$+36.0$	7	20.4	$-''18$	$-''28$
IX	11 45	-24.5	13	20.5	$-''22$	$-''05$
X	12 29	$+12.5$	13	20.9	$-''22$	$-''12$
XI*	12 38	$+32.5$	31	20.7	$-''23$	$-''16$
XII	14 04	$+17.6$	12	20.9	$-''06$	$-''13$
XIII	15 15	$+52.7$	6	20.0	$-''28$	$-''21$
XIV	18 54	$+62.4$	10	20.3	$-''07$	$+''05$
XV	21 17	-11.7	4	20.2	$-''03$	$-''22$
XVI	23 40	$+14.0$	14	20.8	$+''09$	$-''11$

* Area V represents the average for seven plates in the Hyades region, area XI that for
4 plates near the North Galactic Pole.

The total number of stars represented in this table is 204, with a mean photographic magnitude of 20.7; one star (LP 658-2) was so widely different in position and much brighter (15.7) that it could not easily be fitted in and has accordingly been left out. Of the 204 stars used in the solution 169 were fainter than $m = 20.0$ and only 4 brighter than 18.0. I have therefore not reduced the motions to the same apparent magnitude but have simply taken straight averages for both magnitudes and motions.

Making the usual least-squares solution we obtain:

$$
\begin{aligned}
X &= -\,''085 & A &= 296° \\
Y &= +\,.173 \text{ giving} & D &= +43° & \bar{m} &= 20.7 \\
Z &= -\,.181 & q &= 0''27 & \overline{H} &= 23.1
\end{aligned}
$$

With a declination as high as this the solar velocity may well be as high as 45 km/sec hence the mean parallax would be of the order of $p = 0''028$ corresponding to an absolute magnitude around $M = 18.0$ and a *mean* absolute magnitude around $M = 17.7\,pg$.

The apparent, photographic magnitudes used are simple eye estimates made from the plates and are probably subject not only to large accidental errors but also possibly to systematic errors, especially near the plate limit, where my magnitudes could well be too faint by, say, half a magnitude.

As a check on the values derived above, therefore, it may be of interest to make another solution, using only the brightest stars (with, naturally, the largest motions). To this end I have selected from our list of 205 stars only those not fainter than the faintest of the twelve known before, or those with $m \leqslant 19.4$ which are fifteen in number, and one more, found by Plaut on the same 48″ Schmidt plates during a variable star program. This gives us a total of twenty-eight stars, and, while the general group of 205 stars used before has mainly statistical interest only, these twenty eight may be of individual interest and the salient data about them are therefore given in full in table II. The first seven columns of this table are self-explanatory, while the last three give, in order, the quantity $H = m + 5 + 5 \log \mu$, the trigonometric parallax and the corresponding absolute magnitude for those eleven stars for which these last two quantities have been determined. With a total of only twenty-eight stars, ranging in magnitude from 14.2 to 19.4 (pg) and in proper motion from 5″40 to 0″50 the data cannot be used individually. All motions have therefore been reduced to the standard apparent magnitude 18.0 before they were used for the calculation of the solar motion.

Since faint companions often differ slightly from single stars or brighter components, another solution was made by rejecting the seven stars marked with an asterisk in table II.

TABLE II

Star	R.A. 1950 Dec.		m_{pg}	color	μ	θ	H	p	M
* LP 464-521 B	0h 14m 9	+12°01′	19.4	m	0″50	95°	22.9		
G 69-47	1h 02m 8	+28°14′	16.5	m	1″91	94°	22.9		
G 34-15	1h 13m 7	+24°04′	16.8	m	1″90	112°	23.2		
LP 468-66	1h 36m 0	+11°07′	16.8	m	1″62	145°	22.9		
LP 768-500	1h 45m 4	−17°26′	18.3	a	1″18	188°	23.7		
LP 658-2	5h 52m 7	− 4°09′	15.7	g	2″38	167°	22.6	.148	16.5
* L 745-46 B	7h 38m 1	−17°17′	17.6	m	1″26	117°	23.1	.150:	18.5
* −33: 4113 B	7h 43m 8	−33°49′	18.3	m	1″69	350°	24.4		
R 619	8h 09m 2	+9°02′	14.2	m	5″40	167°	22.8	.151	15.1
LP 425-140	8h 37m 7	+18°35′	19.2	m	0″90	240°	24.0	.139	19.9
LP 316-400	10h 34m 7	+30°27′	19.4	m	1″00	233°	24.4		
W 359	10h 54m 1	+ 7°20′	15.7	m	4″71	235°	24.1	.402	18.7
* +44: 2051 B	11h 03m 0	+43°47′	16.0	m	4″53	295°	24.3	.173	17.2
LP 851-446	11h 57m 5	−23°18′	19.2	m	0″50	176°	22.7	.	
LP 320-434	12h 19m 1	+29°12′	18.3	m	1″03	254°	23.4		
* L 68-27	12h 25m 6	−71°13′	17.2	k-m	1″17	339°	22.5	.152:	18.1
W 489	13h 34m 4	+ 3°58′	15.5	k	3″87	253°	23.4	.131	16.1
LP 323-239	13h 39m 0	+30°17′	16.5	m	1″59	274°	22.5		
LP 439-321	14h 12m 7	+14°31′	19.4	m	0″42	141°	22.5		
LP 174-181	14h 13m 5	+48°02′	17.1	m	1″45	237°	22.9		
Pl 1	16h 05m 5	−10°17′	17.7	m	1″44	195°	23.5		
* −8: 4352 C	16h 52m 9	− 8°18′	18.:	m	1″19	223°	23.4	.152	18.9
LP 102-10	17h 13m 6	+60°51′	18.5	m	1″01	241°	23.5		
LP 102-320	17h 54m 8	+58°24′	18.7	m	0″88	17°	23.4		
* +4: 4048 B	19h 14m 6	+ 5°07′	19.4	m	1″46	203°	25.2	.168	20.6
LP 106-38	20h 13m 9	+61°36′	18.7	m	0″67	26°	22.8		
W 1084	20h 41m 8	+55°08′	16.8	m	1″87	21°	23.2	.069	16.0
LP 757-13	21h 04m 8	−13°38′	18.7	m	0″68	228°	22.9		

* Stars marked with an asterisk are faint companions.

The resultant Solar Motion comes out as:

$$X = - 0″30 \qquad A = 292° \qquad 28 \text{ stars}$$
$$Y = + 0″74 \quad \text{giving} \quad D = +39° \qquad m = 18.0$$
$$Z = - 0″65 \qquad q = 1″03 \qquad \overline{H} = 23.7$$

This gave

$$X = - 0''17 \qquad A = 283° \quad 21 \text{ stars}$$
$$Y = + 0''77 \quad \text{or} \quad D = + 40° \quad m = 18.0$$
$$Z = - 0''67 \qquad q = 1''03 \qquad \bar{H} = 23.7$$

I have not calculated the mean errors of these quantities by the usual least-squares method since I believe that a more realistic indication of them may be obtained from a comparison of the three sets of values of A and D and we may estimate them to be of the order of 4° in A and 2° in D. Assuming, as before, a solar velocity around 45 km/sec would give a mean parallax around 0''10 and a corresponding absolute magnitude of + 18.1 *pg*. The *mean* absolute magnitude then would be about + 17.8 *pg*.

For the eleven stars with known trigonometric parallaxes we find $\bar{M}$ = + 17.8, $\bar{H}$ = 23.5 while, when rejecting the five faint companions from among these we obtain $\bar{M}$ = 17.1, $\bar{H}$ = 23.2. These agree so closely with the corresponding values from our three sets of solar motions that we may finally adopt as the mean values for all 216 stars:

$$A = 293°$$
$$D = + 41°$$
$$V_\odot = 45 \text{ km/sec}$$
$$\bar{M} = 17.6 \, pg$$

Counting the numbers of stars between given limits of H we obtain the following tail of the frequency curve in H

H	n	n'
22.5	63	150
23.0	86	110
23.5	29	33
24.0	19	21
24.5	13	13
25.0	5	5
25.5	1	1

Since the limis chosen were 22.75 to 23.25 etc., the number given for H = 22.5 which contains only the values H = 22.5, 22.6, and 22.7 but obviously not those of 22.3 and 22.4 should be multiplied by at least 5/3, and thus become at least 105. Furthermore, it should be pointed out that from the plates not completely measured only the largest motions have been included, whereas, if all stars had been measured the total number with

H $\geqslant$ 22.5 would probably have reached at least 300 and possibly 350. The missing stars would be almost entirely in the first two groups and the actual distribution might well appear somewhat like the numbers given in the last column labeled n'.

First we might draw individual attention to the five stars with H $\geqslant$ 25.0 as these are undoubtedly the faintest stars now known. Table III gives the data for them.

TABLE III

Star	R.A. 1950 Dec.	m_{pg}	Color	μ	θ	H
LP 468-190	1h 42m 8 +12°51	21.0	m	0"69	103°	25.2
* LP 357-150	4h 02m 4 +22°22	21.+	m	0"51	133°	25.0
LP 414-165	4h 16m 6 +17°50	21.0	m	0"68	162°	25.1
* LP 495-25	12h 18m 5 + 9°14	21.+	m	0"66	245°	25.6
+4:4048 B	19h 14m 6 + 5°07	19.4	m	1"46	203°	25.2

* These two stars are invisible on the blue plates and in the calculation of H the photographic magnitude has been assumed to be 21.5.

Accepting a possible total number of from 300-350 stars with H $\geqslant$ 22.5 for all areas blinked would indicate that there might be some 6 500 in the entire sky. Furher accepting from the solution for all 205 stars a mean parallax of 0"028 for them would indicate around 2 000 stars nearer than this distance of 37 parsecs or of the order of 4-5 stars nearer than 5 parsecs. In the luminosity function I derived from the Bruce Proper Motion Survey in 1939 (Luyten, 1939) a total of 7.5 stars nearer than five parsecs and of absolute photographic magnitude 17-20 was predicted. These two values agree as well as one has a right to expect from so crude and preliminary analysis as the present one, and it gives one confidence in the feeling that, when the 48" Schmidt proper motion survey is completed we shall really, and definitely be able to say that we have passed the maximum of the luminosity function.

REFERENCES

HARRIS, D.L., 1963, *Basic Astron. Data*, (ed. K. Strand, Chicago, University of Chicago Press), p. 265.
LUYTEN, W.J., 1939, *Pub. Astron. Obs. Univ. of Minn.* **II**, No 7.

The abundances of the rare earths in six F stars

George WALLERSTEIN

University of California at San Diego

The strengths of the rare earth lines have been noted for many years to be a good indication of peculiarity of stellar spectra. In fact the identification of many rare earth lines in the spectrum of α^2 CVn by STRUVE and SWINGS [1943] opened the way to the analyses that have demonstrated that the peculiar A stars do indeed have atmospheres with outlandishly peculiar chemical compositions. Other types of stars with abnormally strong lines of the rare earths are the S stars, Ba II stars, CH stars, and some carbon stars. Such analyses as have been completed of these objects have always been "relative" analyses in which the peculiar star has been compared with a normal star. Thus absolute f-values were not needed but rather the analysis was performed by deriving empirical line strengths from the normal star and applying them to the peculiar star. Thus abundances could be obtained as a ratio with respect to the normal star. Such abundance ratios clearly do not yield absolute abundances until the composition of the normal star has been established. The lack of absolute f-values for lines of the rare earths has been alleviated with the publication of the extensive lists by CORLISS and BOZMAN [1962].

In this paper we shall derive the abundances of such rare earths as appear in the spectra of six F stars. The stars were chosen because extensive tables of their equivalent widths have been published. In addition, they represent a considerable range in overall metal content. The stars are listed in table I. The first three columns are self-explanatory. The fourth column lists the logarithm of the ratio of iron to hydrogen minus the same quantity in the sun. The fifth column lists the reference from which the equivalent widths have been obtained. For the first three stars the dispersion is the highest available and the number of plates is large; however, the spectral region is limited to the violet. For the next two stars the spectral region extends into the red but the dispersion is lower. The last star is much fainter than the others but has been included since it is representative of the extremely metal-poor subdwarfs. Many of the equivalent widths are derived from a single plate of 4.5 A/mm since quite a number of the lines are either blended or too weak to appear on other spectrograms of lower dispersion.

Gauthier-Villars, Paris - Modern Astrophysics - 1967.

G. WALLERSTEIN

TABLE I

Star	B-V	Spectral Type	[Fe/H]	Reference
σ Boo	+0.36	F2 V	−0.4	(1)
α CMi	+0.40	F5 IV-V	0.0	(1)
110 Her	+0.46	F6 V	0.0	(1)
γ Ser	+0.48	F6 IV-V	−0.3	(2)
β Vir	+0.55	F8 V	+0.3	(3)
HD 19445	+0.46	sd F	−1.6	(4)

(1) WRIGHT et al., 1964.
(2) KEGEL, 1962.
(3) NAMBA, 1964.
(4) ALLER and GREENSTEIN, 1960.

The equivalent widths and f-values are listed for nine elements in table II. Only ionized lines have been used so as to minimize the ionization correction. Scandium has been used as a standard element. The intermediate weight elements, Sr, Y, and Zr, have been included to facilitate comparisons with other stars. Some strong lines have been omitted, since they are not useful for a comparison with scandium.

The analysis of the data has been carried out in the simplest way possible. Curves of growth for each element have been plotted using an excitation temperature of 5 500°K for the first three stars and 5 000°K for the last three stars. These are estimates from other analyses and effective temperatures; but the final abundances will not be sensitive to the excitation temperature since most of the lines arise from levels of about the same excitation potential, between 0 and 1.5 e.v. Since we are dealing with ionized lines the horizontal shifts of the curves of growth yield the relative abundances once the differences in partition functions as well as any second ionization have been taken into account. The partition functions have been calculated, using all the levels in the Multiplet Table of Astrophysical Interest (MOORE, 1945), and were found to agree closely with the partition functions as computed by CORLISS and BOZMAN [1962].

In table III we list the shifts of each element relative to scandium, as well as the partition functions. The correction for second ionization is 20% for barium in the first three stars and is negligible in all other cases provided that the second ionization potential of the rare earths are greater than 11.0 electron volts and the partition functions of the doubly ionized rare earths are no

TABLE II

Element and Line	log gf	Log W					
		σ Boo	α CMi	110 Her	γ Ser	β Vir	HD 19445
Sc II							
4246.83	+0.19	2.15	2.31	2.25	—	—	1.77
4294.77	−1.27	1.58	1.91	1.88	1.95	—	—
4305.66	−1.20	—	—	—	—	—	1.11
4320.76	−0.22	—	—	—	—	—	1.53
4325.01	−0.37	2.00	2.23	2.25	—	—	—
4354.61	−1.50	1.41	1.83	1.80	1.95	—	—
4400.36	−0.72	1.89	2.17	2.10	—	—	1.25
4415.56	−0.84	1.90	2.12	2.02	—	—	1.11
4420.07	−2.32	—	—	—	—	1.38	—
4431.37	−2.13	1.08	1.58	1.54	1.56	1.70	—
4670.40	−0.51	—	—	—	—	1.96	—
5239.82	−0.50	—	—	—	1.84	—	—
5318.34	−1.82	—	—	—	—	1.60	—
5526.81	+0.03	—	—	—	1.97	—	—
5640.97	−1.17	—	—	—	—	1.78	—
5657.87	−0.68	—	—	—	—	1.98	—
5669.03	−1.23	—	—	—	1.67	—	—
6245.63	−1.05	—	—	—	1.62	1.63	—
6320.85	−1.96	—	—	—	—	1.40	—
6604.60	−1.54	—	—	—	1.60	1.62	—
Sr II							
4077.74	+0.18	—	—	—	—	—	1.99
4215.53	−0.10	—	—	—	—	—	1.93
Y II							
3950.36	−0.71	1.72	1.97	—	—	—	1.18
4177.54	−0.24	—	—	—	—	—	1.22
4374.94	−0.14	—	—	—	—	—	1.18
4398.02	−1.25	1.48	1.86	1.77	—	1.81	—
4883.69	−0.50	—	—	—	1.90	—	—
5087.42	−0.87	—	—	—	1.81	1.78	—
Zr II							
3998.97	−0.50	1.58	1.86	1.86	—	—	—
4050.33	−0.96	1.00	1.45	1.43	—	—	—
4179.81	−0.48	0.60	1.08	—	—	—	—
4208.98	−0.54	1.52	1.80	1.73	1.69	1 83	—

TABLE II *(Cont.)*

Element and Line	Log W						
	log gf	σ Boo	α CMi	110 Her	γ Ser	β Vir	HD 19445
4211.88	−1.21	—	—	—	1.77	—	1.08
4317.31	−1.48	—	—	—	—	1.52	—
4414.54	−1.06	—	—	—	—	1.52	—
4442.99	−0.49	—	—	—	—	1.53	—
4629.07	−0.12	—	—	—	—	1.23	—
Ba II							
4130.66	+0.66	1.46	1.72	1.81	—	1.87	—
4554.03	+0.15	—	—	—	—	—	1.74
5853.68	−1.59	—	—	—	1.93	1.94	—
La II							
3995.75	−0.58	—	—	—	—	1.76	1.83
4042.91	+0.07	1.11	1.30	1.25	—	—	—
4123.23	−0.40	1.38	1.72	1.74	—	1.80	—
4238.38	−0.80	1.08	1.32	1.42	1.28	1.69	—
4263.59	+0.03	0.78	1.08	0.78	—	—	1.18
4322.51	−1.62	—	—	—	1.48	1.38	—
4333.74	−0.60	1.41	1.59	1.61	1.87	1.71	—
4429.90	−0.94	1.18	1.46	1.57	—	—	—
4522.37	−0.33	—	—	—	—	1.08	—
4662.51	−2.04	—	—	—	—	1.18	—
6262.30	−2.13	—	—	—	1.08	—	—
Ce II							
3940.34	−0.43	—	—	—	—	—	1.32
4014.90	−0.18	0.90	1.15	—	—	—	—
4137.65	+0.09	1.26	1.47	1.49	—	—	—
4222.60	−0.44	1.15	1.32	1.28	—	—	—
4270.72	−0.22	—	—	—	—	1.20	—
4349.79	−0.42	—	—	—	—	1.23	—
4399.20	−0.78	—	0.78	1.12	—	1.36	—
4418.78	+0.03	—	1.18	1.30	1.43	1.36	—
4449.34	−0.34	—	—	—	—	1.40	—
4486.91	−0.62	—	—	1.27	—	1.36	—
4544.96	−1.12	—	—	—	—	1.08	—
4560.28	−0.15	—	—	—	—	1.20	—
4562.36	−0.07	—	—	—	1.54	—	—
4582.50	−0.55	—	—	—	—	1.20	—

Table II (Cont.)

Element and Line	log gf	σ Boo	α CMi	110 Her	γ Ser	β Vir	HD 15944
				Log W			
4628.16	−0.14	—	—	—	1.23	1.48	—
4773.94	−0.56	—	—	—	—	1.30	—
5274.24	−0.30	—	—	—	1.15	—	—
Nd II							
4061							
4061.09	+0.03	1.48	1.75	1.74	—	—	—
4075.12	−1.07	1.15	1.55	—	—	—	—
4358.17	−0.98	—	—	22	—	1.52	—
4446.39	−1.29	—	—	—	—	1.25	—
4597.02	−1.79	—	—	—	—	1.08	—
4703.57	−1.69	—	—	—	—	1.18	—
4706.54	−1.50	—	—	—	—	1.58	—
4959.13	−1.60	—	—	—	—	1.58	—
5319.82	−0.96	—	—	—	—	1.60	—
4262.68	−0.84	—	1.08	0.78	—	—	—
4329.02	−0.91	—	—	—	1.26	1.23	—
4467.34	−0.39	—	1.20	1.12	—	1.30	—
4537.95	−1.08	—	—	—	—	1.08	—
4577.69	−1.40	—	—	—	—	1.11	—
4642.24	—	—	—	—	—	1.20	—

larger than the partition functions of the singly ionized rare earths. The abundances are derived in table IV where we have *arbitrarily* set the scandium abundance at log N_{Sc} = 2.8 as is found for the sun. We note that this is indeed arbitrary because the general metal abundance of these stars is not solar. On this scale the number of silicon atoms is log N_{Si} = 7.5.

The uncertainties in the quantities in table IV are substantial. When no parentheses appear the abundance is based upon at least three lines showing rather good agreement, and the random uncertainty should be less than 0.2 in the log. A single parenthesis indicates that either two good lines or three lines of less certainty were employed. In that case the uncertainty is probably less than 0.3 in the log. If only one good line was used, double parentheses are indicated as a warning that errors as large as 0.4 in the log are quite possible.

In no case have we used only one line if its identification is in doubt. To these uncertainties must be added any possible systematic error in the f-values For a number of elements lines were found in the original line lists that yielded much higher abundances than listed in table IV. A careful examination of these lines indicated that they were either blends or misidentifications. Such lines were eliminated prior to compiling table II.

TABLE III

Element	Horizontal Shift						
	U(T)	σ Boo	α CMi	110 Her	γ Ser	β Vir	HD 19445
Sc	23.2	—	—	—	—	—	—
Sr	2.3	—	—	—	—	—	+0.6
Y	16.2	—0.8	—0.9	—1.0	—0.5	—0.8	—0.7
Zr	46.6	—1.0	—1.0	—1.0	—1.1	—0.9	—
Ba	4.3	—0.4	—0.55	—0.35	—0.95	0.2	—0.45
La	30.2	—1.35	—1.50	—1.40	—1.5	—1.6	—1.0
Ce	190	—2.0	—2.2	—2.0	—2.3	—2.35	—
Nd	86	—1.7	—1.8	—1.75	—	—1.50	—
Sm	57	—	—1.9	—2.0	—2.5	—2.1	—

TABLE IV

Logarithmic Abundances Based Upon log N_{Sc} = 2.8

Element	log Ni					
	σ Boo	α CMi	110 Her	γ Ser	β Vir	HD 19445
Sr	—	—	—	—	—	(2.6)
Y	1.75	1.65	((1.55))	(2.05)	(1.75)	1.85
Zr	2.0	2.0	2.0	(1.9)	(2.1)	—
Ba	((1.7))	((1.55))	((1.75))	((1.15))	(1.8)	((1.6))
La	(1.45)	(1.3)	(1.4)	1.3	1.2	((1.8))
Ce	1.6	1.4	1.6	1.3	1.3	—
Nd	(1.6)	(1.5)	(1.55)	—	(1.8)	—
Sm	—	1.2	1.1	((0.6))	1.0	—

In table V we have prepared a mean of the composition of the six F stars for comparison with the sun (WALLERSTEIN, 1966) and the chondritic meteorites (UREY, 1964, SCHMIDT et al., 1963). Again we have employed parentheses to indicate the less reliable data, though they are less precisely defined than in table IV. We see general agreement among the three classes of objects. In the sun the main discrepancy with the meteorites was the ratio of La to its two neighbors, Ba and Ce. The F stars do not solve the dilemma. The La abundance falls between that for the sun and the meteorites. Thus we cannot conclude that there is an indisputable discrepancy between stellar and meteoritic material nor can we state that the high lanthanum abundance in the sun is spurious. One further point of interest is to be seen primarily in table IV. There is no significant difference between metal-rich and metal-poor stars so far as the ratio of heavy elements to scandium is concerned.

TABLE V

Comparison of Abundances

	log N		
Element	Sun	Mean of 6 Stars	Meteorites
Sc	2.8	2.8	2.8
Sr	((2.6))	(2.6)	2.9
Y	2.1	1.8	2.2
Zr	2.2	2.0	2.7
Ba	(1.7)	(1.55)	2.2
La	1.7	1.4	1.1
Ce	1.4	1.45	1.6
Nd	1.6	(1.6)	1.3
Sm	1.1	1.0	0.9
Eu	(0.8)	—	0.4
Gd	(0.8)	—	1.0

Note added in proof : Several of the NBS f-values for Ba II have been found to be in error by Garstang (1966). It is not clear whether or not we should revise our abundances since the relative abundances among barium and the rare earths are as important as the absolute abundances and any systematic errors in the experimental f-values of barium may have been present in the heavier elements. Using Garstang's f-values we revise the abundances of barium in table VI as follows:

β Vir   (1.55)

HD 19445   ((1.55))

The barium abundance in the sun (Table V) is also revised to (1.4). The Goldberg, Müller, and Aller (1960) abundance of barium remains at very nearly 2.1 since their f-values were quite close to the values recommended by Garstang.

REFERENCES

ALLER, L.H. and GREENSTEIN, J.L., 1960, *Ap. J. Suppl.* 5, No. 46, p. 139.

CORLISS, G.H. and BOZMANN, W.R., 1962, *NBS Monograph* No. 53.

GOLDBERG, L., MÜLLER, E.A. and ALLER, L.H., 1960, *Ap. J. Suppl.*, 5, 1.

KEGEL, W.H., 1962, *Zs. f. Ap.* 55, 221.

MOORE, C.E., 1945, *Cont. from the Princeton Univ. Obs.*, No. 20.

NAMBA, O., 1964, *Rev. Geophys.*, 2, 1.

SCHMIDT, R.A., SMITH, R.H., LASCH, J.E., MOSEN, A.W., OLEHY, D.A. and VASILEVSKIS, J., 1963, *Geochim. Cosmochim. Acta*, 27, 577.

STRUVE, O. and SWINGS, P., 1943, *Ap. J.* 98, 361.

UREY, H.C., 1964, *Rev. Geophys*, 2, 1.

WALLERSTEIN, G., 1966, *Icarus*, 5, 75.

WRIGHT, K.O., LEE, E.K., JACOBSON, T.V., and GREENSTEIN, J.L., 1964, *Pub. D.A.O. Victoria*, 12, No. 7, p. 173.

Hydrogen-poor stars

Margherita HACK

Astronomical Observatory, Trieste, Italy

Only a few stars are known, which are hydrogen deficient. v Sagittarii and R Coronae Borealis are the best known representatives of the group.

It should be interesting to review the properties of all these stars, comparing them in an attempt to understand the reasons for their hydrogen depletion, and for the other abundance peculiarities.

1 — General properties of the hydrogen-poor stars

Table I gives a list of hydrogen-poor stars, in order of decreasing temperature, collecting all the data found in the literature for each star.

The position of these stars on the two-color diagram is shown in figure 1. We note that all of them are above the curve for normal stars, the hydrogen deficiency resulting in a lower opacity of the atmosphere, and especially so for $\lambda < 3647$. The theoretical curve for hydrogen-deficient stars computed by NARIAI [1963a] is also given.

The position on the HR diagram is known with a very low degree of accuracy. The absolute magnitudes are generally estimated by the strength of the interstellar absorption lines, or by the radial velocity, assuming that this is due only to the galactic differential rotation. In four cases, β Lyrae, HD 128220 B, HD 113001 B and σ Orionis E, the stars are members of binary or multiple systems and the companion have normal spectra to which the usual luminosity criteria can be applied.

The hydrogen-poor stars can be divided into five groups. The first group contains the hot sub-dwarfs (M_v $+3 \div +4$), which fall several magnitudes below the main sequence. They do not show lines of carbon and oxygen, and are found in high galactic latitudes. The second group contains hot stars with absolute magnitudes ranging from 0 to -3. These show lines of carbon and often also of oxygen, and generally have high galactic latitudes. The third group presenting a moderate hydrogen deficiency, is composed of stars above or close to the main sequence. The fourth group includes close binaries showing evidence of exchange of mass between the two components.

Gauthier-Villars, Paris - Modern Astrophysics - 1967.

TABLE

N°.	Star	α (1900)	δ (1900)	b	m	M
1	BD +75°325	6h 59m	+75°18′	+32°	8.9	
2	HD 49798	6h 45m	−44°13′	−18°	8.3	+1÷+3
3	GS 259-8	22h 44m	+37°23′	−18°	12.5	∼+4
4	HD 127493	14h 27m	−22°13′	+34°	10.0	
5	HZ 44	13h 19m	+36°39′	+78°		+1÷+4
6	BD+25°4655	21h 56m	+25°27′	−23°	9.0	
7	HD 160641	17h 36m	−17°51′	+5	9.8	−3
8	HD 113001 B	12h 56m	+36°17′	+83°	10.6	+3.6
9	HD 128220 B	14h 31m	+19°39′	+63°	7.3	+0.7
10	HD 96446	11h 2m	−59°24′	0	6.6	
11	HD 124448	14h 9m	−45°49′	+13°	10.0	−3
12	MV Sgr	18h 39m	−21° 3′	−10°	12.7−15.0	
13	BD+13°3224	16h 43m	+13°27′	+32°	9.5	0÷+1
14	BD+10°2179	10h 34m	+10°34′	+55°	9.95	⩽ −1.6
15	HD 37479	5h 34m	− 2°39′	−15°	6.53	−2.2
16	HD 168476	18h 15m	−56°41′	−20°	9.4	−1÷−2
17	HD 135485	15h 10m	−14°19′	+35°	8.3	
18	β Lyr	18h 46m	+37°15′	+13°	3.4÷4.3	−3.5
19	υ Sgr	19h 16m	−16° 9′	−16°	4.3−4.4	⩽ −5.5
20	HD 30353	4h 42m	+43° 6′	0°	7.76	⩽ −1.6
21	R Cr B	15h 44m	+28°28′	+48°	5.8−14.8	
22	HD 25878	4h 1m	+53° 6′	+ 2°	7.1−8.7	
23	HD 182040	19h 18m	−10°53′	−14°	7.04	

1　Spectroscopic characteristics: He II > H; He II > He I; N IV > N III; Si III (ELVIUS and SINNERSTAD, 1958; GREENSTEIN, 1960; GOULD, HERBIG, and MORGAN, 1957).

2　Spectroscopic characteristics: He II > H; He II > He I; N IV > N III; Si III . V_r variable from −88 to +86 in few months (JASCHEK and JASCHEK, 1963).

3　Spectroscopic characteristics: He II, He I, Si IV, N III (MÜNCH and SLETTEBAK, 1959).

4　Spectroscopic characteristics: He II > H; N III > N II; Si IV, Si III (GREENSTEIN, 1960).

5　Spectroscopic characteristics: He II > H; N III, N II; He I, Ne II, Si IV, Si III (MÜNCH, 1958).

6　Spectroscopic characteristics: He II > H; N II > N III; Si III, C III, Ne II (GREENSTEIN, 1960).
1 to 6: no lines of O are visible; 1 to 5: no lines of C are visible.

7　Spectroscopic characteristics: C-and O-lines are normal (BIDELMAN, 1952; ALLER, 1954; HILL 1965).

8　Spectroscopic characteristics: no lines of C and O are visible. Visual binary. The companion is F 2 V or IV (WALLERSTEIN and SPINRAD, 1960; STURCH and WALLERSTEIN, 1962).

9　Spectroscopic characteristics: H, He I, He II, C III, N III, O III, Ne II; the Si lines are missing and the O lines are very strong. Visual binary. The companion is GO III (WALLERSTEIN, STURCH and KLEMOLA, 1963).

I

B-V	U-B	Sp.	T	log P_e	log g	log Σ Nhμ	Turbulence
extremely blue		O 5	45 000-70 000		4-8		
−0.24	−1.18	O 6					
		O 6					
		O 6					
		O 6	35 000	+4.5	6		
		O 6					
		O 9	31 500	+3.1			14
−0.25	−1.25	O 9					
(+0.21)AB	(−0.85)AB	O 9					
		B 1					
−0.07	−0.80	B 2	16 800	+2.4	3.7	23.10	7
		B 2					
−0.19	−0.97	B 2					
−0.18	−0.90	B 3	16 800	+2.4	3.6	23.21	6
−0.21	−0.91	B 3					
−0.01	−0.67	B 5	13 300	+1.6	2.4	24.02	14.5
		B 6					
		B 8-B 9	13 400-12 400	+1.25		24.74	6
		B 8-B 9	12 800- 8 000	+1.8 - −0.1	2	24.07	6
+0.48	−0.18	F 0	7 400-6 000	−0.9		26.90	22
		F 5	6 600	+0.9			7
		F 5					
		C 1,2					

10   Spectroscopic characteristics: He I > H; C II, C III, N II, N III, O II, O III, Ne II, Mg II, Si III, S II, S III, Fe III (BUSCOMBE, 1965).
11   Spectroscopic characteristics: see quantitative analysis (POPPER, 1942, 1946, 1947, HILL, 1963, 1965).
12   Spectroscopic characteristics: The spectrum is very similar to HD 124448. Variable type R Cr B (HOFFLEIT, 1959).
13   Spectroscopic characteristics: Very similar to BD + 10°2179 (BERGER and GREENSTEIN, 1963).
14   Spectroscopic characteristics: see quantitative analysis. High space velocity: 320 km/s (KLEMOLA, 1961).
15   Spectroscopic characteristics: Balmer lines well visible. Multiple system σ Ori E (BERGER, 1956; GREENSTEIN and WALLERSTEIN, 1958).
16   Spectroscopic characteristics: see quantitative analysis; high velocity star (THACKERAY and WESSELINK, 1952; HILL, 1963, 1965).
17   Spectroscopic characteristics: He is 10 times more abundant than normal, H is almost normal, C, N, O, Si, S are normal, Mg is deficient by a factor of 10. The star is about one magnitude below the main sequence (STEWART, 1956).   (Continuation page 168).

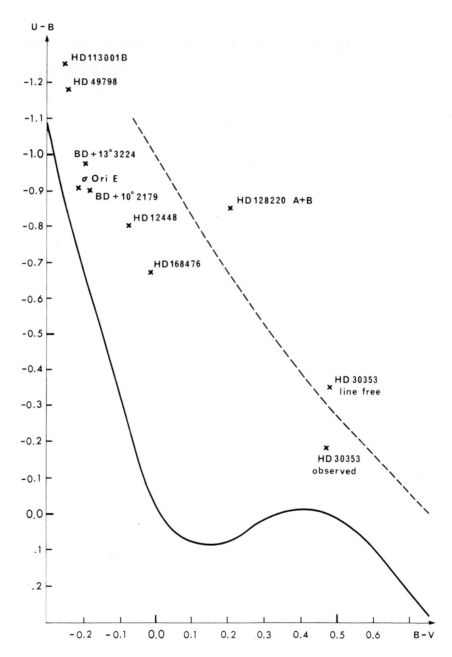

Fig. 1 — Position of the hydrogen-deficient stars in the two-color diagram. The broken line represents the theoretical relation computed by Nariai.

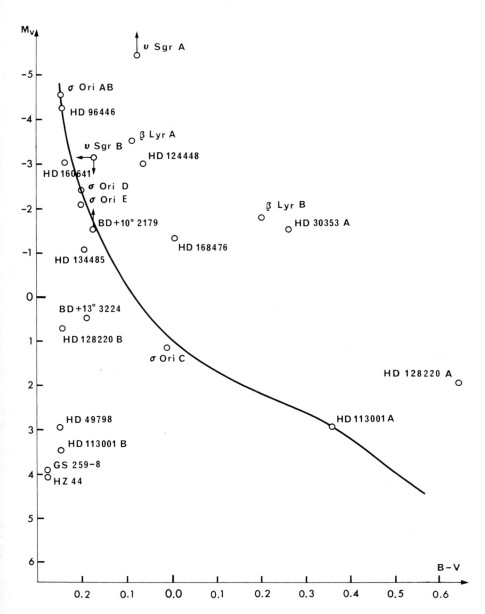

Fig. 2 — Position of the hydrogen-deficient stars in the HR diagram.

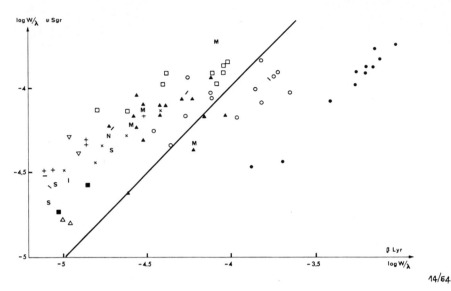

Fig. 3 — Comparison of υ Sgr and β Lyr. The symbols represent: ● H I; ○ He I; N N II; M Mg II; ▯ Si II; ■ Si III; S S II; |Sc II; × Ti II; \ V II; + Cr II; △ Fe I; ▲ Fe II; ▽ Fe III; / Ni II; — Sr II.

Continuation from page 165.

18   Close binary, eclipsing variable. The two values of the temperature are derived by the ionization equilibria of Si III and Si II and Fe II and Fe I respectively. Evidence of exchange of matter with the invisible companion (STRUVE, 1958; SAHADE *et al.*, 1959; BOYARCHUK, 1959; STRUVE and ZEBERGS, 1961; HACK and JOB, 1965).

19   Close binary, eclipsing variable. The two values of the temperature and of the electron pressure are derived by the ionization equilibria of Si III and Si II and of Fe II and Fe I respectively. Evidence of exchange of matter with the unvisible hotter component (GREENSTEIN, 1940, 1943, 1950; GREENSTEIN and ADAMS, 1947); GAPOSCHKIN, 1945; BIDELMAN, 1949; HACK, 1960; HACK and PASINETTI 1963).

20   Spectroscopic binary: intrinsic variable. H α in emission. The first values of the temperature is given by the ionized elements, the second by the neutral elements. The colors corrected for blanketing effect and for interstellar reddening are: B-V = + 0. 18; U-B ⩽ −0.37 (BIDELMAN, 1950; HEARD, 1962; NARIAI, 1963a and 1963b; OSAWA, NISHIMURA and NARIAI, 1963).

21   log $\varkappa$ = −1.6 i.e. higher than that for δ C Ma, in spite of the very low abundance of hydrogen. The opacity is imputed to photoionization of neutral carbon (BERMAN. 1935); SEARLE, 1961; PAYNE GAPOSCHKIN, 1963).

22   Very similar to R Cr B (BIDELMAN, 1948; CHANG YUIN, 1948).

23   CH is weak. The lines in the yellow region of the spectrum are stronger than in other stars of the same spectral type. These facts suggest a lower abundance of hydrogen and therefore a lower atmospherical opacity (BUSCOMBE, 1953, 1955).

And finally the fifth group is composed of carbon-rich stars, like R Cr B and HD 25878, to which the hot hydrogen-poor star MV Sgr is correlated because it presents the same type of variability.

TABLE II

Subdivision of hydrogen-poor stars

Hot sub-dwarfs ($M_v \simeq +3 \div +4$)		
BD $+75°315$	$b = +32°$	
HD 49798	-18	
GS 259-8	-18	
HD 127493	$+35$	Spectral class O; no lines of C and O are
HZ 44	$+78$	visible
BD $+25°4655$	-25	
HB 113001 B	$+83$	
Hot hydrogen-poor stars ($M_v \simeq 0 \div -3$)		
HD 160641	$b = + 5°$	
HD 128220 B	$+63$	
HD 124448	$+13$	
MV Sgr	$- 9$	The Balmer lines are very weak or not
BD $+13°3224$	$+32$	visible at all; C lines are present and often
BD $+10°2179$	$+55$	also the O lines
HD 168476	-20	
Stars with moderate hydrogen-deficiency		
HD 96446	$b = 0°$	
HD 37479	-15	The Balmer lines are almost normal; the
HD 135485	$+35$	He lines are stronger than normal
β Lyr	$+14$	
Close binaries		
β Lyr	$+14$	
υ Sgr	-15	
HD 30353	0	
Carbon stars		
R Cr B	$+50$	
HD 25878	$+ 2$	
HD 182040	-15	

A comparison of the line intensities has been made for a few stars for which intensity measures were available.

The three close binary systems β Lyrae, υ Sagittarii and HD 30353 are compared in figures 3 and 4. It is clearly visible that the degree of excitation of β Lyrae and υ Sagittarii is about the same, but the latter star displays much stronger spectral lines (with the exception of the Balmer lines), because of its low atmospherical opacity. HD 30533 on the other hand is cooler than υ Sagittarii, and it has a lower opacity due to the lower atmospherical abundance of hydrogen and to the lower temperature.

BD $+$ 10°2179 and HD 124448 are compared in figure 5. They are very similar; although we note that the majority of He lines at $\lambda < 3647$ are stronger in BD $+$ 10°2179, a fact hard to explain. It would suggest that the opacity of BD $+$ 10°2179 at $\lambda < 3647$ is lower than that of HD 124448, and therefore that the former star has a lower hydrogen abundance. However the contrary is true because weak Balmer lines are visible and measurable in BD $+$ 10°2179 and not in HD 124448.

HD 168476 is very similar to υ Sagittarii but it has a higher degree of excitation than υ Sagittarii. Moreover the Balmer lines are not visible in HD 168476 (Fig. 6).

HD 96446 is compared with the normal star 10 Lacertae (Fig. 7). Although 10 Lacertae is hotter than HD 96446 the Balmer lines are much stronger and the He lines slightly weaker in the standard star.

The abundance determinations are given in table III. The abundances for normal stars are usually compared with that of hydrogen. However in the case of hydrogen-deficient stars a comparison with the normal stars is more meaningful if we compare the abundances of the elements with respect to their total atmospheric mass. If we assume for normal stars $\log N(H) = 12.00$ and $\log N(He) = 11.21$ it follows that $\log \Sigma N \mu = 12.23$. Hence we adjust the number of atoms of each element contained in the atmospheres of the hydrogen-deficient stars to give $\log \Sigma N \mu = 12.23$. At the end of each column of table III we give also $\log \Sigma Nh \mu$, which is indicative of the opacity of the atmosphere. However we observe that this value, which depends mainly upon the H and He abundance, is strongly affected by the value assumed for the temperature and a small error in this temperature estimate has a great influence upon the computation of the degree of ionization of hydrogen and helium. For this reason we compare also the abundances of the elements with respect to iron (table IV). From an examination of tables III and IV we are able to deduce the following conclusions: The group of hot stars HD 160641, HD 124448, BD $+$ 10°2179 and HD 168476, have a rather uniform composition; the main peculiarities being an excess of carbon and a defect of oxygen (with the exception of HD 160641), and a defect of chromium and manganese, as well as, of course, the hydrogen deficiency.

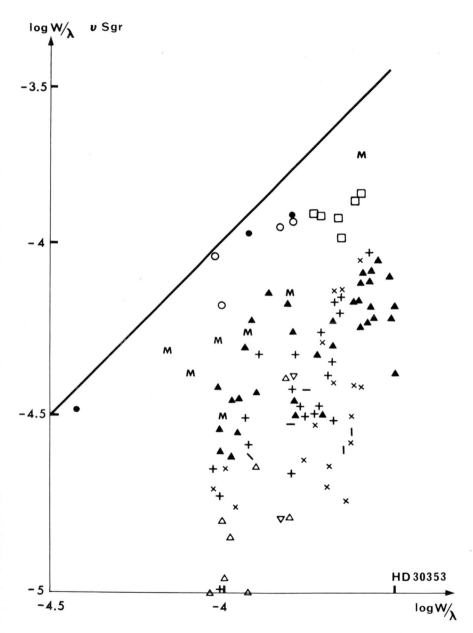

Fig. 4 — Comparison of υ Sgr and HD 30353. The symbols represent: ● H I; ○ He I; ▽ Mg I; M Mg II; □ Si II; | Sc II; × Ti II; ＼ V II; + Cr II; △ Fe I ▲ Fe II; — Sr II.

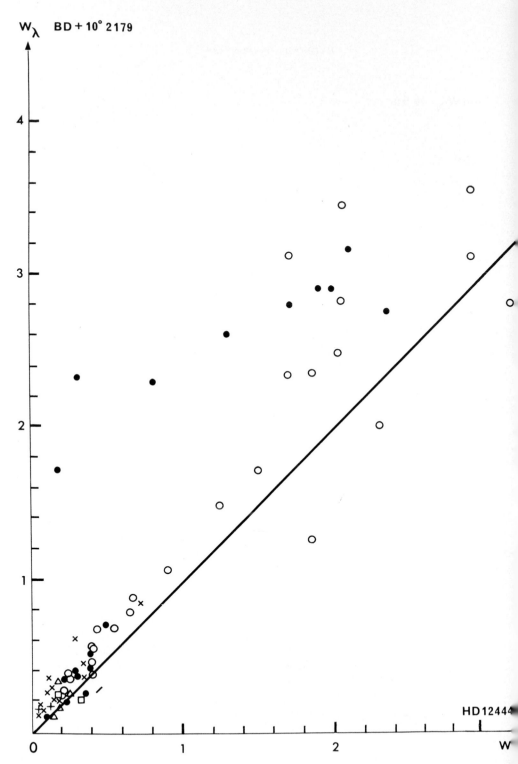

Fig. 5 — Comparison of BD +10°2179 and HD 124448. The symbols represent:
● He I ($\lambda < 3647$); ○ He I ($\lambda > 3647$); × C II; ☐ N II; + Si III, △ Si II; / Mg II.

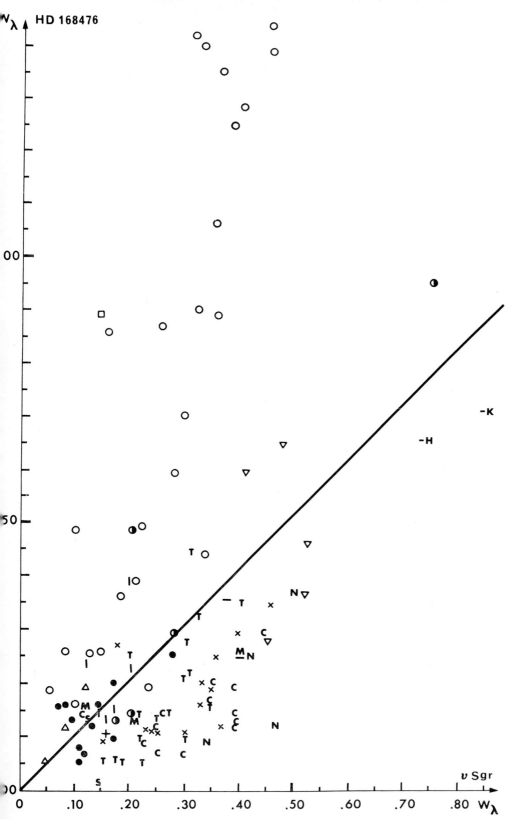

Fig. 6 — Comparison of HD 168476 and υ Sgr. The symbols represent: ○ He I; □ C II; | N II; ◖ Mg II; — Ca II; △ Si III; ▽ Si II; ● S II; T Ti II; C Cr II; S Sc II; M Mn II; N Ni II; × Fe II; + Fe III.

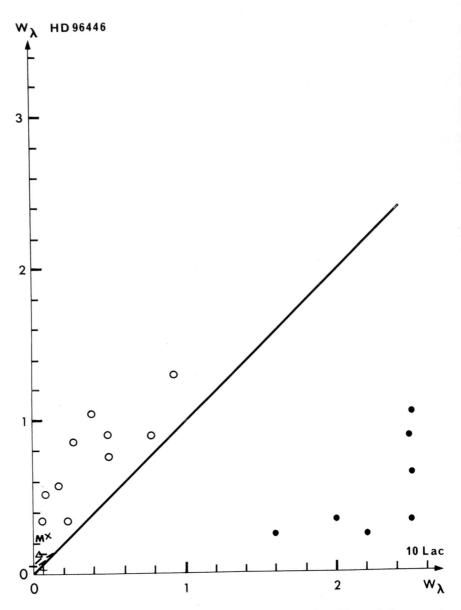

Fig. 7 — Comparison of HD 96446 and the standard star 10 Lac. The symbols represent:
● H I; ○ He I; × C II; + C III; △ N II; / O II; — Si III; M Mg II.

TABLE III

	β Lyr	υ Sagr	HD 30353	Average Normal Stars	HD 168476	HD 124448	BD +10°2179	HD 160641
H	11.23	9.90	7.73	12.00	<7.1	<7.8	8.49	—
He	11.58	11.54	12.23	11.25	11.61	11.62	11.61	11.61
C	7.45	8.70		8.18	9.16	9.01	9.51	8.66
N	7.78	10.06		8.38	8.35	8.38	8.67	8.77
O		8.06		8.91	<8.3	<8.4	<8.2	8.91
Ne		9.44		8.88	9.05			9.42
Na		7.23		6.51				
Mg	7.16	9.00	7.13	7.70	7.53	7.75	7.2	7.61
Al		5.78		6.60	6.19	6.61	5.8	
Si	6.04	7.92	7.43	7.62	7.12	7.21	7.42	7.61
S	8.13	8.50		7.15	6.75	7.19		
Ca		5.32		6.46	6.00	6.40	5.91	
Sc	2.61	3.83	2.83	3.55	4.3			
Ti	4.15	5.33	4.43	5.40	5.98	6.3		
V		4.27	2.73	4.30	4.65			
Cr	4.50	6.82	4.93	6.30	5.20	4.8		
Mn		4.55		6.10	4.57	4.84		
Fe	7.18	7.85	7.13	7.95	7.42	7.58		
Co		5.73		5.64				
Ni		7.58		7.17	5.4	5.2		
Sr	2.23		2.33	2.90				
Ba		1.01		2.21				
log ΣNhμ	24.75	24.07	26.90		24.02	23.10	23.21	

TABLE IV

log N_i/N_{Fe}	β Lyr	υ Sgr	HD 30353	Average Normal Stars	HD 168476	HD 124448	R Cr B	BD +10°2179	HD 160641
H	+4.05	+2.05	+0.60	+4.05	<−0.32	<+0.2			
He	+4.40	+3.69	+5.10	+3.30	+4.19	+4.04			
C	+0.27	+0.85		+0.23	+1.74	+1.43	−0.31		
N	+0.60	+2.21		+0.43	+0.93	+0.80	+0.79		
O		+0.21		+0.96	<+0.9	<+0.8			
Ne		+1.59		+0.93	+1.63				
Na	−0.02	−0.62	0.00	−1.44			+0.15		
Mg		+1.15		−0.25	+0.11	+0.17			
Al	−1.14	−2.07		−1.35	−1.23	−0.97			
Si	+0.95	+0.07	+0.30	−0.33	−0.30	−0.37			
S		+0.65		−0.80	−0.67	−0.39			
Ca	−4.57	−2.53		−1.49	−1.42	−1.18	−1.75		
Sc	−3.03	−4.02	−4.30	−4.40	−3.12		−3.90		
Ti		−2.53	−2.70	−2.55	−1.44	−1.3	−2.30		
V		−3.58	−4.40	−3.65	−2.77		−3.35		
Cr	−2.60	−1.03	−2.20	−1.65	−2.22	−2.8	−1.45		
Mn		−3.30		−1.85	−2.85	−2.74	−1.75		
Fe	0.00	0.00	0.00	0.00	0.00	0.00	0.00		
Co		−2.12		−2.31					
Ni		−0.27		−0.78	−2.0	−2.4			
Sr	−4.95		−4.80	−5.05					
Ba		−6.84		−5.74			−5.65		
Number — He/H	2.35	44	3 × 10⁴	1/5.6	>3 × 10⁴	>6 × 10³		1.3 × 10³	
Ratio — N/C	2.1	23		1.6	0.15	0.23		0.14	1.3

The group of A-type stars (β Lyrae, υ Sagittarii and HD 30353, which are all members of close binary systems, with evidence of loss and exchange of mass, have not a general behavior, The degree of hydrogen deficiency with respect to normal stars ranges from a factor of 10 in β Lyrae to a factor of 100 in υ Sagittarii and of 10^4 in HD 30353, suggesting very different stages of evolution for these three objects.

We note the very low opacity of the atmosphere of HD 30353, where H does not play an appreciable role, due to its low abundance, and the bound-free and free-free transitions of He are ineffective, because helium is practically all in the neutral state at the relatively low temperature of this star.

It is interesting to consider the abundances of the elements with respect to iron (table IV) whose abundance is very probable unaffected by nuclear reactions. The abundance ratios with respect to iron are indicative of the processes which have occurred in the star and for some reason have become visible at the surface. It is evident from the graph that the abundances of the elements in the iron peak are normal (Fig. 8). Also calcium and heavy elements (Sr and Ba) have normal abundances. The main peculiarities are general excess of C and N, a slight defect of O, excess of Ne, Mg, and S. He is in excess with respect to Fe by a factor of 2 in υ Sagittarii and of 100 in HD 30353.

Table IV also summarizes the ratios of abundances which are more significant in explaining the nuclear processes which take place in the star: H/He, N/C. There is evidence of the following processes: H $\rightarrow$ He in all these stars, though in a different degree; carbon cycle, with production of nitrogen in υ Sagittarii, where N/C = 23. The theoretical value resulting from the carbon cycle for the ratio N/C is 25, to be compared with the solar value N/C = 1/5.5 (GOLDBERG, MÜLLER and ALLER, 1960) and with the average value for 10 stars of spectral type ranging from O9 to B3, N/C = 1.6 (HACK, 1959). Moreover there is evidence of the process of the 3 α particles giving an excess of carbon in υ Sagittarii, R Coronae Borealis and especially in HD 168476 and HD 124448 and of oxygen burning with production of Ne, Mg, Si, S in υ Sagittarii or only Ne in HD 168476.

CAMERON [1955, 1959] has shown that C^{12} will be the principal product of the process of the 3 α particles, when the rate of energy generation during helium burning is 10^6 ergs $g^{-1} s^{-1}$ or more. These energy generation rates will be attained in very massive stars which evolve in a few million years. In the less massive stars, where He is burned less rapidly, the final product is likely to be O^{16} and Ne^{20}. The main effect of oxygen and neon burning is to produce large quantities of Mg^{24}, Si^{28}, and S^{32}.

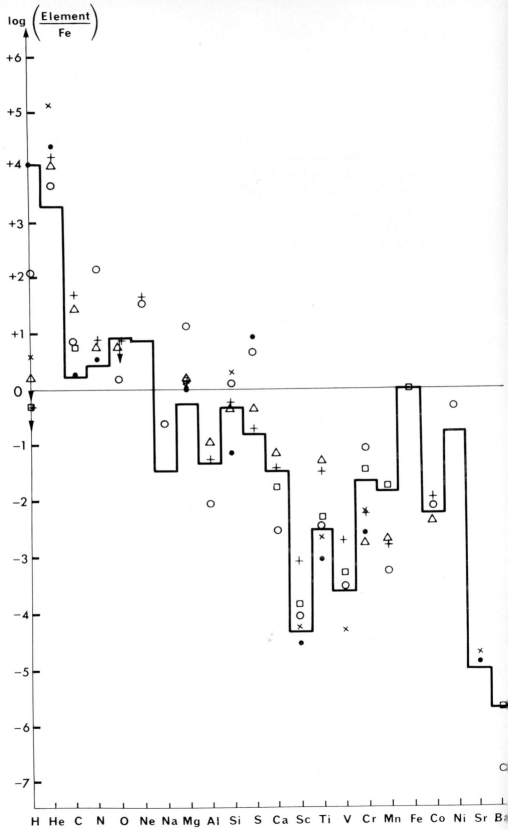

Fig. 8 — Abundance of the elements relative to iron. The full line represents the average value for normal stars. The symbols represent: ● β Lyr; ○ υ Sgr; × HD 30353; + HD 168476; △ HD 12 □ R C r B.

υ Sagittarii shows the products of a number of reactions greater than the other stars, probably not because it is in a more advanced stage of evolution (in fact H/He for υ Sgr is greater than for the group of hot stars), but because it has lost its outer envelope by tidal effects due to the presence of a close companion, and shows the products of burning of the different envelopes.

The group of hot subdwarfs which are characterized by the complete absence of carbon and oxygen lines in their spectra, are probably the objects in the most advanced evolutionary stage, already on the way to become white dwarfs, and have completely burned up carbon and oxygen.

2 — The close binary systems

The three close binary systems υ Sagittarii, HD 30353 and β Lyrae have the common particularity of presenting evidence of loss and exchange of mass to the companion and hydrogen-deficiency, though in a very different degree.

HD 30353 presents the hydrogen-depletion in the highest degree, and phenomena imputed to exchange of mass or loss of mass from the system in the lowest degree, the only evidence of this being the H α emission.

β Lyrae has a slight hydrogen deficiency but strong evidence of loss and exchange of mass and an extended shell which probably envelopes the whole system. υ Sagittarii is in the middle, both with respect to the hydrogen deficiency and to the loss of mass. The existence of an envelope is not so evident as in the case of β Lyrae but the irregular variations in the contours of the lines can be explained by the existence of a shell. Moreover emission and absorption components of H α and H β indicate the existence of jets of gas from one star to the other and vice versa (HACK, 1950).

By consequence of these observations we are tempted to suggest that the stars which just begin to fill their equipotential lobe, and therefore are still in possession of their outer hydrogen-rich layers, may eject matter in greater quantity. In this sense β Lyrae should be the less evolved of the three close systems here considered.

Table V gives the characteristics of these three systems.

The probable position of the three pairs in the HR diagram is shown in figure 2. For υ Sagittarii it is not impossible that the values of the masses derived by the Mass-function are in agreement with the Mass-Luminosity relation. The primary could be a supergiant evolving in the direction of the red-supergiant region, while the secondary would still be on the main

TABLE V

	β Lyrae	υ Sagittarii	HD 30353
P	$12^d.9$	$137^d.94$	$360^d.47$
γ	−16 km/s	9 km/s	6 km/s
K	187 km/s	56 km/s	50 km/s
$a \sin i$	32.9×10^6 km	106×10^6 km	243×10^6 km
$f(\mathcal{M})$	$8.5\ \mathcal{M}_\odot$	$1.582\ \mathcal{M}_\odot$	$4.41\ \mathcal{M}_\odot$

Masses for

β Lyrae: $i = 90°\ (\alpha = \mathcal{M}_1/\mathcal{M}_2)$
υ Sagittarii: $i = 90°$
HD 30353: $i = 90°$ and $i = 45°$

α	β Lyrae $\mathcal{M}_1$	β Lyrae $\mathcal{M}_2$	υ Sgr $\mathcal{M}_1$	υ Sgr $\mathcal{M}_2$	HD 30353 $i=90°$ $\mathcal{M}_1$	HD 30353 $i=90°$ $\mathcal{M}_2$	HD 30353 $i=45°$ $\mathcal{M}_1$	HD 30353 $i=45°$ $\mathcal{M}_2$
4	840	210	160	40	440	110	—	—
2	152	76	28	14	80	40	150	100
1.5	78	52	15	10	40	27	65	65
1	34	34	6.5	6.5	17.5	17.5	18.5	37
0.5	9	19	1.7	3.5	5	10	6.3	15.5
0.25	4.4	13.5	0.6	2.5	1.7	6.8	4.8	24
0.2	2.4	12	0.5	2.3	1.25	6.4		

	β Lyrae	υ Sagittarii	HD 30353
	Eclipsing variable. The primary is eclipsed at the principal min. No trace of sec. spectrum.	Eclipsing variable. The secondary is eclipsed at the principal min. No trace of sec. spectrum.	No eclipse. No trace of the secondary spectrum
Sp. prim.	B 8-B 9	B 8-B 9	F 0
M_{bol} prim.	−4.5	$\leqslant -5.75$	~ -1.6
M_{bol} sec.	> -2.5	> -3.7	$> +0.4$
	The secondary is over-massive		The secondary is over-massive

sequence. But it is also possible that the primary is the less massive having suffered great loss of mass.

For β Lyrae the model which best explains the observed facts is that proposed by HUANG [1963]. β Lyrae has filled the equipotential lobe and is a giant overluminous for its mass, while the companion is underluminous, is surrounded by a disk and is still in the contraction phase.

HD 30353 is a giant with visual magnitude $M_v = -1.6$ according to NARIAI [1963] who judges its luminosity from the color excess. He corrects the observed color for the blanketing effect and compares this corrected color with the color computed for a hydrogen-deficient atmosphere having the same temperature of HD 30353, deriving in this manner the color excess. BIDELMAN [1950] has estimated a distance of 2 000 parsecs by the interstellar reddening, assuming a color normal for the atmospherical temperature. From this it follows that $M_v = -3.7$. The value given by NARIAI, taking into account the influence of the hydrogen-depletion upon the color, is the more reliable. The secondary is at least two magnitudes fainter, since no trace of its spectrum is visible. The mass function indicates that the secondary is strongly overmassive for its luminosity. Since this is not an eclipsing system we cannot tell if the secondary is hotter or cooler than the primary.

3 — Visual binary or multiple systems

The visual binary or multiple systems having a member which is hydrogen-poor are HD 113001 (O 9 + F 2 V), HD 128220 (Osd + G 0 III) and σ Orionis.

HD 113001 B is a hot subdwarf, while the companion is a main sequence star. The hot subdwarf was probably a massive and bright star which has completed almost the whole evolutionary path in a time less than one billion years, this being the time which is necessary for the present primary to evolve out of the sequence.

HD 128220 B is also a hot star placed below the main sequence, but this star has arrived at a less advanced stage of evolution than HD 113001 B. Its companion is a G 0 giant. Also in this case the secondary was probably the original primary and has described a great part of its evolutionary path while the companion has just begin to move on the giant branch.

σ Ori E is only slightly hydrogen-deficient and is located practically on the main sequence. The close system σ Ori AB and the wider components σ Ori C, σ Ori D and σ Ori E all fall on the main sequence. It is difficult to explain why σ Ori E which is less massive than σ Ori A has evolved faster than the more massive companion, at least if we accept the idea that the slight excess of helium indicated by visual inspection of the spectrum (GREENSTEIN and WALLERSTEIN, 1958), necessarily indicates an evolutionary effect in spite of the position on the main sequence occupied by σ Ori E. A quantitative analysis of the spectrum of this star would be necessary to decide the extent of the He excess, and if this can be explained by atmospherical anomalies rather than by abundance anomalies.

REFERENCES

ALLER, L.H., 1954, *Liège Mem.*, **14**, No. 357, p. 353.

BERGER, J., 1956, *Contr. Inst. Ap.*, Paris, No. 217.

BERGER, J. and GREENSTEIN, J.L., 1963, *P.A.S.P.*, **75**, 336.

BERMAN, L., 1935, *Ap. J.*, **81**, 369.

BIDELMAN, W.P., 1948, *Ap. J.*, **107**, 413.

BIDELMAN, W.P., 1949, *Ap. J.*, **109**, 544.

BIDELMAN, W.P., 1950, *Ap. J.*, **111**, 333.

BIDELMAN, W.P., 1952, *Ap. J.*, **116**, 227.

BOYARCHUCK, A.A., 1959, *Soviet Astron.*, **3**, 748.

BUSCOMBE, W., 1953, *Ap. J.* **118**, 459.

BUSCOMBE, W., 1955, *Ap. J.*, **121**, 312.

BUSCOMBE, W., 1965, *M.N.R.A.S.*, **129**, 1.

CAMERON, A.G.W., 1955, *Ap. J.*, **121**, 144.

CAMERON, A.G.W., 1959, *Ap. J.*, **130**, 329 and 895.

ELVIUS, T. and SINNERSTAD, U., 1958, *Arkiv f. Astron.*, **2**, 189.

GAPOSCHKIN, S., 1945, *A.J.*, **51**, 109.

GOLDBERG, L., MÜLLER, E.A., and ALLER, L.H., 1960, *Ap. J. Suppl.* **5**, 1.

GOULD, N.L., HERBIG, G.H., and MORGAN, W.W., 1957, *P.A.S.P.*, **69**, 242.

GREENSTEIN, J.L., 1940, *Ap. J.*, **91**, 438.

GREENSTEIN, J.L., 1943, *Ap. J.* **97**, 252.

GREENSTEIN, J.L., 1950, *Ap. J.*, **111**, 20.

GREENSTEIN, J.L., 1960, *Stellar Atmospheres*, (ed. J.L. Greenstein, Chicago, University of Chicago Press), p. 703.

GREENSTEIN, J.L. and ADAMS, W.S., 1947, *Ap. J.*, **106**, 339.

GREENSTEIN, J.L. and WALLERSTEIN, G., 1958, *Ap. J.*, **127**, 237.

HACK, M., 1959, *Mem. Soc. Astron. Ital.*, **30**, 89.

HACK, M., 1960, *Mem. Soc. Astron. Ital.*, **31**, 43.

HACK, M. and JOB, F., 1965, *Zs. f. Ap.* **62**, 203.

HACK, M. and PASINETTI, L., 1963, *Contrib. Merate Milano*, No. 215.

HEARD, J.F., 1962, *Publ. David Dunlap Observ.*, **2**, No. 9.

HILL, P.W., 1963, *M.N.R.A.S.*, **127**, 113.

HILL, P.W., 1965, *M.N.R.A.S.*, **129**, 137.

HOFFLEIT, E.D., 1959, *A.J.*, **64**, 241.

HUANG, S.S., 1963, *Ap. J.*, **138**, 342.

JASCHEK, C. O. R., and JASCHEK, M., 1963, *P. A. S. P.*, **75**, 365.

KLEMOLA, A. R., 1961, *Ap. J.*, **134**, 130.

MÜNCH, G., 1958, *Ap. J.*, **127**, 642.

MÜNCH, G., and SLETTEBAK, A., 1959, *Ap. J.*, **129**, 853.

NARIAI, K., 1963*a*, *Publ. A. S. Japan*, **15**, 7.

NARIAI, K., 1963*b*, *Publ. A. S. Japan*, **15**, 449.

OSAWA, K., NISHIMURA, S. and NARIAI, K., 1963, *Publ. A.S. Japan*, **15**, 313.

PAYNE GAPOSCHKIN, C., 1963, *Ap. J.*, **138**, 320.

POPPER, D. M., 1942, *P. A. S. P.*, **54**, 160.

POPPER, D. M., 1946, *P. A. S. P.*, **58**, 370.

POPPER, D. M., 1947, *P. A. S. P.*, **59**, 320.

SAHADE, J., HUANG, S. S., STRUVE, O., and ZEBERGS, V., 1959, *Trans. Amer. Phil. Soc.*, **49**, 1.

SEARLE, L., 1961, *Ap. J.*, **133**, 531.

STEWART, J. Q., 1956, *A. J.*, **61**, 13.

STRUVE, O., 1958, *P. A. S. P.*, **70**, 5.

STRUVE, O. and ZEBERGS, V., 1961, *Ap. J.*, **134**, 161.

STURCH, C. and WALLERSTEIN, G., 1962, *P. A. S. P.*, **74**, 325.

THACKERAY, A. D. and WESSELINK, A. J., 1952, *Observatory*, **72**, 248.

WALLERSTEIN, G. and SPINRAD, H., 1960, *P. A. S. P.*, **72**, 486.

WALLERSTEIN, G., STURCH, C. and KLEMOLA, A. R., 1963, *P. A. S. P.*, **75**, 61.

YUIN, C., 1948, *Ap. J.* **107**, 413.

The helium-hydrogen ratio for Population I stars deduced from binary data

Bengt STRÖMGREN

The Institute for Advanced Study, Princeton, N.J.

In a recent investigation KELSALL and STRÖMGREN [1965] have calculated evolutionary model sequences for main-sequence B and A stars for six different assumptions regarding the initial chemical composition. In the present investigation these results are utilized for a determination of the initial helium-hydrogen ratio for a number of main-sequence B and A stars with well-determined masses, radii and luminosities. The stars in question consist of components of eclipsing binary systems and one visual binary component, Sirius A.

The basis for the selection of the eclipsing binaries was the table of data on "reliable" systems given by HARRIS, STRAND and WORLEY [1963]. These authors assembled the list from compilations by KOPAL [1955] and POPPER [1957a], and their list was critically reviewed by POPPER.

The values of the masses M and the radii R were taken from the table by HARRIS, STRAND and WORLEY. These data were combined with effective temperatures T_e derived from the results of photoelectric photometry with the help of model-atmosphere calculations. The bolometric magnitudes M_{bol} followed from the known values of R and T_e.

I am very much indebted to Dr. D.H. McNAMARA for putting at my disposal in advance of publication the results of photoelectric measures of a number of eclipsing binaries. For the B stars photoelectric UBV photometry was used in the determination of T_e, for the A stars cl photometry (B. STRÖMGREN, 1958).

For the derivation of T_e from $(U - B)_0$ for B stars I used a temperature scale obtained from model-atmosphere calculations (B. STRÖMGREN, 1964). For the A stars the first step was the conversion of the results of the cl photometry to $b-y$ (B. STRÖMGREN, 1963); the effective temperature could then be derived from $b-y$ using a temperature scale obtained on the basis of model atmosphere calculations by OSAWA [1956], see (B. STRÖMGREN, 1963). Actually, an improved $T_e - (b-y)$ relation obtained from model atmospheres calculated by D. MIHALAS was used. D. MIHALAS kindly communicated to me the results of these calculations before publication.

Gauthier-Villars, Paris - Modern Astrophysics - 1967.

Table I gives the observational data used in this investigation. For WW Aur, AR Aur, RX Her, TX Her and U Oph the adopted values of the mass and the radius are means of the values for the two components, weighted according to the light ratio. The effective temperature T_e was derived from photoelectric photometry referring to the combined light of the components. For Z Vul the $(U-B)_0$-value of the brighter component was derived from the measures of the combined light with the help of the B and V data for the two components given by POPPER [1957b], and the given values of mass, radius and effective temperature refer to the bright component.

For Sirius A the mass and the visual absolute magnitude were taken from the compilation by HARRIS, STRAND and WORLEY [1963]. Thd effective temperature was derived from $uvby$ photometry (STRÖMGREN and PERRY, 1965) see also (STRÖMGREN, 1963) on the basis of the model atmospheres computed by D. MIHALAS.

TABLE I

Star	log M/M$_\odot$	log T$_e$	M$_{bol}$
WW Aur	0.25	3.92	$+1\overset{m}{.}7$
AR Aur	0.39	4.06	$+0.4$
RX Her	0.42	4.06	-0.2
TX Her	0.30	3.88	$+2.3$
U Oph	0.70	4.26	-2.9
Z Vul	0.73	4.27	-3.7
Sirius A	0.33	4.02	$+1.0$

The following procedure was used for the determination of the initial helium-hydrogen ratio of the stars in question. Separate calculations were made for each of the six initial chemical compositions X, Y, Z (hydrogen content X, helium content Y, heavy-element content Z) of the KELSALL-STRÖMGREN evolutionary model sequences. First, the zero-age value of M_{bol} was found from T_e (KELSALL-STRÖMGREN, table II) and the difference ΔM_{bol} between this value and the actual M_{bol}-value computed. With the help of KELSALL-STRÖMGREN, table I, the value of log M/M$_\odot$ corresponding to T_e and ΔM_{bol} was computed, and the residual observed minus computed log M/M$_\odot$ followed.

Table II gives the residuals for the six combinations of Z = 0.02, 0.03, 0.04, respectively, with X = 0.60 and X = 0.70. The last column gives for the stars in question the value of X that corresponds to zero mass-residual, separately for each of the three Z-values.

TABLE II

	Observed log $M/M_\odot$	Assumed Z	Residual (O-C) in log $M/M_\odot$ for $X = 0.60$	Residual (O-C) in log $M/M_\odot$ for $X = 0.70$	X corresponding to assumed Z
WW Aur	0.25	$Z = 0.02$	$+0.06$	0.00	0.70
		0.03	$+0.03$	-0.03	0.65
		0.04	$+0.01$	-0.05	0.62
TX Her	0.30	$Z = 0.02$	—	$+0.11$	—
		0.03	$+0.14$	$+0.08$	—
		0.04	$+0.13$	$+0.06$	~ 0.8
AR Aur	0.39	$Z = 0.02$	$+0.06$	-0.01	0.69
		0.03	$+0.03$	-0.03	0.65
		0.04	$+0.01$	-0.06	0.61
RX Her	0.42	$Z = 0.02$	$+0.04$	-0.02	0.67
		0.03	$+0.02$	-0.04	0.63
		0.04	0.00	-0.06	0.60
U Oph	0.70	$Z = 0.02$	$+0.02$	-0.04	0.63
		0.03	0.00	-0.06	0.60
		0.04	-0.02	-0.08	0.57
Z Vul	0.73	$Z = 0.02$	-0.02	-0.08	0.57
		0.03	-0.04	-0.10	0.54
		0.04	-0.05	-0.13	0.54
Sirius A	0.33	$Z = 0.02$	$+0.05$	-0.01	0.68
		0.03	$+0.03$	-0.04	0.64
		0.04	$+0.01$	-0.06	0.61

We shall now consider the changes in the resulting X-values caused by observational errors in M, R and T_e. An increase in log M of 0.01 gives an increase in X approximately equal to 0.02, while an increase in log R of 0.01 corresponds to a decrease in X of about 0.006. Finally, if log T_e is increased by 0.01, the corresponding X decreases by 0.02.

From these considerations it follows that the differences between the X-values for the stars in table II (with the exception of TX Her), are not greater than the uncertainties corresponding to possible observational errors in M, R and T_e. For TX Her further analysis of the observational data is necessary before it can be safely concluded whether or not the X-value is abnormal.

The sample of stars available for this type of discussion is, of course, small. It should be emphasized that a larger sample of Population I stars might contain cases with X-values well outside the range of those given in table I. In particular, X-values as low as those indicated by EGGEN's [1963] investigation of visual binaries in the Hyades might occur, although they are not present in our sample of X-values for stars with well-determined values of mass, radius and luminosity.

The average values of X for the stars of table II (excluding TX Her) are given in table III for the three different assumed values of Z.

TABLE III

Z	X	Y	Y/4X	Y/Z
0.02	0.66	0.32	0.12	16
0.03	0.62	0.35	0.14	12
0.04	0.59	0.37	0.16	9

It is interesting to compare these values with those obtained for the sun by GAUSTAD [1964], SEARS [1964], and DEMARQUE and PERCY [1964]. GAUSTAD's values are X = 0.72, Y = 0.26 and Z = 0.020, and the two other investigations yielded very nearly the same values.

If the sample of table II is typical of Population I main-sequence B and A stars, then we may conclude that stellar masses derived from M_{bol} and T_e on the basis of evolutionary model sequences have a fairly high degree of accuracy, better than 5-10 per cent. This would also be the case with regard to calculated values of the gravitational acceleration g at the surface of the star, so that g-values computed in this way could be trusted in stellar-atmosphere investigations.

Acknowledgements I wish to express my thanks to Dr. D.H. McNAMARA and to Dr. D. MIHALAS for their kindness in putting unpublished results at my disposal in advance of publication. This investigation was supported by a grant from the National Science Foundation.

REFERENCES

DEMARQUE, P. R. and PERCY, J. R., 1964, *Ap. J.*, **140**, 541.

EGGEN, O. J., 1963, *Ap. J. Suppl.*, **8**, 125.

GAUSTAD, J. E., 1964, *Ap. J.*, **139**, 406.

HARRIS, D. L., STRAND, K. AA, and WORLEY, C. E., 1963, *Stars and Stellar Systems*, **3**, Ch. 15 (ed. K. Aa. Strand, University of Chicago Press, Chicago).

KELSALL, T. and STRÖMGREN, B., 1965, *Vistas in Astronomy*, **6** (ed. A. Beer, Pergamon Press, London).

KOPAL, Z., 1955, *Ann. d'Ap.*, **18**, 379.

OSAWA, K., 1956, *Ap. J.*, **123**, 513.

POPPER, D. M., 1957a, *J. R. A. S. Canada*, **51**, 51.

POPPER, D. M., 1957b, *Ap. J.*, **126**, 53.

SEARS, R. L., 1964, *Ap. J.*, **140**, 477.

STRÖMGREN, B., 1958, *Stellar Populations* (ed. D. J. K. O'Connell, Amsterdam, North-Holland Pub. Co. and New York, Intersciences Publishers), p. 385.

STRÖMGREN, B., 1963, *Quarterly J. R. A. S.* **4**, 8.

STRÖMGREN, B., 1964, *Rev. Mod. Phys.*, **36**, 532.

STRÖMGREN, B. and PERRY C., 1965, *Photoelectric uvby photometry for 1217 stars* (unpublished).

Quelques réflexions sur l'astrophysique moléculaire

P. SWINGS

Institut d'Astrophysique, Liège (Belgique)

Lorsque, en 1931, je préparais mon premier séjour dans une institution astronomique américaine, je m'étais enquis de l'Observatoire où j'aurais le plus de chance de pouvoir discuter les deux questions qui m'intéressaient le plus à cette époque, à savoir les étoiles à raies d'émission et le rôle des molécules dans les astres. J'ai rapidement compris que l'endroit où je pourrais le plus efficacement travailler ces deux problèmes pendant quelques mois était l'observatoire Yerkes où le jeune professeur Otto STRUVE était en train de créer une florissante École d'Astrophysique. STRUVE commençait à s'occuper fort activement des étoiles Be et il se rendait compte aussi des possibilités d'applications astronomiques de la physique des molécules.

Dès ce premier séjour aux Etats-Unis, j'ai entamé avec STRUVE, dans le domaine des étoiles Be, une intime et fructueuse collaboration qui devait durer plus de vingt ans. En fait, dans son premier long mémoire sur les étoiles chaudes à raies d'émission [1931], STRUVE a bien voulu associer généreusement mon nom (STRUVE and SWINGS, 1932). Dans cette première publication commune, nous discutons, sur la base de spectres pris au réfracteur de quarante pouces, l'hypothèse de l'origine des raies brillantes dans les enveloppes d'étoiles en rotation rapide. Pendant près de vingt ans, nous avons, dans une cinquantaine de publications, étudié, en collaboration, les spectres d'astres divers à raies d'émission, ainsi que des problèmes connexes concernant des objets normaux ou exceptionnels.

STRUVE s'intéressait intensément aux problèmes spectroscopiques soulevés par les astres chauds à raies brillantes, mais les questions d'identification nous amenaient fréquemment aussi à des études spectrographiques d'étoiles chaudes normales ou même d'astres froids. Nous trouvions ainsi de fréquentes occasions d'appliquer les travaux expérimentaux et théoriques de spectroscopie atomique, notamment ceux qui concernaient les raies interdites, les mécanismes de fluorescence et les effets de dilution. Les contributions de Struve et de ses associés dans le domaine des étoiles à raies brillantes sont bien connues et je ne m'occuperai pas ici de ce chapitre de l'Astrophysique.

Gauthier-Villars, Paris - Modern Astrophysics - 1967.

STRUVE commençait aussi, en 1931, à s'intéresser aux spectres moléculaires. Il avait eu l'occasion d'en discuter avec H. N. RUSSELL, R. S. MULLIKEN, A. CHRISTY et d'autres physiciens. C'est avec enthousiasme que, durant l'été et l'automne 1931, nous avons associé nos efforts dans une première recherche sur le comportement des bandes de CH et CN dans les spectres stellaires (SWINGS and STRUVE, 1932). Notre but essentiel était d'estimer les abondances relatives de H et N en comparant les comportements des bandes de CH et CN (deux molécules ayant l'atome C en commun) en fonction du type spectral et de la magnitude absolue. Nous ne disposions que de spectres à dispersion moyenne, obtenus au spectrographe Bruce du réfracteur de quarante pouces. Nous avons trouvé que, sur nos clichés, la limite supérieure de visibilité de la bande λ 4300 de CH était la classe F 8, c'est-à-dire nettement moins chaude que les limites adoptées auparavant (classes F 2 à A 0).

L'erreur de nos prédécesseurs était due à la présence d'un spectre atomique très riche, superposé à la bande de CH; dans la bande G le rôle de CH est moins important que celui des raies atomiques. Quant à la bande λ 4200 de CN, la limite trouvée était F 8, en bon accord avec les estimations antérieures. La disparition simultanée, en F 8, des bandes des deux radicaux CN et CH dont les énergies de dissociation diffèrent fortement, résulte de ce que l'hydrogène est beaucoup plus abondant que l'azote, le rapport des abondances étant de l'ordre de 1000. Certes, notre traitement du problème était rudimentaire, car nous ne connaissions pas les forces oscillantes des deux bandes, les énergies de dissociation étaient très incertaines et bien d'autres sources d'erreur étaient présentes; d'ailleurs notre matériel d'observation était fort modeste. Mais, comme S. ROSSELAND l'exposait, peu après, dans son ouvrage d'astrophysique theorique (1936), c'était la seule façon d'obtenir une idée des abondances relatives de H et N, dont les raies atomiques du domaine observable possèdent un potentiel d'excitation très élevé.

Durant ce premier séjour à Yerkes Observatory, j'avais, également, sur la base de spectres de dispersion très modeste, obtenus au réfracteur de quarante pouces, étudié le comportement des bandes de CN et CH dans δ Cephei (1931). Plus tard, STRUVE et moi avons observé plusieurs autres effets moléculaires, parfois avec succès (spectres cométaires), parfois en vain (comparaison des spectres du disque et des anneaux de Saturne; recherche de bandes éventuelles de NH_2 dans Jupiter).

Quoique essentiellement « atomiste », STRUVE n'a jamais, au cours de sa carrière, perdu de vue les problèmes d'astrophysique moléculaire. Son travail en collaboration avec G. SHAJN sur l'absorption intense dans la région violette des spectres d'étoiles carbonées avancées (1947) a inspiré, au moins en partie, les travaux de A. McKELLAR, M. N. RAO et moi-même, sur les étoiles N avancées.

Les réflexions qui suivent et que je dédie à la mémoire de notre ami regretté n'ont pas la prétention de couvrir toute l'astrophysique moléculaire. Plusieurs exposés systématiques de ce sujet ont, d'ailleurs, été publiés récemment (HERZBERG, 1965; SWINGS, 1958; et les *Colloques Internationaux d'Astrophysique de Liège*, 1954, 1956, 1962 et 1963). Dès 1933, d'importants travaux théoriques effectués à Liège par L. ROSENFELD [1933] et Y. CAM-BRESIER et ROSENFELD [1933] et à Princeton par H. N. RUSSELL [1934] per-mettaient de mieux comprendre le comportement des bandes moléculaires essentielles dans les étoiles avancées. Ces travaux théoriques ont été suivis de nombreux autres concernant les abondances moléculaires; les calculs les plus récents et les plus complets sont ceux du groupe de Y. FUJITA [1957, 1964], notamment de TAKASHI TSUJI [1964] et de VARDYA.

Au cours des dernières années, les observations spectroscopiques par télescopes traditionnels au sol et les recherches théoriques correspondantes ont fait faire des progrès considérables à nos connaissances des planètes (y compris la terre), des comètes, des étoiles avancées (y compris le soleil) et de la matière interstellaire. Si les astrophysiciens ont tiré grand profit des travaux de laboratoire, la réciproque est aussi vraie (SWINGS, 1958; HERZBERG, 1965; *Colloques de Liège*, 1954, 1956, 1962, 1963). Les bandes telluriques de O_2 dans le rouge et le proche infrarouge ont fourni les premiers exemples de transitions magnétiques dipolaires ($^1\Sigma_g^+ - {}^3\Sigma_g^-$ et $^1\Delta_g - {}^3\Sigma_g^-$) d'une molécule diatomique. Les bandes telluriques ont aussi permis d'étudier des molécules isotopiques comme $^{16}O\,^{18}O$ et $^{16}O\,^{17}O$. La structure de la molécule H_2O a été basée sur les transitions de vibration-rotation observées en absorption tellurique. Un impressionnant effet de prédissociation inverse de la molécule Al H a été observé en émission dans des variables à longue période, comme Ki Cygni. Ce sont les observations astronomiques qui, pour une large part, ont suscité les importants travaux expérimentaux récents sur les spectres permis de diverses molécules comme C_3, NH_2, CH^+ et sur les transitions interdites quadrupolaires de H_2. Je ne m'occuperai ici que des étoiles et du milieu interstellaire et non des planètes et comètes.

Nous savons à présent que le comportement des bandes de CN et de CH n'est plus seulement fonction du type spectral et de la magnitude absolue comme nous le pensions il y a une trentaine d'années; le type de population joue aussi un rôle essentiel.

La séparation en étoiles froides à oxygène et à carbone continue à être attribuée essentiellement — comme l'avaient déjà montré L. ROSENFELD et

H.N. RUSSELL — à des différences d'abondances relatives de l'oxygène et du carbone. Mais, du moins dans les étoiles les plus froides, on ne pense plus que le rôle essentiel soit joué exclusivement par la molécule CO[1]; on doit y ajouter l'influence des molécules polyatomiques (FUJITA et al., 1957, 1964; TSUJI, 1964) et, peut-être, même des poussières de graphite. Jusqu'ici, les atmosphères stellaires n'ont révélé que trois molécules polyatomiques : C_3, SiC_2 et H_2O. Des bandes intenses de H_2O ont été observées récemment dans la région infrarouge des étoiles les plus froides, par observations au sol (G.P. Kuiper : bande de 1.4 μ dans Mira Ceti, R Leonis et d'autres étoiles M 7 et M 8; P.B. Boyce et W.M. Sinton : dans Mira, R Leonis, U Orionis, Ki Cygni, T Cephei, R Cassiopeae, HD 207076) et par observations en ballon (*Stratoscope* II : R.E. DANIELSON, W.K. ROSE, M. SCHWARZSCHILD et N.J. WOOLF, spectres[2] de 1 à 3 μ de Mu Cephei, Betelgeuse, Mira, R Leonis, Rho Persei et Mu Geminorum). L'effet de magnitude absolue des bandes de H_2O est très prononcé.

En fait, les observations stellaires dans l'infrarouge fourniront encore de grandes surprises[3]. La découverte par H. SPINRAD [1964] de la transition infrarouge quadrupolaire $2-0$ de H_2 dans des étoiles froides[4] est de grande importance. On peut s'attendre à trouver, dans les étoiles C, les bandes permises, fondamentales et harmoniques, de vibration-rotation de diverses molécules polyatomiques (FUJITA et al. 1964; TSUJI, 1964) comme HCN, C_2H_2, C_2H, etc. En fait, les transitions électroniques de la plupart des molécules polyatomiques[5] se trouvent dans l'ultraviolet; leur détection dans les étoiles nécessite des observations par engins spatiaux, mais le succès de tels essais est douteux, étant donné la basse température des étoiles C et M.

Suivant les abondances relatives de H : C : N : O, les spectres infrarouges seront très différents (FUJITA et al., 1957, 1964; TSUJI, 1964). Comme l'a montré R. WILDT [1957], les molécules constituent le facteur principal déter-

---

[1] Ce n'est que tout récemment que les bandes infrarouges de CO ont été observées dans des étoiles autres que le soleil (intenses dans les étoiles M, faibles dans les étoiles R).

[2] Le spectre d'Aldebaran (K 5) ne présente pas d'absorption aux environs de 1.6 μ, là où l'opacité due à H^- et H_2^- est faible.

[3] Même dans le spectre solaire au sol, on n'a observé aucune raie non tellurique avec certitude, au-delà de 5 μ. L'étude à haute résolution du spectre infrarouge du soleil par ballon est très désirable.

[4] Spinrad a observé les raies S(2) et S(3) de $2-0$. Les transitions quadrupolaires $3-0$ et $4-0$ de vibration-rotation de H_2 ont été observées dans Jupiter. Dans Uranus et Neptune on a observé des bandes diffuses dues au spectre de H_2 induit par pression.

[5] Quelques radicaux polyatomiques, comme C_3, SiC_2, NH_2, HCO possèdent des transitions électroniques dans le domaine ordinaire. Plusieurs molécules diatomiques (H_2, N_2, O_2, NO et SiO ont leurs transitions électroniques de résonance dans l'ultraviolet lointain.

minant la structure des atmosphères des étoiles très froides[6]. En fait, déjà en 1934, H. N. Russell se rendait bien compte de l'importance des molécules polyatomiques au sein des atmosphères stellaires et avait inclus H_2O et CO_2 dans ses calculs d'abondances moléculaires; il avait aussi envisagé HCN et C_2N_2. Depuis longtemps, il a été suggéré que, aux basses températures (T < 2200° K), les atmosphères d'étoiles carbonées pourraient contenir des particules de graphite. Il est possible qu'on découvre les molécules stables CH_4 et NH_3 dans les étoiles les plus froides.

L'interprétation du comportement des bandes de MERRILL-SANFORD attribuées à SiC_2 n'est pas encore claire. Il semble bien (FUJITA et al., 1957, 1964; TSUJI 1964; HUMBLET et MANNINO, 1955) qu'il n'y ait qu'une corrélation fort peu marquée entre l'intensité des bandes de SiC_2 et la classe spectrale (aussi bien C que $R - N$). Peut-être existe-t-il un important effet de luminosité ? Un vague maximum d'intensité aux environs de C 4 est, peut-être, dû à la réduction de l'abondance de Si due à la formation de molécules polyatomiques à base de silicium (HSiN, Si_2H_2 ...) (FUJITA et al., 1957, 1964; TSUJI, 1964). L'analyse plus détaillée du spectre de laboratoire de SiC_2 actuellement en cours à Ottawa, est attendue avec impatience.

L'analyse du spectre de laboratoire de C_3 a fait des progrès considérables récemment (GAUSSET et al., 1963, 1965), de même que l'étude théorique de son abondance dans les étoiles (FUJITA et al., 1957, 1964; TSUJI, 1964; HUMBLET et MANNINO, 1955). La présence du spectre discret de C_3 dans les étoiles N paraît extrêmement probable, mais on n'est pas encore tout à fait convaincu que l'affaiblissement considérable des étoiles N pour λ < 4200 étudié, entre autres, par O. STRUVE et G. SHAJN, est dû au continuum de C_3.

Si la bifurcation en étoiles à oxydes et à composés carbonés est due aux abondances relatives de C et O, la séparation entre la séquence M (caractérisée par les bandes intenses de TiO et VO et faibles de ScO, YO, AlO, CaH, AlH, MgH, SiH) et la séquence S (surtout ZrO et LaO, plus bandes faibles de TiO, YO et SiH) paraît due aux abondances relatives des métaux lourds (5e et 6e périodes) et des métaux plus légers (4e période). Certes, on a longtemps considéré comme solution de facilité, le recours à des effets d'abondances. A présent, il faut pourtant bien admettre qu'il existe, par suite de divers mécanismes (nucléogénèse, brassage, effet betatron, etc.) de grandes différences d'abondances d'éléments ou de leurs isotopes dans les

---

[6] A T_e < 2.500 °K, l'hydrogène est presque complètement sous forme moléculaire. Récemment on a envisagé que des molécules telles que HeH^+ peuvent jouer un rôle dans l'ultraviolet des étoiles chaudes. De même le rôle de H_2, H_2^+ et H_2^- dans l'opacité continue a été discuté.

divers astres. Les bandes moléculaires fournissent, au sujet des isotopes, des renseignements précieux, notamment dans le cas du carbone.

Les progrès expérimentaux effectués dans l'analyse des spectres moléculaires d'intérêt astronomique, dans la mesure des forces d'oscillation et dans la détermination des énergies de dissociation permettent d'espérer des progrès parallèles dans l'établissement des modèles d'atmosphères, les déterminations d'abondances, les mesures de températures et les études d'équilibres de dissociation.

Les molécules jouent aussi un rôle de plus en plus important dans l'étude du milieu interstellaire. Depuis longtemps, on connaît les raies interstellaires de CH, CH$^+$ et CN[7]. Récemment, la radio-astronomie a fait de grands progrès grâce à la découverte des radicaux interstellaires de OH (raies à 1667, 1665 et 1612 Mc/sec) (transition d'une composante à l'autre dans le dédoublement Λ du sous-niveau inférieur $^2\pi_{3/2}$ de l'état électronique normal). Sans doute, observera-t-on, un jour prochain, dans la région centimétrique, les transitions d'autres radicaux interstellaires, comme CH ? On pense de plus en plus qu'une partie importante de l'hydrogène interstellaire se trouve sous forme de la molécule H$_2$ (GOULD et al., 1963). On a envisagé la détection de transitions interdites de H$_2$ dans l'infrarouge (GOULD and HARWIT, 1963). Le système ultraviolet lointain de H$_2$ est toutefois beaucoup plus sensible que les transitions quadrupolaires dans l'infrarouge. La transition électronique de LYMAN (B $^1\Sigma_u^+$ $-$ X $^1\Sigma_g^+$) apparaîtra sûrement lorsqu'on obtiendra par télescope orbitant (3e OAO; instrumentation de L. Spitzer, SPITZER et al., 1964) des spectres d'étoiles chaudes à haute résolution dans l'ultraviolet lointain. D'après les forces oscillantes calculées par NICHOLLS, il semble bien que les raies interstellaires les plus sensibles de H$_2$ seraient les transitions R(0) de 5$-$0 ($\lambda = 1036.456$) et 4$-$0 (λ 1049.368). Peut-être détectera-t-on aussi la molécule interstellaire HD ? Comme dans le cas de CH, CH$^+$, CN et Ti$^+$, on n'observera probablement que les raies de H$_2$ (et HD ?) correspondant aux niveaux rotationnels les plus bas.

Il reste encore plusieurs bandes d'absorption interstellaire diffuses inexpliquées. Certains astronomes pensent qu'elles sont dues à des poussières interstellaires[8], par exemple des grains métalliques (UNSÖLD, 1963), peut-être recouverts de glace (WHITNEY, 1964), ou des grains de graphite (éjectés par les étoiles carbonées) (HOYLE and WICKRAMASINGHE, 1962), ou encore des particules solides de SiO$_2$ (KAMIJO, 1963) (condensées dans les enveloppes

---

[7] G. MÜNCH [1964] a observé un nuage interstellaire, particulièrement riche en CN.

[8] La bande d'absorption de la glace à 3.1 μ, n'a pas été trouvée dans Mu Cephei, une étoile supergéante froide, rougie interstellairement (DANIELSON et al., 1965).

d'étoiles M), ou encore des particules de Platt constituées de molécules polyatomiques carbonées (C_2H_2, CH_4, C_2H_4, ...) (FUJITA et al., 1957, 1964; TSUJI, 1964). HERBIG [1963] et MALVILLE [1964] ont, de leur côté, émis l'hypothèse que certaines bandes diffuses sont dues à H_2 emprisonné dans de la glace. Mais HERZBERG [1965] pense que l'on ne peut pas encore exclure que ces bandes diffuses soient dues à des gaz et il considère qu'il s'agit là d'un « challenge to spectroscopists ».

OTTO STRUVE avait une connaissance très vaste et profonde de l'Astrophysique, comme le montrent, non seulement ses importantes recherches personnelles, mais aussi ses livres et ses articles mensuels à *Sky and Telescope*. Il a certes publié beaucoup moins dans le domaine moléculaire que dans plusieurs autres chapitres de l'astrophysique. Mais les quelques travaux qu'il a effectués dans cette voie et les références aux molécules que l'on trouve dans ses traités ou articles généraux montrent qu'il a toujours apprécié la grande importance de l'astrophysique moléculaire. Un de ses tout derniers articles mensuels de *Sky and Telescope*, paru dans le numéro de janvier 1963, trois mois avant sa mort, était intitulé *Molecular Spectra*.

BIBLIOGRAPHIE

CAMBRESIER, Y., and ROSENFELD, L., 1933, *M.N.R.A.S.*, **93**, 710.
DANIELSON, R.E., WOOLF, N.J., and GAUSTAD, J.E., 1965, *Ap. J.*, **141**, 116.
FUJITA, Y., YAMASHITA, Y., and NISHIMURA, S., 1957, *Proc. Japan Academy*, **33**, 386.
FUJITA, Y., YAMASHITA, Y. and TSUJI, T., 1964, *Proc. Japan Academy*, **40**, 664.
GAUSSET, L., HERZBERG, G., LAGERQUIST, A., and ROSEN, B., 1963, *Faraday Soc. Disc.*, **35**, 113; 1965, *Ap. J.*, **142**, 45.
GOULD, R.J., GOLD, T., and SALPETER, E.E., 1963, *Ap. J.*, **138**, 393 et 408.
GOULD, R.J. and HARWITT, M., 1963, *Ap. J.*, **137**, 694.
HERBIG, G.H., 1963, *Ap. J.*, **137**, 200.
HERZBERG, G., 1965, *J.O.S.A.*, **55**, 229.
HOYLE, F. and WICKRAMASINGHE, N.C., 1962, *M.N.R.A.S.*, **124**, 417.
HUMBLET, J. et MANNINO, G., 1955, *Ann. d'Ap.*, **18**, 321.
KAMIJO, F., 1963, *P.A.S. Japan*, **15**, 440.
MALVILLE, J.M., 1964, *Ap.J.*, **139**, 198.
MÜNCH, G., 1964, *Ap. J.*, **140**, 107.
ROSENFELD, L., 1933, *M.N.R.A.S.*, **93**, 742.
ROSSELAND, S., 1936, *Theoretical Astrophysics*, **93**, (Clarendon Press, Oxford), p. 251.
RUSSELL, H.N., 1934, *Ap. J.*, **79**, 317.
SHAJN, G. and STRUVE, O., 1947, *Ap. J.*, **106**, 86.
SPINRAD, H., 1964, *Ap. J.*, **140**, 1639.

Spitzer, L., Dressler, K., and Upton, W. L., 1964, *P. A. S. P.*, **76**, 387.
Struve, O. and Swings, P., 1932, *Ap. J.*, **75**, 161.
Swings, P., 1931, *M. N. R. A. S.*, **92**, 140.
Swings, P., 1958, *Handbuch der Physik*, **50**, 109.
Swings, P. and Struve, O., 1932, *Physical Review*, **39**, 142.
Tsuji, T., 1964, *Annals of the Tokyo Astr. Obs.*, **9**, no. 1.
Unsöld, A., 1963, *Zs. f. Ap.*, **56**, 221.
Whitney, C. A., 1964, *A. J.*, **69**, 564.
Wildt, R., 1957, *Mém. Soc. R. Sc.* **18**, 319 (*Colloque 1956 de Liège*).

Voir aussi :

Colloques Internationaux d'Astrophysique de Liège : 1954 (*Les particules solides dans les astres*); 1956 (*Les molécules dans les astres*); 1962 (*La physique des planètes*); 1963 (*Les spectres infrarouges des astres*) et 1965 (*Nature et Origine des comètes*).

Centre-limb variation of line profile in a moving atmosphere

K. D. ABHYANKAR

Nizamiah Observatory and Astronomy Department, Osmania University, Hyderabad, India

Abstract

From the radiation field in a moving atmosphere, obtained earlier (ABHYANKAR, 1964 b) for a Gaussian scattering function and a linear velocity law, line profiles have been computed for various angles of emergence. An optical thickness of $10/\sqrt{3}$ for the reversing layer and a maximum outward velocity of $10\sqrt{3}/\Delta\nu$ at the top of the atmosphere, where $\Delta\nu$ is the Gaussian parameter of the scattering function, were assumed. Line profiles at various points of the disc are shown in figures 1 and 2 for isotropic scattering (full line) and for a phase function with scattering in forward and backward directions only (dashed line). Figure 3 shows the integrated line profiles for a uniform disc with no limb darkening ($X = 0$) and for a disc with complete darkening at the limb ($X = 1$). These results support STRUVE's hypothesis of a network of prominences in supergiant stars.

1 — Mass motions in stellar atmospheres

In a review article with copious references HUANG and STRUVE [1960] have discussed two important factors, rotation and turbulence, responsible for the geometrical Doppler broadening of lines in stellar spectra. They concluded that "While we have no doubt about the rotation of early-type main-sequence stars, the question of line broadening in supergiant stars is far from settled." STRUVE [1951*a*, *b*; 1952] had pointed out earlier that the profiles and behaviour of absorption lines in supergiant stars like ε Aur and τ CMa indicate a network of prominences to which the theory of aerodynamic turbulence cannot be applied. This view is upheld by others including MCKELLAR *et al.* [1952], HUANG and STRUVE [1953], and BHATNAGAR *et al.* [1955]. Ejection of matter plays an important role in many peculiar stars (SWINGS and STRUVE, 1940; STRUVE, 1951*c*) and close binary systems (STRUVE, 1948; BIDELMAN, 1949). MERRILL [1956] has summarized the information concerning stars with expanding atmospheres.

Theoretical treatment of line profiles produced on account of haphazard motions of ejection by prominence activity would be quite difficult. The solution of the problem should be simpler in the case of more orderly motions

found in pulsating variables and P Cygni stars. In their case the movement
of matter is not only continuous, but it is also shared by the whole atmosphere. In the latter sense the ejection of matter in shell stars and novae is also
simpler though more violent than prominence activity. In all these cases one
can assume a monotonic variation of velocity with height and consider the
problem of line formation on the basis of a Schuster-type scattering atmosphere. But even then the differential motions of the various layers of the
atmosphere introduce mathematical complexities in this Schuster problem
for a moving atmosphere.

Following the earlier work of MCCREA and MITRA [1936] and CHAN-
DRASEKHAR [1945][1] the author developed a numerical method for solving
this problem; ABHYANKAR [1964a, b; 1965]. This new method can be applied
to any general scattering function and to any monotonic velocity law of
atmospheric motion. Results for squareroot, linear, parabolic, and exponential velocity laws in conjunction with a Gaussian scattering function have
been reported in the earlier three papers. Here we present the computations
of line profiles for various angles of emergence in one representative case.

2 — The fundamental equations

In the present problem a plane parallel stratified atmosphere scatters
radiation in selected line frequencies according to a Gaussian scattering
function

(1) $$\sigma(v) = \sigma_0 \exp\left\{- \left[(v - v_0)/\Delta v\right]^2\right\}$$

The geometrical height, z, and the optical depth, τ, at the centre (v_0) of the
line scattering coefficient are both measured outward from the photosphere.
The outward normal velocity, $v(\tau)$, of the atmosphere increases monotoni-
cally from zero at the photosphere to V at the top of the atmosphere where
$z = z_1$, and $\tau = \tau_1$. The problem of the formation of absorption lines in
this atmosphere can be solved by the two beam approximation of the method
of discrete ordinates. Let I^+ and I^- represent the intensities of the outgoing
($\mu = + \mu_1 = + 1/\sqrt{3}$) and ingoing ($\mu = - \mu_1 = - 1/\sqrt{3}$) beams, respectively, μ being the cosine of the angle made by the beam with the outward

---

[1] I would like to take this opportunity to thank Professor V. Kourganoff for introducing
me to these papers during a seminar held by him in Berkeley Astronomical Department
during 1958-59.

normal. Then CHANDRASEKHAR [1945] has shown that the mean intensity $J(v, \tau, \mu)$ at frequency v, as judged by a stationary observer, is given by

$$
(2) \qquad J(v, \tau, \mu) = \tfrac{1}{2}\left\{ I^+\left[v - v_0\,\frac{v(\tau)}{c}\,\mu + v_0\,\frac{v(\tau)}{c}\,\mu_1, \tau\right] + \right.
$$

$$
\left. + I^-\left[v - v_0\,\frac{v(\tau)}{c}\,\mu - v_0\,\frac{v(\tau)}{c}\,\mu_1, \tau\right]\right\}
$$

This is CHANDRASEKHAR's [1945] equation (133). Here J depends on μ in spite of the assumed isotropic scattering on account of the differential motions in the atmosphere which cause different Doppler shifts of frequencies in different directions. Integrating the equation of transfer through the atmosphere we obtain for the emergent intensity $I(v, \tau_1, \mu)$ in the direction μ:

$$
(3) \qquad I(v, \tau_1, \mu) = I_0(v, 0, \mu)\exp\left\{-\int_0^{\tau_1}\frac{\sigma\left(v - \frac{v_0}{c}v\mu\right)}{\sigma_0}\,\frac{d\tau}{\mu}\right\}
$$

$$
+ \int_0^{\tau_1}\frac{\sigma\left(v - \frac{v_0}{c}v\mu\right)}{\sigma_0}\,J(v, \tau, \mu)\exp\left\{-\int_\tau^{\tau_1}\frac{\sigma\left(v - \frac{v_0}{c}v\mu\right)}{\sigma_0}\,\frac{d\tau}{\mu}\right\}\frac{d\tau}{\mu}
$$

This is CHANDRASEKHAR's [1945] equation (131); but the first term on the right-hand side of equation (3), which is necessary, was missing from his equation as printed in the above paper. Since $I_0(v, 0, \mu)$ is taken equal to unity for positive μ in all frequencies, equation (3) reduces to

$$
(4) \qquad r_v(\mu) = I(v, \tau_1, \mu) = \exp\left\{-\int_0^{\tau_1}\frac{\sigma\left(v - \frac{v_0}{c}v\mu\right)}{\sigma_0}\,\frac{d\tau}{\mu}\right\}
$$

$$
+ \int_0^{\tau_1}\frac{\sigma\left(v - \frac{v_0}{c}v\mu\right)}{\sigma_0}\,J(v, \tau, \mu)\exp\left\{-\int_\tau^{\tau_1}\frac{\sigma\left(v - \frac{v_0}{c}v\mu\right)}{\sigma_0}\,\frac{d\tau}{\mu}\right\}\frac{d\tau}{\mu}
$$

When $v - (v/_0c)\,v\,\mu$ lies outside the line at all levels in the atmosphere, the first term is equal to one and the second term is zero so that $r_v(\mu)$ is unity.

3 — Line profiles for isotropic scattering

In our numerical method the atmosphere is divided into N layers in such a way that the mean velocity of separation between any two consecutive layers is DNU = P/N, where P = $V\mu_1$, in the direction of the two beams at $\pm \mu_1$. V, P, and DNU are measured as Doppler shifts in units of Δv. For a general velocity law, $v = f(\tau)$, the thickness of the layers is determined by making the optical thickness at the top of the I' th layer above the photosphere conform to: $f\{\tau(I)\} = $ IV/N. In general the layers have different thicknesses; but, for the linear velocity law, $v = a\tau$, they are all of equal thickness τ_1/N.

The frequencies as observed by a stationary observer are denoted by integers L through

$$v(L) = \text{REDNU} + (L-1)\text{DNU},$$

(5)

where

$$\text{REDNU} = v_0 - (M/2)\text{DNU},$$

M being the number of strips of width DNU into which $\sigma(v)$ is divided. Similarly the apparent frequencies as observed from the I'th layer, having an average outward velocity $\bar{v} = (I - \frac{1}{2})$ V/N, are denoted by integers J through

(6) $$v(J) = \text{REDNU} - (N - \frac{1}{2})\text{DNU} + (J-1)\text{DNU}$$

where,

$$J = L + N - I \qquad \text{for the outgoing beam,}$$

(7)

$$J = L + N + I - 1 \quad \text{for the ingoing beam.}$$

Further, according to earlier definitions, FOUT (I, J) is the intensity of the outgoing beam falling on the bottom of the I'th layer and having an apparent frequency J, and FIN (I, J) is the intensity of the ingoing beam falling on the top of the I'th layer and having an apparent frequency J. FOUT (I, J) and FIN (I, J) represent the radiation field in the moving atmosphere; the method of computing these quantities is described in the earlier papers.

The apparent frequencies, J, are related to L, the frequency as observed by a stationary observer through equation (7). Then, since the optical depth at the bottom of the I'th layer is $(I - 1)\,\tau_1/N$ in the case of a linear velocity law,

$$FOUT(I, J) = I^+ \left\{ REDNU + (L-1)DNU, \frac{(I-1)\tau_1}{N} \right\}$$

becomes

$$(8) \quad FOUT(I, J) = I^+ \left\{ REDNU + (J-N+I-1)DNU, \frac{(I-1)\tau_1}{N} \right\}$$

Similarly,

$$(9) \quad FIN(I, J) = I^- \left\{ REDNU + (J-N-I)DNU, \frac{I\tau_1}{N} \right\}$$

Equations (8) and (9) can be utilised for computing I^+ and I^- at the boundaries of the N layers for any frequency v by interpolation. It may be recalled that FOUT $(1, J) = 1$ and FIN $(N, J) = 0$ for all J, while FIN $(0, J))$ and FOUT $(N + 1, L) = r \{v (L)\}$ are given by the equations (12b) and (21), respectively, of paper III; ABHYANKAR [1965]. Now,

$$\frac{v_0 v}{c} \mu_1 = \frac{P \tau}{\tau_1} \text{ in units of } \Delta v.$$

Or,

$$(10) \qquad \frac{v_0 v}{c} \mu_1 = \frac{N \tau}{\tau_1} DNU$$

Therefore we have:

$$(11a) \quad v(L) - v_0 \frac{v}{c} \mu + v_0 \frac{v}{c} \mu_1 = REDNU + (L-1)DNU + \frac{N\tau}{\tau_1} DNU \left(1 - \frac{\mu}{\mu_1} \right),$$

and

$$(11b) \quad v(L) - v_0 \frac{v}{c} \mu - v_0 \frac{v}{c} \mu_1 = REDNU + (L-1)DNU - \frac{N\tau}{\tau_1} DNU \left(1 + \frac{\mu}{\mu_1} \right)$$

Consequently we can write equation (2) as

$$J \left\{ v(L), \frac{(I-1)\tau_1}{N}, \mu \right\} =$$

$$\tfrac{1}{2} \left\{ I^+ \left[REDNU + (L-1)DNU + (I-1)\left(1 - \frac{\mu}{\mu_1}\right)DNU, \frac{(I-1)\tau_1}{N} \right] \right.$$

$$(12) \qquad \left. + I^- \left[REDNU + (L-1)DNU - (I-1)\left(1 + \frac{\mu}{\mu_1}\right), \frac{(I-1)\tau_1}{N} \right] \right\}$$

Although L's and I's are integers, $(I-1)(1 \pm \mu/\mu_1)$ are no longer integers; hence we have to make use of equations (8) and (9) for obtaining $J(v, \tau, \mu)$ by interpolation. On evaluating $J\{v, [(I-1)\tau_1/N], \mu\}$ for $I = 1$ (Photosphere) to $I = N + 1$ (top of the atmosphere) the computation of the emergent intensity $I(v, \tau_1, \mu)$ is straight-forward according to equation (4) where we put $(v_0 v)/c = (P\tau)/\mu_1 \tau_1$ in units of Δv for the linear velocity law. The accuracy of the numerical integration depends upon the number of layers, N. But reduction to $N \to \infty$ can be made by making computations for N and 2 N as indicated in the earlier papers. It may be pointed out here that N should be so chosen that REDNU comes out to be the same for both N and 2 N numbers of layers.

In the case of non-linear velocity laws the thickness of the N layers is not constant; so the numerical integration of equation (4) would be more complicated. But otherwise there is no difficulty in following the above procedure.

Computations of line profiles were made for $\mu = 1.0$ to 0.1 at intervals of 0.1 in a representative case with a linear velocity law in which $P = 10$ and $x_1 = \tau_1/2\mu_1 = 5$. The resultant profiles are shown as full line curves in figures 1 and 2. They indicate that the profile is broad and shallow at the centre of the disc, $\mu = 1.0$, and it becomes narrower and deeper as we go toward the limb, $\mu = 0$. For each μ the extent of the violet edge of the line corresponds to the maximum velocity of approach in that direction given by $V\mu = P\mu/\mu_1$.

4 — Profiles for forward and backward scattering phase function

It was pointed out in section V of paper II (ABHYANKAR, 1964b) that when the phase function corresponds to a predominantly forward and backward scattering the numerical method for two beams described in papers I to III can be applied if we define:

(13) $$x_1 = \tau_1/2\mu, \quad \text{and} \quad P = V\mu$$

for all μ. Following this recipe we have calculated the line profiles for various values of μ in the above case of linear velocity law where $V = 10\sqrt{3}$ and $\tau_1 = 10/\sqrt{3}$. These profiles are shown as dashed curves in figures 1 and 2. On comparing them with the profiles for isotropic scattering we find that the two sets do not differ much near the centre of the disc. But as we go toward the limb the forward and backward scattering phase function gives a deeper line although the width of the line is unchanged. This is easily understood,

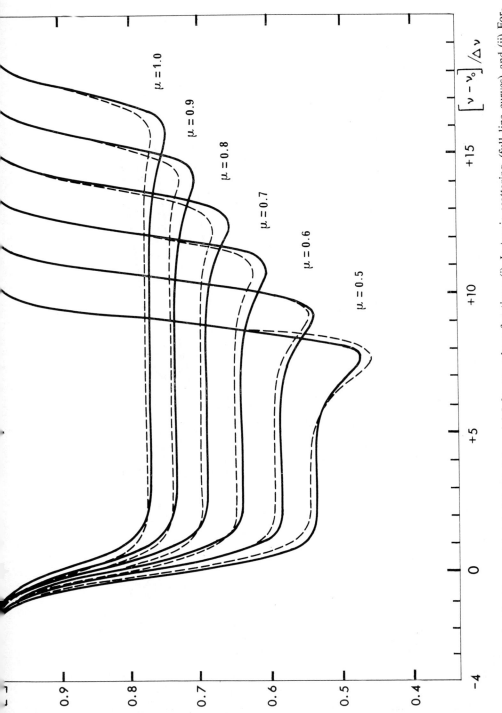

Fig. 1 — Line profiles for $\mu = 1.0, 0.9, 0.8, 0.7, 0.6,$ and 0.5 for two phase functions: (i) Isotropic scattering (full line curves), and (ii) Forward and backward scattering (dashed line curves).

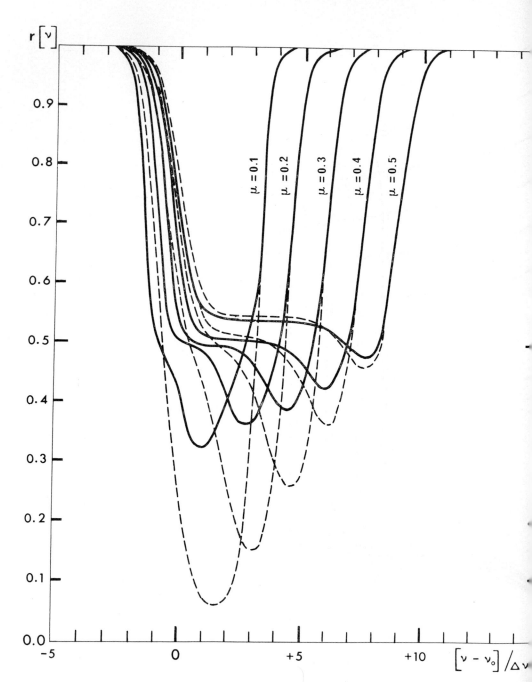

Fig. 2 — Line profiles for $\mu = 0.5$, 0.4, 0.3, 0.2, and 0.1 for the two phase functions of figure 1.

because, in this case the increasing depth of the atmosphere in the line of sight as we approach the limb reduces the residual intensity in the line, but there is no addition of radiation from other directions which occurs when isotropic scattering is prevalent.

5 — The integrated profile

After obtaining the variation of the line profile over the disc from the centre to the limb it is easy to derive the line profile in the integrated flux over the whole disc. Let the intensity $I_c(\mu)$ in the continuum be represented by

$$(14) \qquad I_c(\mu) = I_0(1 - X + X\mu)$$

where X is the limb darkening coefficient. $X = 0$ for a uniformly bright disc, and $X = 1$ for complete darkening at the limb ($\mu = 0$). Then the integrated flux in the continuum will be

$$(15) \qquad F_c = \int_0^1 I_c(\mu)\,\mu\,d\mu = I_0(3 - X)/6$$

In line frequencies we have

$$(16) \qquad I_v(\mu) = r_v(\mu)\,I_c(\mu),$$

so that

$$(17) \qquad F_v = \int_0^1 r_v(\mu)\,I_c(\mu)\,\mu\,d\mu.$$

Then the line profile $r_F(v)$ is given by

$$(18) \qquad r_F(v) = \frac{F_v}{F_c} = \frac{6}{3 - X}\left[\int_0^1 r_v(\mu)\,(1 - X)\,\mu\,d\mu + \int_0^1 r_v(\mu)\,X\,\mu^2\,d\mu\right].$$

For a uniform disc ($X = 0$) we have

$$(19) \qquad r_F(v) = 2\int_0^1 r_v(\mu)\,\mu\,d\mu.$$

For a disc which is completely darkened at the limb ($X = 1$) we obtain,

$$(20) \qquad r_F(v) = 3\int_0^1 r_v(\mu)\,\mu^2\,d\mu.$$

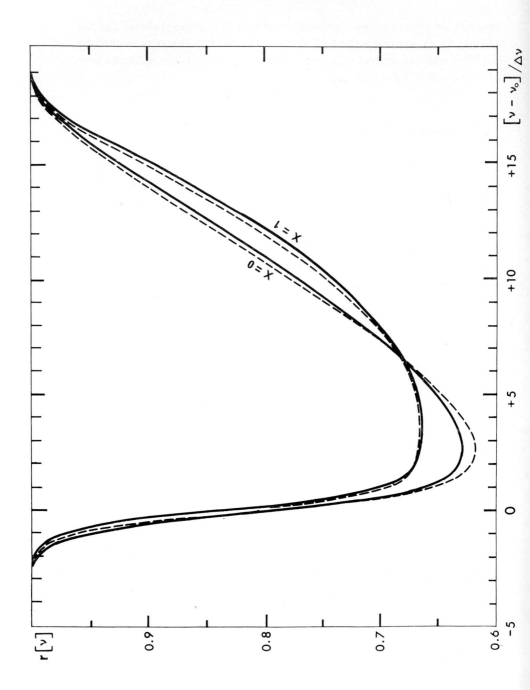

Line profiles obtained from equations (19) and (20) are shown in figure 3; the full line curves correspond to isotropic scattering and the dashed curves represent the case of forward and backward scattering. It is seen that the difference between the curves for the two phase functions of scattering is small compared to the difference caused by a variation of limb darkening coefficient X.

6 — Conclusions

On comparing the line profiles of figures 1 and 2 with the corresponding line profile in figure 4 of paper II (ABHYANKAR, 1964b) we notice that the characteristics of the integrated profile obtained from the two beam ($\mu = \pm 1/\sqrt{3}$) approximation are retained in the profiles at various points of the disc. In particular the violet core at the maximum frequency shift of ($P\mu/\mu_1$) Δv is visible at all values of μ. On the other hand the integrated profiles of figure 3 are entirely different. They give a broad, shallow and asymmetric line without any fine detail; the width of the line corresponds to the maximum velocity of approach in the line of sight, and the intensity at the deepest point is undoubtedly determined by the optical thickness of the atmosphere. But the integration over the disc has smoothed out the effects of the differential motions. It will be interesting to see how this smoothing differs with P, x_1, and the velocity law.

Most of the observed contours of absorption lines in stellar spectra are profiles integrated over the whole disc of the star. Hence the value of the profiles for various μ's appears to lie in their being a step for obtaining the integrated profile. But this need not be the case. The bewildering variety of line profiles in ε Aur reported by STRUVE [1951b] can be understood in the light of the present work. If we assume that some atoms are spread over the whole disc they could give rise to line shapes of Struve's types C, D, and F (cf. Fig. 3). On the other hand if the concentration of atoms responsible for the formation of the line is not uniform over the disc line shapes of his types A, B and E can be produced (cf. Fig. 1 and 2). Our computations thus confirm in an indirect way STRUVE'S hypothesis of a network of prominences in supergiant stars.

The computations described in this paper were performed on the 7090 electronic computer of the University of Toronto during 1963-64. I am highly grateful to the staff of David Dunlap Observatory, and particularly to Dr. J.F. HEARD, Director, for giving me an opportunity to work in Toronto and for providing the facilities at the Institute of Computer Science.

REFERENCES

ABHYANKAR, K.D., 1964a, *Ap. J.*, **140**, 1353 (Paper I).

ABHYANKAR, K.D., 1964b, *ibid.*, **140**, 1368 (Paper II).

ABHYANKAR, K.D., 1965, *ibid.*, **141**, 1056 (Paper III).

BHATNAGAR, P.L., KROOK, M., MENZEL, D.H., and THOMAS, R.N., 1955, *Vistas in Astronomy*, **1**, 296 (ed. A. Beer; Pergamon Press, London).

BIDELMAN, W.P., 1949, *Ap.J.*, **109**, 544.

CHANDRASEKHAR, S., 1945, *Rev. Mod. Phys.*, **17**, 138.

HUANG, S.S. and STRUVE, O., 1953, *Ap. J.*, **118**, 463.

HUANG, S.S. and STRUVE, O., 1960, *Stellar Atmospheres*, Ch. **8** (ed. J.L. Greenstein; Univ. of Chicago Press: Chicago).

McCREA, W.H. and MITRA, K.K., 1936, *Zs. f. Ap.*, **11**, 359.

McKELLAR, A., ODGERS, G.J., ALLER, L.H. and McLAUGHLIN, D.B., 1952, *Nature (London)*, **169**, 990.

MERRILL, P.W., 1956, *Vistas in Astronomy*, **2**, 1375 (ed. A. Beer; Pergamon Press, London).

STRUVE, O., 1948, *Ap. J.*, **107**, 327.

STRUVE O., 1951a, *P.A.S.P.*, **63**, 138.

STRUVE, O., 1951b, *A.J.*, **56**, 114.

STRUVE, O., 1951c, *P.A.S.P.*, **63**, 82.

STRUVE, O., 1952, *ibid*, **64**, 118.

SWINGS, P. and STRUVE, O., 1940, *Ap. J.*, **91**, 546.

Effect of non-synchronous rotation on close binary stars

Su-Shu HUANG*

Department of Space Science and Applied Physics, Catholic University of America and Goddard Space Flight Center, National Aeronautics and Space Administration

1 — Abstract

The effect of non-synchronous rotation of the component star in close binaries on its limiting surface is analyzed and the difficulties in the previous investigations are examined. It has been shown that no potential function exists in a coordinate system following the axial (non-synchronous) rotation of the component star. Consequently, no equilibrium surfaces can be obtained in this way. It is therefore suggested that we should retain the conventional coordinate system that rotates with the binary motion. Since a simple energy integral exists in this coordinate system, we can obtain a physical picture for the problem of the non-synchronously rotating star in the binary systems. Indeed we have found that the non-synchronously rotating star will modify its rotation gradually and become eventually synchronous with its orbital revolution.

In this multifarious activities and achievements that make him one of the greatest astronomers in the modern time, Professor Otto Struve has never forsaken the binary stars. After having spent some years of successful researches in other fields of astronomy now and then he always returned to this field of his early interest. Therefore, few astronomers have observed spectroscopically as many binary stars as he has done. Fewer still have left such a distinct mark as his in the history of double stars.

In a close association and collaboration with him for a decade during which I am proud to have received his confidence and learned the process of his mental perceptions and responses as a result of our daily afternoon meetings in cafes outside the North Gate of the Berkeley Campus of the University of California, I have always been impressed by his open mindedness to new ideas, his enthusiasm for and devotions to astronomy. Because of his open mindedness he saw any problem in its multi-faceted angles, thus making him not only an outstanding scientist but also a great leader. Because of his enthusiasm, he enlisted many astronomers into the fields of his interest. Our daily contact also induced me to become a novice in the study of binary

---

* On leave from Dearborn Observatory, Northwestern University.

Gauthier-Villars, Paris - Modern Astrophysics - 1967.

stars in the mid fifties: It is therefore befitting for me ten years later to write this article on binary stars in this memorial volume as my attribute to a great leader as well as a dear friend whom I have both respected and admired.

2 — A Critical Review of the Previous Investigations

The shape of stellar surfaces in the close binary system has been given as a first approximation by what has been predicted by the Roche Model (e.g., STRUVE and HUANG, 1957). According to this model, the axial rotation of component stars and their orbital revolution are synchronized. While the majority of close binaries indeed obey the rule of synchronization (SWINGS, 1936; STRUVE, 1950; PLAUT, 1959) there are some exceptions to which belongs β Lyrae — a peculiar binary system that Professor STRUVE [1941, 1958] had a life-long interest. Therefore, in recent years attempts have been made to predict the stellar surfaces, especially the limiting surface, when the component star does not rotate in synchronization with its orbital revolution (KOPAL, 1956; PLAVEC, 1958; KRUSZEWSKI, 1963; and LIMBER, 1963).

In the restricted three-body problem one can define a potential function U in a coordinate system that rotates with the binary's orbital motion (e.g., MOULTON, 1914). Also an energy integral can be obtained in the form that the sum of the potential energy and the kinetic energy is constant. It is the existence of the energy integral in this form that enables us to predict the stellar surfaces of close binaries. Thus, we should emphasize that the mere existence of a potential function does not necessarily warrant a prediction of the equilibrium surface of a star. Indeed, this is the reason that the calculations by previous investigators have to be regarded as unsatisfactory.

KOPAL [1956] first studied the limiting surface of the non-synchronously rotating star, using a potential function which KRUSZEWSKI [1963] has since pointed out to be incorrect. Later PLAVEC [1958], KRUSZEWSKI [1963] and LIMBER [1963] have all derived a potential function and obtained the limiting surface. However, even though their potential function is correct, their result is still open to debate as we may see in the following way.

Let us first choose a dimensionless system of units of measurement with the total mass of the binary as the unit of mass, with the separation between the two components as the unit of length and with $P/2\pi$ as the unit of time, where P stands for the orbital period. Thus, if we denote $1 - \mu$ as the mass of one component, μ will be the mass of the other. Let us further choose a rotating (x, y, z) system such that the origin is at the center of the $1 - \mu$ component, the x-axis points always towards the μ component, and the xy

plane coincides with the orbital plane. We have the equations of motion for a test particle in the (x, y, z) system:

1) $$\frac{d^2 x}{dt^2} - 2\frac{dy}{dt} = \frac{\partial U_1}{\partial x}, \quad \frac{d^2 y}{dt^2} + 2\frac{dx}{dt} = \frac{\partial U_1}{\partial y}, \quad \frac{d^2 z}{dt^2} = \frac{\partial U_1}{\partial z},$$

where

(2) $$U_1(x, y, z) \equiv \tfrac{1}{2}[(x-\mu)^2 + y^2] + \frac{1-\mu}{r_1} + \frac{\mu}{r_2}$$

and r_1 and r_2 are respectively the distances of the test particles from the two component stars. Note that U_1 is a function of time only through the co-ordinates (x, y, z) of the test particle.

We now introduce a new rotating (ξ, η, ζ) system such that it is rigidly fixed to the $1 - \mu$ component, sharing the latter's axial rotation. Although the axial rotation of the $1 - \mu$ component is not synchronous with the orbital motion, its rotating axis (chosen as the ζ-axis) is still assumed to be perpendicular to the orbital plane. Thus, if the (ξ, η, ζ) system is rotating with an angular velocity, ω, with respect to the (x, y, z) system, it rotates with an angular velocity, $1 + \omega$, with respect to the rest frame of reference. The transformation equations between (x, y, z) and (ξ, η, ζ) are as follows:

(3) $x = \xi \cos \omega t - \eta \sin \omega t, \; y = \xi \sin \omega t + \eta \cos \omega t, \; z = \zeta$

The equations of motion in the (ξ, η, ζ) system are

(4) $$\frac{d^2 \xi}{dt^2} - 2(\omega+1)\frac{d\eta}{dt} = -\mu \cos \omega t + \frac{\partial U_2}{\partial \xi}$$

(5) $$\frac{d^2 \eta}{dt^2} + 2(\omega+1)\frac{d\xi}{dt} = \mu \sin \omega t + \frac{\partial U_2}{\partial \eta}$$

(6) $$\frac{d^2 \zeta}{dt^2} = \frac{\partial U_2}{\partial \zeta}$$

where

(7) $$U_2(\xi, \eta, \zeta) \equiv \tfrac{1}{2}(\omega+1)^2(\xi^2 + \eta^2) + \frac{1-\mu}{r_1} + \frac{\mu}{r_2}$$

may be regarded as the negative value of the potential function. Actually, it is a misleading name as we shall see presently.

U_2 (ξ, η, ζ) as given by equation (7) does not give the limiting surface of the non-synchronous $1 - \mu$ component. In the first place, we encounter the time-dependent terms $\mu \cos \omega t$ and $\mu \sin \omega t$ in equations (4) and (5). Secondly r_2 which is given by

$$(8) \qquad r_2^2 = (\xi - \cos \omega t)^2 + (\eta + \sin \omega t)^2 + \zeta^2 ,$$

is now an explicit function of time. Therefore U_2 (ξ, η, ζ), unlike U_1 in the (x, y, z) system, is no longer an implicit function of time through the space coordinates alone but involves time explicitly. For brevity we write $U_2(t)$ for $U_2(\xi, \eta, \zeta)$. Because of the two complications, we can no longer derive from equations (4)-(6) the simple result that the sum of the potential energy and the kinetic energy is a constant of motion. Consequently, the surfaces defined by equation (7) do not represent equilibrium surfaces of the star. We can see this point analytically in the following way.

Multiplying equations (4)-(6) respectively by $d\xi/dt$, $d\eta/dt$ and $d\zeta/dt$ and adding the resulting equations together, we obtain after integration with respect to time that

$$(9) \qquad \tfrac{1}{2} [V^2(t) - V^2(t_o)] - [U_2(t) - U_2(t_o)]$$

$$= \int_{t_0}^{t} \left[\mu \left(\frac{d\eta}{dt} \sin \omega t - \frac{d\xi}{dt} \cos \omega t \right) - \frac{\partial U_2}{\partial t} \right] dt,$$

where $V(t)$ and $V(t_0)$ denote respectively the velocity of the test particle at time t and at the initial time t_0. $\partial U_2 / \partial t$ may be evaluated from equations (7) and (8). When the result is substituted into equation (9), we obtain finally

$$(10) \qquad \tfrac{1}{2} [V^2(t) - V^2(t_0)] - [U_2(t) - U_2(t_0)]$$

$$= \mu \int_{t_0}^{t} \left[\left(\frac{d\eta}{dt} - \frac{\omega \xi}{r_2^3} \right) \sin \omega t - \left(\frac{d\xi}{dt} + \frac{\omega \eta}{r_2^3} \right) \cos \omega t \right] dt.$$

It is obvious from equation (10) that the sum of the potential and kinetic energy is no longer constant. Since the integral in equation (10) actually depends upon the path of the test particle, $- U_2$ does not behave exactly like a potential.

The previous investigators have introduced

$$(11) \qquad U_3(\xi, \eta, \zeta) = U_2(\xi, \eta, \zeta) + \mu(\eta \sin \omega t - \xi \cos \omega t)$$

In doing so, they can replace the right hand sides of equations (4)-(6) respectively by $\partial U_3/\partial \xi$, $\partial U_3/\partial \eta$, and $\partial U_3/\partial \zeta$. Because of the transformation relation (3), $U_3(\xi, \eta, \zeta)$ can now be expressed in terms of x, y and z. In this new expression for U_3, time appears only implicitly through x, y, z but does not enter explicitly. Consequently, they have independently derived the limiting surface in the (x, y, z) system by considering U_3 as the potential function.

However, we should remember that it is the (ξ, η, ζ) system that is rigidly fixed to the rotating star. Any stationary surface of the non-synchronous rotating star $(1 - \mu$ component) must be expressed as a function of ξ, η and ζ alone without the explicit appearance of time. It does not appear that an expression in $x, y,$ and z can represent the stationary surfaces of the non-synchronous component because in the (x, y, z) system the component has a net rotation. Since, as we have seen before, we cannot obtain a potential function in the (ξ, η, ζ) system, we have no means to compute the stationary surfaces of a non-synchronous rotating component star, a conclusion contrary to the previous investigators.

3 — Physical Interpretation

Because of the difficulties we have just observed, it is advisable to retain the (x, y, z) coordinate system that rotates with the binary motion. In this coordinate system we have for the test particle a simple energy integral

$$(12) \qquad\qquad 2 U_1 - V^2 = C$$

where $U_1(x, y, z)$ is given by equation (2).

We should now recall that the zero-velocity surfaces are labelled by C (e.g., MOULTON, 1914). Let the C value that is associated with the innermost contact surface S_1 (KUIPER, 1941) be C_1. Therefore, all particles inside the S_1 surface with $C < C_1$ could penetrate the S_1 surface. As a result, these particles will gradually escape from the star. Now the $1 - \mu$ component is rotating with an angular velocity ω in the x, y, z coordinate system along the z-axis. Particles in the stellar surface layers have velocities

$$(13) \qquad\qquad V = (x^2 \times y^2)^{\frac{1}{2}} \omega$$

if thermal motion or other kinds of motion are neglected. Hence, all particles in the $1 - \mu$ component star that are above the surface (called the R surface hereafter) given by

$$(14) \qquad\qquad 2 U(x, y, z) - \omega^2 (x^2 + y^2) = C_1$$

and consequently have C values less than C_1 may be regarded as unstable and could easily escape out of the S_1 surface. Figure 1 illustrates the cross sections in both the xy plane and the xz plane of a few R surfaces for the case $\mu = 0.4$ and $\omega = 0, 2, 4$ and 8. The case $\omega = 0$ is simply the S_1 surface for $\mu = 0.4$. The elongated shape of the cross sections in the xz plane is easy to understand because those particles near the equatorial plane that have the highest linear velocities due to non-synchronous rotation are the easiest to be ejected out of the S_1 surface.

However, it should be noted that the R surfaces represent neither the limiting nor equilibrium surface. Particles below the R surface for a given value of ω can move up although they cannot escape through the S_1 surface without collisions. Statistically, we can state that most particles that are originally located above the R surface are lost and are replaced by particles coming from below the R surface. These new particles will naturally fill up the entire lobe of the S_1 surface. Therefore, the limiting surface of the $1-\mu$ component is still given by the S_1 surface. Since the angular momentum per unit mass due to the axial rotation of the $1-\mu$ component decreases downward in the star if it rotates as a rigid body, the new material above the R surface will rotate less rapidly (with respect to the xyz system) than the old material before the latter's escape. The simultaneous transfer of mass from below the R surface to above the R surface and from inside the S_1 surface to outside the S_1 surface will continue until the orbital revolution and the axial rotation become synchronized. Perhaps this is one of the most effective mechanisms for synchronizing orbital revolution and axial rotation of close binary stars. Therefore, non-synchronization observed in those close binaries must be a temporary phenomenon triggered by rapid evolution of the component star itself as is suggested by KOPAL [1959].

Finally, one may question our argument on the ground that it has not proven that the particles are necessarily flying away from the star. If all particles on some surface of a non-synchronously rotating star should tend to move inward, this surface could be regarded as a stable surface for the star. This is however not true because when the particles move inward they collide with other particles. Since the average C value [the C value of each particle being defined by equations (12)] of all particles participating in a collision remains constant (HUANG, 1965) and since directions of the velocities will be modified after the collision, the chance of escape from the surface increases with time whatever are the directions of their intitial velocities (in the xyz system). Therefore, our conclusion about the non-synchronously rotating star is valid without qualification for the Roche model.

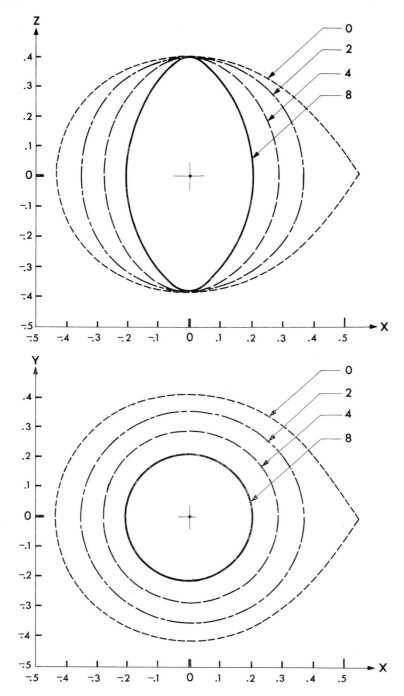

Fig. 1 — The R surfaces for different values of ω (0, 2, 4, 8) for $\mu = 0.4$. The R surfaces are defined by equation (14). The case ω = 0 represents simply the innermost contact surface (denoted by S_1). When the rotation of a component star is not synchronous with its orbital motion, the gaseous particles above the R surface may escape the S_1 surface and are replaced by gaseous particles moving out from below the R surface. This process will go on until the star finally becomes synchronized to its orbital motion.

It is my pleasure to note my thanks to Mr. CLARENCE WADE, JR. who has performed the computation involved in obtaining diagrams in figure 1.

REFERENCES

HUANG, S.S., 1965, *Ap. J.*, **141**, 201.
KOPAL, Z., 1956, *Ann. d'Ap.*, **19**, 298.
KOPAL, Z., 1959, *Close Binary Systems* (Chapman and Hall, London).
KRUSZEWSKI, A., 1963, *Acta Astronomica*, **13**, 106.
KUIPER, G.P., 1941, *Ap. J.*, **93**, 133.
LIMBER, D.N., 1963, *Ap. J.*, **138**, 1112.
MOULTON, F.R., 1914, *An Introd. to Celestial Mechanics*, chap. 8, 2nd ed. (Macmillan: New York).
PLAUT, L., 1959, *P.A.S.P.*, **71**, 167.
PLAVEC, M., 1958, *Liège Symp.*, No. 8, p. 411.
STRUVE, O., 1941, *Ap. J.*, **93**, 104.
STRUVE, O., 1950, *Stellar Evolution* (Princeton University Press: Princeton).
STRUVE, O., 1958, *P.A.S.P.*, **70**, 5.
STRUVE, O. and HUANG, S.S., 1957, *Occasional Notes R.A.S.*, **3**, 161.
SWINGS, P., 1936, *Zs. f. Ap.*, **12**, 40.

The spectroscopic binary HD 698*

JORGE SAHADE[†]

Observatorio Astronómico, La Plata, Argentina

Abstract

High dispersion spectrograms of HD 698 definitely confirm that the lines of the secondary component are not present in the spectrum, We are probably dealing here with another system where the mass of the fainter component is larger than that of the primary. The period of the orbital motion has been corrected to 55.927 days. The system is no longer a case for the existence of very large stellar masses.

HD 698 (B 5) [α = 0h 09m 0; δ = + 57°56′ (1950 . 0). GC 193 (cB 8 e: 7.08 mag)] is a spectroscopic binary which we have discussed briefly some time ago in connection with the problem of the maximum stellar masses (SAHADE, 1962). The system was first studied by PEARCE [1932] who described the spectrum as B 9 + B 5 and derived masses of

$$\mathfrak{M}_1 \sin^3 i = 113 \odot \quad \text{and} \quad \mathfrak{M}_2 \sin^3 i = 45 \odot.$$

According to PEARCE, the high luminosity B 9 primary displayed "a well-developed metallic-line spectrum" and H emission, outstanding at H α and II β. The spectrum of the B 5 secondary was faint, only measurable at the times of maximum separation of the lines, and displayed lines of He, I, H, Mg II, C II and Ca II. Pearce's earlier plates had a dispersion of 49 A/mm, while the later ones were taken with a dispersion of 29 A/mm, presumably also at H γ.

In 1948, STRUVE and RUDKJØBING [1948] became concerned with the luminosity that PEARCE'S masses implied, because such a luminosity was too high as compared with the luminosity that is suggested by the spectral features of the B 9 star and by the intensity of the interstellar Ca II lines, namely, the luminosity that corresponds to luminosity class III. The spectrograms of HD 698 secured by STRUVE and RUDKJØBING with a dispersion of 40 A/mm at λ 3934 threw some doubts in regard to the presence of lines of

* Part of this work was done while the author was an AAS-NSF Foreign Visiting Professor at the Astronomy Department of Indiana University, in the first part of 1965. The 1963 spectrograms were taken by the author as a guest investigator at the Mount Wilson Observatory.

† Member of the Carrera del Investigador Cientifico, Consejo Nacional de Investigaciones Cientificas y Técnicas, Argentina.

the secondary component and made it clear that additional material, particularly of higher dispersion and very good definition, were highly desirable. As a consequence, an attempt was made to try to secure new material on the star and J. L. GREENSTEIN and J. JUGAKU were extremely kind in obtaining for me three spectra with the 200-inch Hale reflector at Mount Palomar in October 1961 and November 1962, and five spectra with the 60-inch reflector at Mount Wilson in October and November, 1961. and January 1962, respectively. This material was supplemented by four spectra obtained by the author in November 1963 with the 60-inch reflector at the Mount Wilson Observatory. The dispersion of each plate is indicated in table I, where the radial velocities are also listed.

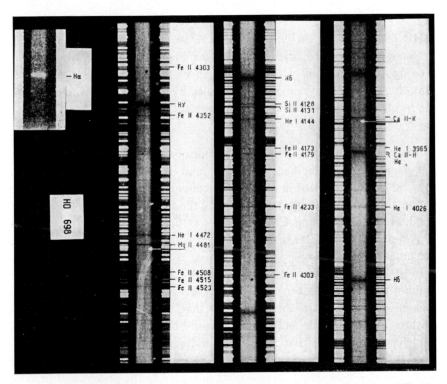

Fig. 1 — The spectrum of HD 698 at phase 53.517 days (see table I, under "S"). The white arrows at Ca II — K and Mg II 4481 indicate the positions at which the lines of the secondary component should be, according to Pearce's velocity curves.

Definitely, the new material (see Fig. 1) shows only the spectrum of the B 9 III component, and even at the quadrature that is covered by our plates, when, according to PEARCE. the relative radial velocity of the two components

TABLE I

Radial Velocities of HD 698

Date of mid-exposure	Phase (Days) P[1]	Phase (Days) S[2]	Emulsion (Eastman)	Disp. (A/mm)	Radial Velocities (in km/sec) from absorption lines	Radial Velocities (in km/sec) from Hα emission	Radial Velocities (in km/sec) from interstellar lines	Number of measured absorption lines
1961								
Oct. 21.353	51.521	46.621	IIa-O	9	−50.3	−28.5	−14.3	39
27.342	1.604	52.611	IIa-O+103a−F	20; 40	+ 3.6	−56.4		18
28.252	2.516	53.517	IIa-O+103a−E	20; 40	+11.6	−42.3		18
28.346	2.611	53.612	IIa-O+103a−E	20; 40	+11.9	−49.5		3
Nov.17.212	22.479	17.550	IIa-O+103a−E	20; 40	+ 4.4			16
1962								
Jan. 18.160	28.522	23.573	IIa-O+103a−E	20; 40	−53.2	−54.4		16
Nov.16.310	51.152	46.089	103a−F	13; 5	−55.0	−35.9	−12.5	15
16.355	51.197	46.134	IIa-O	9	−52.6	− 8.6[3]	−13.8	58
1963								
Nov.27.303	35.812	30.592	IIa-O+103a−E	20; 40	−99.4	−31.4		18
28.159	36.673	31.448	IIa-O+103a−E	20; 40	−102.7	−42.0		19
28.301	36.813	31.588	IIa-O+103a−E	20; 40	−95.8	−36.6		8
29.186	37.696	32.477	IIa-O+103a−E	20; 40	−105.2	−34.1		16

[1] The phases under P were computed by considering Pearce's period (55.904 days) and, as origin, Pearce's time of periastron passage (JD 2425634.780).

[2] The phases under S were computed by considering the period suggested by the present work, namely, 55.927 days, and, as origin, Pearce's time of periastron passage.

[3] From H β.

should be of the order of 300 km/sec (nearly 4 A separation at Ca II-K and about 4.5 A separation at Mg II λ 4481), the lines of the secondary component do not show. The tentative conclusion that was suggested by the McDonald material is thus confirmed. The question then arises as to what had Pearce measured. It seems unlikely that whatever lines he was able to measure originated in the secondary component of HD 698 as they were not present in 1948 and in 1961-3. An obvious conclusion is, therefore, that the large masses that were assigned to the system are not real and should be dropped from the list of reliable stellar masses.

The Mount Wilson plates were measured for radial velocity with the Grant comparator at the Astronomy Department of Indiana University and were reduced with the CDC 3900 electronic computer of the I.U. Computing Center. The Mount Palomar plates were measured and reduced in the conventional manner. Information on the program used with the electronic computer will be given elsewhere (SAHADE, *in preparation*).

Neither PEARCE's period (55.904 days) nor the period that was suggested by STRUVE and RUDKJØBING (55.935 days) represent the new observations, and, as a consequence, a new value for the period, namely, 55.927 days, was derived. The new period brings together Pearce's velocity curve, the McDonald radial velocities and those discussed in the present paper. Figure 2 shows that the agreement is good and that Pearce's orbital elements for the B 9 component do represent the 1948 and 1961-3 observations.

Pearce's orbital elements for the primary component suggest a mass-function

$$f(\mathfrak{M}) = 3.63 \; \odot.$$

Let us discuss the possible mass-values that are consistent with such a mass-function; such values are listed in table II.

The luminosity of a B 9 III star corresponds to a bolometric absolute magnitude of the order of -3. When on the main sequence the mass of the star, according to the mass-luminosity relation, would have been of the order of 5 $\odot$ and since table II shows that for $\mathfrak{M}_1 \sin^3 i < \sim 14 \; \odot$, $\mathfrak{M}_2 \sin^3 i > \mathfrak{M}_1 \sin^3 i$, it seems reasonable to conclude that HD 698 is probably another member of the group of binaries (SAHADE, 1966) where the more massive component is underluminous for its mass and most likely the older of the two stars evolution-wise. As it was suggested earlier (SAHADE, 1962), HD 698 is no longer a case for the existence of the very large stellar masses. Unfortunately, the object does not undergo eclipses and, therefore, we cannot say very much about the relative sizes of the two components.

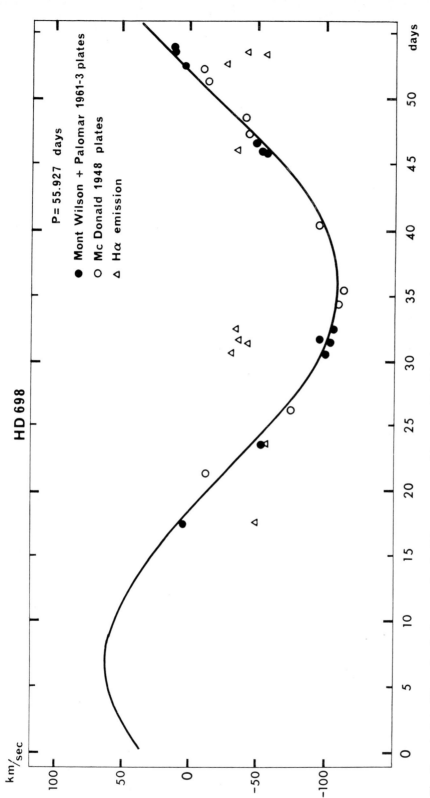

Fig. 2 — A plot of Pearce's velocity curve for the B 9 component, of Struve and Rudkjøbing's and of our radial velocities, by considering the period derived in the present paper and, as origin, Pearce's time of periastron passage, namely, JD 2425634.780. Our radial velocities from H α emission are also plotted.

TABLE II

Possible Values of the Masses of the Components of HD 698 *Consistent with*
$f(\mathfrak{M}) = 3.63 \odot$

$\mathfrak{M}_1/\mathfrak{M}_2$	$\mathfrak{M}_2 \sin^3 i$	$\mathfrak{M}_1 \sin^3 i$
0.2	5.2	1.0
0.4	7.1	2.8
0.6	9.3	5.6
0.8	11.8	9.4
1.0	14.5	14.5
1.5	22.7	34.0
2.0	32.7	65.4

The radial velocities from the center of the emission at H α are also plotted in figure 2. They fall below the γ-velocity and suggest that probably arise in an expanding envelope around the system.

It is unfortunate that neither the McDonald observations nor the Mount Wilson and Palomar spectrograms cover the quadrature where the velocities of the B 9 star are of recession.

It is a pleasure to record my indebtedness to Drs. J.L. GREENSTEIN and J. JUGAKU for taking most of the plates used in the present investigation, to MISS SUSAN HAGERMANN for kindly doing the punching of the cards and to Mr. T.D. FAŸ for taking care of everything related with the running of the program in the CDC 3600 electronic computer. Miss HAGERMANN and Mr. FAŸ are students at the Astronomy Department of Indiana University.

REFERENCES

PEARCE, J.A., 1932, *M.N.R.A.S.*, **92**, 877.
SAHADE, J., 1962, *Symposium on Stellar Evolution*, J. Sahade, ed. (Observatorio Astronômico: La Plata), p. 145.
SAHADE, J., 1966, *Stellar Evolution*, A.G.W. Cameron and R.F. Stein, ed. (Plenum Press, New York), p. 449.
SAHADE, J. and FAŸ, T.D., *a paper on δ Librae* (in preparation).
STRUVE, O. and RUDKJØBING, M., 1948, *Ap. J.*, **108**, 537.

Stellar multiplicity: an aspect of the observational approach to stellar evolution

J. A. HYNEK

Dearborn Observatory, Northwestern University, Evanston, Illinois

In his classical papers on the observational approach to stellar evolution SANDAGE, (1957) demonstrated that the observed luminosity function is in good accord with the present theory of stellar evolution and that the "general scheme presented appears to be confirmed by kinematical results." In particular, he concluded that the kinematic properties of about two out of every three giant stars are in agreement with those of F 3 – F 7 dwarfs, and one out of three appears to have space motion in accord with the A stars. Most of the K 0 – K 2 giants, Sandage concluded, have come from the F dwarfs.

Additional avenues of marked sensitivity and power for observational confirmation of the present theory of stellar evolution are offered by a comparison of the frequency of binary systems among giant and dwarf sequences, of the Δm's of the visual binaries in these respective sequences, and of the linear separation of the components of giant and dwarf visual binaries.

Since such a study of binary systems involves considerable data-processing and statistical analysis, it was clearly important to adapt this work for computer use. This has resulted in a *Directory of Bright Star Stellar Systems*, in which each star is considered as a potential triple visual system. For example, single stars are considered as "zero-order" stellar systems (code number 100), a visual binary whose primary is a double line spectroscopic binary but which has a close visual companion and a distant common proper motion companion, carries the code 348, etc. A description of the *Directory* is given at the end of this chapter, both to illustrate the manner in which the data germane to the present topic were processed and also to call attention to the existence of the *Directory*. With such a data processing system, one can ask many questions of the bright star stellar systems; e.g., "What percent of giant stars are spectroscopic binaries and also have distant companions", or "Is there any relation between axial rotation of a star and its membership in a binary system?" Before the advent of electronic computers, it might have been considered far too wasteful of the astronomer's time to have pursued such lines of inquiry unless one had strong indication of productive results. Today, however, it is a matter of a moment to query the system: "Is there a relation between Δm and space motion?" Such immediate capability to correlate and process data should not be an invitation to adopt Sir Francis BACON's general approach to scientific experimentation, namely that to gain all possible knowledge, all possible experiments should be tried! Such an attitude puts a low premium on thinking, but modern computers do allow one to ask questions which thinking has indicated might have fruitful answers, and to get those answers in a remarkably short time.

In the context of the present chapter, we are asking whether the numbers, kinds, and motions of giant and dwarf binary systems support modern theories of stellar evolution.

1 — Δm's of Bright Giant and Dwarf Visual Binaries

Although the measured Δm's of the components of visual binaries vary greatly in accuracy, itself a function of the separation and of Δm, the theory of stellar evolution calls for such major changes in the brightness of the evolving component of a double star system, that they should be easily detected by comparing Δm's of giants and dwarfs. We should expect that the mean Δm's of K 0 III stars, for example, would be about three magnitudes greater than those of the F stars, their probable progenitors. The results of the tabulation of Δm's for 900 visual binary systems are given in figure 1 and in table I are given the percentages of bright visual binaries whose Δm's fall within successive integral steps. Because the apparent magnitude cut-off used is the same as that in the Yale Bright Star Catalogue, the number of lower main sequence stars available is severely limited. Figure 1 therefore includes only groups having statistical significance. Table II lists the median and average Δm's for 1331 visual systems in the various spectral subgroups.

Both the median and average values indicate strongly that the normal giants arise primarily from the middle F stars. The average median value of Δm for the giants is 5.0 and that for the main sequence A's and F's is 3.0 and 2.5 respectively. If, then, giants came only from A stars, which differ in absolute magnitude from the giants by less than a magnitude, the observed difference in median Δm's should be much less than it is. For the middle F's, however, the observed difference between their median Δm value and that of giants is 2.5, which matches the observed average difference in absolute magnitude between giant K and main sequence F stars. A similar conclusion

DISTRIBUTION OF ΔM OF 900 BRIGHT BINARY STARS

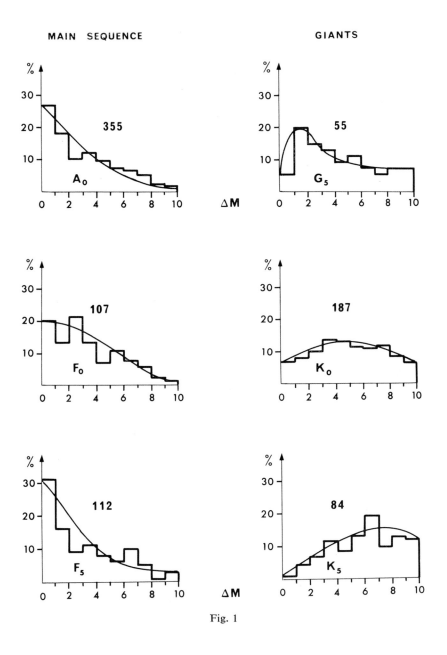

Fig. 1

TABLE I

Spectral Class Δm	0-1	1-2	2-3	3-4	4-5	5-6	6-7	7-8	8-9	9-10	Total No.
→ B 2	5.0	12.9	12.9	5.9	17.8	13.8	9.9	7.9	5.0	8.9	101
B 3 - B 7	19.3	15.9	14.2	6.7	10.9	5.0	10.1	6.8	6.8	4.3	119
B 8 - A 2	26.7	18.0	10.0	12.1	9.5	7.3	5.8	5.4	2.2	2.0	355
A 3 - A 7	21.8	13.5	12.6	12.6	13.5	6.3	9.9	5.4	0.9	3.5	110
A 8 - F 2	19.6	13.0	21.4	13.0	6.6	10.3	7.4	5.7	2.0	1.0	107
F 3 - F 7	31.2	16.0	8.9	10.7	8.0	6.2	10.0	5.4	0.9	2.7	112
F 8 - G 2	34.3	10.0	7.1	14.2	7.2	5.7	5.7	10.0	2.9	2.9	70
G 3 - G 7	5.4	20.1	14.5	12.7	9.1	10.9	7.3	5.4	7.3	7.3	55
G 8 - K 2	6.9	8.0	10.1	13.8	13.3	11.2	10.6	11.7	8.0	6.4	187
K 3 - K 7	1.2	4.8	7.2	11.9	8.3	13.0	19.1	9.6	13.0	11.9	84
K 8 - M2	3.3	9.6	0	19.3	9.6	22.6	12.9	6.5	12.9	3.3	31

Main sequence: B 2 through F 8 - G 2 rows.
Giants: G 3 - G 7 through K 8 - M2 rows.

is reached if average rather than median values of the Δm's of visual binaries are used.

TABLE II

	Median Δm	Average Δm	No. of Stars
⟶ B 2	4.7	4.9	101
B 3 - B 7	3.0	3.8	119
B 8 - A 2	2.4	3.1	355
A 3 - A 7	3.2	3.5	110
A 8 - F 2	2.9	3.3	107
F 3 - F 7	2.2	3.1	112
F 8 - G 2	2.9	3.3	70
G 3 - G 7	3.9	4.3	55
G 8 - K 2	4.8	5.0	187
K 3 - K 7	6.2	6.0	84
K 8 - M2	5.2	5.2	31

In contrast, the differences in magnitude of components of spectroscopic binaries are not directly available, in general, but since, in double-line spectroscopic binaries, the difference in magnitude of the components must be about one magnitude or less, we should expect to find a virtual absence of double-line spectroscopic binaries among K giants. Only those spectroscopic binaries which evolved simultaneously from the main sequence as "twins" might be expected to show double lines as giant systems.

Table III lists the relative numbers of single and double line spectroscopic binaries in the various subgroups among the bright star giants and dwarfs. Only those stars were chosen which could definitely be shown to belong either to luminosity class III or V. From A 8 to G 2, along the main sequence, some twenty-five percent of all the spectroscopic binaries are double-lined; whereas from G 3 to M 2, among the giants, less than six percent of the spectroscopic binaries are double-lined. Another factor enters to diminish the number of double-line binaries, as well as spectroscopic binaries in general, among the giants. As detailed below, some thirty percent of main sequence spectroscopic binaries probably cannot become normal giant binaries because of the "swallowing-up" effect as the primary component expands and tends to engulf the secondary.

TABLE III

Spectral Subgroup	Single Line Binaries		Double Line Binaries	
Main Sequence	n	%	n	%
──→ B 2	55	86	9	14
B 3 - B 7	80	86	13	14
B 8 - A 2	135	85	24	15
A 3 - A 7	44	86	7	14
A 8 - F 2	23	82	5	18
F 3 - F 7	27	71	11	29
F 8 - G 2	14	64	8	36
Normal Giants				
G 3 - G 7	24	89	3	11
G 8 - K 2	79	93	6	7
K 3 - K 7	39	100	0	0
K 8 - M2	14	100	0	0

2 — Relative Frequency of Binaries Among Giants and Dwarfs

In the following section, as throughout the chapter, the stars chosen have been deliberately limited to the stars of the *Yale Bright Star Catalogue*. The bright stars represent, on one hand, by far the best observed stars with respect to radial velocity, accurate spectral class, parallax, and multiplicity; on the other hand, they are precisely those stars which might be said to represent the "playing field of stellar evolution." The progenitors of the present giants were presumably mid-upper main sequence stars, and it is from the present upper main sequence that future giants presumably will come. Although for every naked eye star on the sky, there are probably several hundred telescopic stars within the same general volume of space, these are out of the pale of active stellar evolution. The bright stars thus represent a homogeneous group for our purposes. To make the sample more homogeneous, all stars having space velocities greater than fifty kilometers per second as listed in the *Directory* have been omitted from the discussion.

If our knowledge of the multiplicity of every bright star were complete, we should expect essentially a detailed balancing of the characteristics of giant and the main sequence binaries, from whence came the progenitors of the present giants. In short, the numbers and kinds of spectroscopic and visual binaries among giants and dwarfs should be identical. The major exception to this would be cases of very close binary systems. In these the linear expansion of the originally more massive component can be expected to initiate a mass transfer from one component to another, thus disturbing the normal evolution of the primary and very likely removing it from the domain of normal giants. As we shall see later, main sequence binary systems of Class A and later, with periods greater than ten days, are not likely to be affected by the physical expansion of the primary. After due allowance is made for this, we should expect, therefore, that if two-thirds of the giant stars came from F dwarfs and one-third from A type stars, the dynamic characteristics (masses, mass functions, periods, and frequency of binaries among the giants) should closely resemble those of the F and A binary systems presently on the main sequence. This must indeed be the case if our data were complete or unless we postulate a secular change in the structure of the main sequence since the time the present giants were members there of.

TABLE IV

Frequency distribution of visual and spectroscopic binaries

Spectral Group Main Sequence	N $V < 50$ km/sec	$V \geqslant 50$ km/sec	Visual Binaries		Spectroscopic Systems		All Spectroscopic Systems	
			n	$\%$	n	$\%$	n	$\%$
B 3 - B 7	344	4	56	16.3	107	31.1	128	37.2
B 8 - A 2	1052	24	170	16.2	307	29.2	355	33.7
A 3 - A 7	419	9	65	15.5	119	28.4	138	32.9
A 8 - F 2	282	30	63	22.3	51	18.1	66	23.4
F 3 - F 7	269	44	68	25.3	35	13.0	41	15.2
F 8 - F 9	(105)		(23)	(21.9)	(15)	(16.5)	(17)	(18.7)
Giants								
G 3 - G 7	197	36	25	12.7	20	10.2	23	11.7
G 8 - K 2	628	202	56	8.9	58	9.2	62	9.9
K 3 - K 7	341	101	17	5.0	31	9.1	32	9.4
M 3 $\rightarrow$	78	32	3	3.8	3	3.8	4	5.1

The numbers of visual binaries and spectroscopic binaries for each spectral subgroup of the upper main sequence and for the giant sequence are given in the table IV. The columns give in succession, the spectral subgroup, the numbers of stars in each group having space velocities less than fifty kilometers per second, the number (for comparison) of stars having velocities equal to or greater than fifty kilometers per second, the number and percentage of visual binaries and of spectroscopic systems, and of all spectroscopic systems (including spectroscopic systems which are also members of visual binary systems), among the spectral subgroups. The F 8 − F 9 spectral subgroup is listed separately, within parentheses, because in view of the small number of these stars in the *Yale Bright Star Catalogue* having MK classes or dwarf or giant designation, additional stars were selected on a basis of known parallax and proper motions in order to increase the available number.

Visual Binaries: It would appear that the main sequence progenitors (A 8 − F 7, primarily) have some three times (24%) as many visual binary systems as do the giants (8%). The writer at first believed that this imbalance, along with a similar imbalance in the relative numbers of spectroscopic binaries and the periods of spectroscopic binaries shown later, was too great to be explained as observational selection effects.

It has now become clear that the observed discrepancies actually constitute a support for, rather than a contradiction to, the present theories of stellar evolution. In the case of the visual binaries, the imbalance can be accounted almost entirely for as the result of the arbitrary cut-off at $6^{m}.5$ apparent magnitude of the stars used and is therefore a distance effect.

To examine this problem, the projected separations of visual binaries were plotted for each spectral subgroup, figure 2, and those within each subgroup were plotted as a function of apparent magnitude. Space does not permit showing this array of diagrams. Figure 2 demonstrates that a large part, if not all, of the imbalance can be explained as a simple selection effect of distance. It is clearly apparent among the main sequence stars and is remarkably apparent among the giants. The effect on the giants is two-fold: the earlier Bright Star giants are on the average closer, to the sun, thus leading to the discovery of pairs with smaller separations, but the enhanced Δm of the components as the later giants are reached imposes a second observational selection factor; discovery of close pairs becomes more difficult as Δm increases.

Briefly, if we compare, for example, the F 3 to F 7 main sequence group of visual binaries with the G 8 to K 2, giant binaries, we find that of the dwarfs, thirty-six out of ninety pairs have projected separations less than 50 astronomical units, whereas among the giants only three out of seventy-one pairs have a projected separation less than this. If we were to remove the thirty-six pairs from the main sequence group, the discrepancy would disappear; yet this is, in effect what happens when these stars become giants. In evolving to a giant, the primary increases by approximately two and a half magnitudes, or some ten-fold in brightness. This implies a three-fold increase in distance over which a giant pair can be seen, to the same limiting apparent magnitude. An F-type main sequence star, for instance, of apparent magnitude of 6 will have a parallax of about 0″03. Thus a linear

SEPARATION OF BINARY COMPONENTS

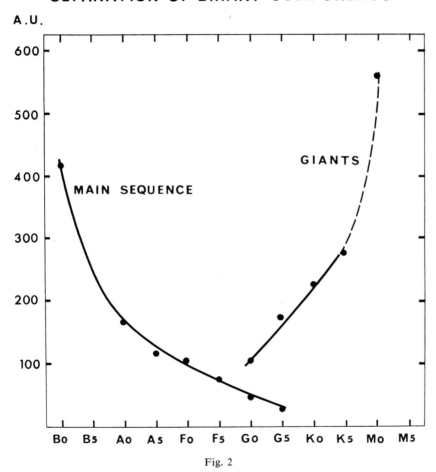

Fig. 2

separation of fifty astronomical units represents an angular separation of some one and one-half seconds of arc, a separation which is fairly easily discernible if the magnitude differences are not great. However, a threefold increase in distance, and a concomitant increase in Δm of two to three magnitudes, makes discovery of a companion that is less than fifty astronomical units from the primary a much more difficult matter.

While this allowance for the distance effect has not appeared to fully remove the discrepancy (this is probably due to the limited statistical sample at our disposal), it appears that the present giants have approximately the same relative number of binaries as do the F main sequence stars, although the majority of these pairs in which one component is a giant have yet to be detected. As further evidence of this, a comparison of the F 3 − F 7 dwarfs with the G 8 − K 2 giants shows that the dwarfs exhibit no diminution in numbers of binaries having projected separations of less than one hundred astronomical units, as one proceeds to the limiting magnitude of 6.5, whereas among the giant binaries there are an order of magnitude more systems below this limiting separation in the apparent magnitude group 4.0 − 5.5 mag. than there are in the group 5.5 − 6.5 mag. This strongly corroborates the previous conclusion.

Spectroscopic Binaries: Since the discovery of spectroscopic binaries is distance-independent, depending only on the quality of the spectrograms, the discovery of a spectroscopic binary in any given spectral subgroup is equally likely. It is surprising, then, to find that some sixteen percent of the late A and F main sequence stars are spectroscopic binaries whereas less then nine percent of the giant stars are spectroscopic systems. Before discussing the selection effects and physical processes which contribute to this imbalance, let us first examine the periods of the spectroscopic binaries in various spectral subgroups. This is shown in figure 3.

The great difference in periods between the dwarf and giant spectroscopic binaries at first appears to be a contradiction of evolutionary theories. It is clear from figure 3 that there is a preponderance of short periods among the main sequence stars, and an excess of long periods among the giants. Since the G 8 − K 7 giants most presumably arise from A 8 − F 7 main sequence stars, the absence of spectroscopic binaries in the A 8 − F 7 group with periods longer than 500 days might seem very surprising. This is a good illustration, however, of the effect of the adopted cutoff in apparent magnitude at 6.5 mag., and it illustrates also the pitfall of regarding spectroscopic binaries and visual binaries as two distinct classes of objects.

The explanation for the absence of long period spectroscopic binaries among the A 8 − F 7 main sequence subgroup is simply that stars in this spectral group which are bright enough to be listed in the *Yale Bright Star Catalogue* must also be close enough for relatively easy detection as visual binaries, hence precluding their being listed in the catalogue of spectroscopic binaries. Giant spectroscopic binaries, on the other hand, which are suffi-

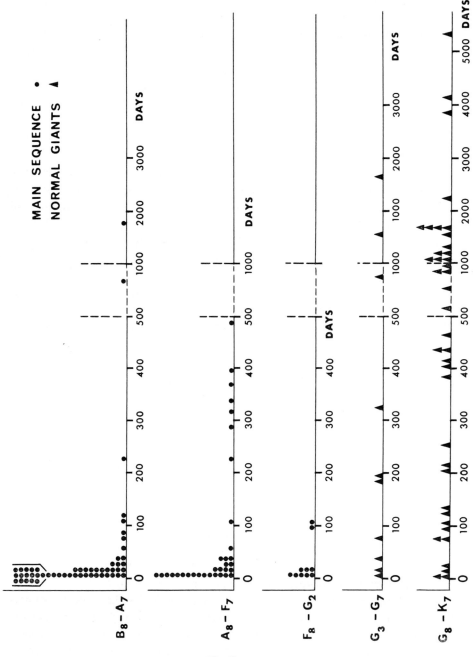

Fig. 3

ciently bright to be included in the *Bright Star Catalogue* can be sufficiently distant not to be detected as visual binaries. The presence of long period giant spectroscopic binaries and the apparent absence of their main sequence progenitors is thus largely explained.

It would seem, however, that the distance effect should tend to increase the number of spectroscopic binaries among the giants relative to those on the main sequence since the close pairs would escape detection as visual binaries. Let us, however, first examine the probable number of spectroscopic binaries that are removed from the giant ranks by virtue of mass-transfer in close binary systems.

Elementary consideration shows that if evolution from the main sequence imposes a ten-fold increase in luminosity and an approximate halving of temperature, the surface area must be increased some one hundred and sixty-fold, and consequently the radius by a dozen times or more. Twenty-fold or thirty-fold increases in radius can be expected for the later giants. Table V gives the minimum periods allowable for contact binaries for various values of the expanding radius of the evolving star. It would appear that for spectroscopic binaries of periods of ten days or more, evolution of one component to the giant sequence can occur without interruption, but shorter period systems will be transformed into "contact" systems as the primary star expands.

TABLE V

Minimum Period		
R$\odot$	2 M$\odot$	10 M$\odot$
5	0.9	0.4
10	2.6	1.2
20	7.3	3.3
40	20.0	9.2

Minimum allowed periods
for given size of primary.

It is interesting to note for how many present spectroscopic systems the orbit of the secondary would lie within the physical boundaries of the primary were it a giant star (figure 4). The curves have been computed for typical B, A, and F stars for two solar masses with the limits of one and fifty solar masses indicated. We see that at least twenty percent of all present spectroscopic systems of classes A and B cannot survive the expansion of the primary and remain as normal systems, and in some cases perhaps as many as thirty percent will be so affected. The absence of very short periods among giant spectroscopic binaries are thus satisfactorily explained.

PERCENT OF PRESENT SPECTROSCOPIC COMPANIONS WHOSE ORBITS WOULD LIE WITHIN AN EXPANDING PRIMARY STAR

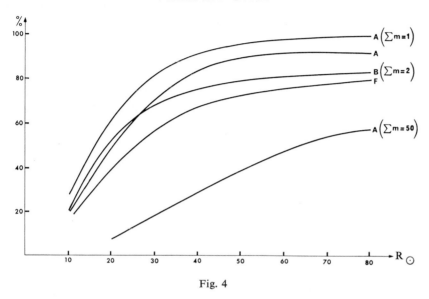

Fig. 4

3 — The Working Directory of Stellar Systems

The following brief description of the working *Directory of Bright Stellar Systems* which is kept on tape and punch cards at the Dearborn Observatory, is primarily given here to call attention to its existence. It is likely that one version of the *Directory* will be published in the *Annals of the Dearborn Observatory* although one of the features of the *Directory* is its fluid nature; its existence on magnetic tape and punch cards allows frequent updating as more data for bright stars becomes available.

The *Directory* was conceived by the writer many years ago partially as a result of his interest in stars with composite spectra, many of which are Bright Stars. It was apparent that even for stars brighter than 6.5, much basic data were still lacking. It seemed expedient, therefore, to devise a working directory, a rather elaborate guide to further observations. Since it is obvious that the Bright Stars will remain the most easily observable stars, there is some point in maintaining an up-to-date survey of our knowledge of these stars. The *Directory* therefore can serve as a catalogue to highlight bright stellar systems for which specific observations are desirable or to consider in detail the role of these stars as primaries in multiple stellar systems, etc. The *Directory* thus serves as a sort of finding list.

Space motions, both with respect to the sun and with respect to an arbitrary local standard of rest, are an important feature of the *Directory*. As better parallax, radial velocity, and proper motion values become available, these velocity data are subject to a constant upgrading, a relatively easy matter when the data are compiled on cards and tape.

The spectrum and luminosity of each star in a multiple system is listed as a three-digit code number. The first two digits represent the spectral class and decimal subdivision; thus 06, 35, and 60 indicate an O6, and F5, and M0 respectively. The absence of the third digit indicates that the luminosity class is unknown; 0 and 1, respectively, indicate luminosity class Ia and I. Digits 2, 3, 4, 5, and 6 indicate the luminosity classes II, III, IV, V, and VI, respectively. Digits 7 and 8 indicate dwarf (d) and giants (g) characteristics and the digit 9 indicates supergiant (c) characteristics. Mean values, respectively, of trigonometric, spectroscopic, and dynamic parallaxes, culled from many sources, and an adopted parallax used for general computation purposes are also listed.

A unique feature of the *Directory* is, however, having each bright star carry a three digit code number with the following significance for each of the digits :

Multiplicity	
First Column	Second and Third Columns
1. Single star	1. Single star
2. Single line sp. bin.	2. Single line sp. bin.
3. Double line sp. bin.	3. Double line sp. bin.
4. Double sep $< 1''$	4. Close visual double
5. Triple spectroscopic system	5. CPM close visual double
6. Composite spectrum	6. CPM dbl. line sp. bin.
7.	7. CPM single line sp. bin.
8. Astrometric double	8. CPM single star
9. No R. V.	9. Poss CPM single star

This multiplicity code allows considerable flexibility in the handling of Bright Stars as multiple systems; the present chapter is an example of this. Listed also are the radial velocities of the primary and secondary components, their axial rotations on a scale 0-5, (the latter number indicating extremely rotationally broadened spectrum lines), and Δm between visual components 1 and 2, and 2 and 3 respectively, and the corresponding separations in seconds of arc. Likewise, the periods of the first and second components when these are spectroscopic binaries are included. The *Directory* also gives the projected separation in astronomical units of the visual binaries, computed from the adopted parallax. Finally, it contains eighteen indicators (in binary notation) which show at a glance, for each star, the presence or

TABLE VI

	Configuration number	Graphic representation	No. of stars
One-component systems	0	0	1
	1	$\bar{0}$	2
Two-component non-CPM systems	2	0-0	2
	3	$\bar{0}$-0	3
	4	0-$\bar{0}$	3
	5	$\bar{0}$-$\bar{0}$	4
CPM	6	0--0	2
	7	$\bar{0}$--0	3
	8	0--$\bar{0}$	3
	9	$\bar{0}$--$\bar{0}$	4
T: peculiar and triple systems	10	0--0-0	3
	11	$\bar{0}$--0-0	4

Legend

0   = single star
$\bar{0}$ = spectroscopic binary
0-0 = visual binary
0--0 = common proper motion pair

absence of various data items as parallax, radial velocity, axial rotation, etc.

The adaptation and evolution of the *Directory* as a computational device is the work of Dr. Walter WELLER and Mr. Jacques VALLEE, whose great aid is gratefully acknowledged. Vallee has incorporated a symbolic indicator for each star which visually portrays immediately the nature of the stellar system and is shown in table VI.

VALLEE has also adapted the *Directory* for correlated information retrieval. A natural language input which the computing machine can interpret directly and provide a printout answer has been devised. This departure is at the moment exploratory but appears to offer great promise in this and other branches of astronomical data processing.

REFERENCE

SANDAGE, A., 1957, *Ap. J.* **125**, 422, 435; **126**, 326.

The masses of nine visual binary systems

O.C. Wilson

Mount Wilson and Palomar Observatories
Carnegie Institution of Washington, California Institute of Technology

Stellar masses are known reasonably well along most of the main sequence. But in the region of the H-R diagram to the right of the main sequence, among the giants and subgiants, such information is almost totally lacking (see HARRIS, STRAND, and WORLEY, 1963) for a recent discussion. This situation is especially unfortunate since, according to current concepts, the giants and subgiants have evolved from various locations on the main sequence, the points of origin determining the masses, and vice versa.

The sum of the masses, in solar units, of the members of a visual binary system of known orbit is given by the well-known equation

$$\text{(1)} \qquad \mathfrak{M} = a^3/\mathrm{P}^2\,\pi^3,$$

in which a and π are the semi-major axis and the parallax, respectively, in seconds of arc, and P is the period in years. For many visual binaries containing intrinsically bright stars the period of revolution is so long compared to the time covered by observation that the orbital elements are not determinable with the necessary accuracy. For others, in which shorter periods may permit the computation of acceptable orbits, the precision of the parallaxes is insufficient to derive satisfactory masses. With the development in recent years of a procedure which appears capable of yielding rather accurate luminosities for stars of spectral types G, K and M (WILSON, 1959), it is timely to consider whether an application of this method to selected visual doubles may significantly improve our knowledge of the masses of evolved stars. The procedure in question employs the empirically determined relationship between the absolute visual magnitude, M_v, and the measured widths of the bright H and K reversals, corrected for instrumental effects, W_0.

Combination of equation (1) with that for the absolute magnitude,

$$\text{(2)} \qquad M = \mathfrak{M} + 5 + 5\log \pi,$$

results in the expression

$$\text{(3)} \qquad \log \mathfrak{M} = 3\log a - 2\log \mathrm{P} - 0.6\,(M - m) + 3.0.$$

This latter equation is utilized here since the method of H-K emission line widths provides a value of M_v directly.

Systems likely to be useful for mass determination were selected originally from the compilation of O. FRANZ [1956], and more recent references to orbital data have been sought in the catalogue of WORLEY [1963]. When, in Worley's opinion, two orbits should be considered of equal weight, computations of mass have been made from both sets of data if the results differ significantly.

To determine the absolute magnitudes, spectroscopic observations at a dispersion of 10 Å/mm have been made at both Mount Wilson and Palomar. A sufficient number of spectrograms, about ten, has been obtained for each object in order to reduce the internal probable error of M_v to approximately 0.1 mag. Hence the principal error in the method is that due to the "cosmic scatter", which has been estimated by comparison with trigonometric parallaxes to be about 0.2 mag. (WILSON, 1959). Zero point and scale errors of the H-K method are not known, but I regard it as unlikely that these together can exceed about 0.1 mag. Thus, at best, masses derived by use of the H-K procedure will be uncertain by about 30 per cent.

Since the H-K method is based on the V magnitudes of the U, B, V system, it is essential that the apparent magnitudes of the stars be known with adequate accuracy on this system also. This information is lacking in the literature for several of the binaries under discussion and I am therefore much indebted to Dr. H. SPINRAD of the University of California, Berkeley, for U, B, V measures of these stars, which were communicated privately, and for permission to use his results.

When the members of a pair which are unresolved on the spectrograph slit are of nearly equal magnitude, or when the difference in brightness is one magnitude or more, the procedure is obvious and straightforward. When, however, the brightness difference is a few tenths of a magnitude, one cannot be certain as to which star is the major contributor to the H-K emission, although it is likely that the brighter member will predominate. In such cases, two values of the total mass are given, on the assumption that the H-K reversals are produced entirely by either the brighter or the fainter component. The true mass is probably between the two values and closer to the smaller one.

An additional source of error in close pairs of nearly equal brightness is the possibility of some widening of the H-K reversals due to the differential radial velocity of the component's orbital motion, on the assumption that both members are contributing to the observed H-K emissions. This effect should at most amount to only a few km/sec in the measured widths and, since the relative contributions of the members to the H-K emissions are not known for any of the close pairs, no attempt has been made to correct for it. However, it should be borne in mind that the effect may have a tendency to increase slightly the computed masses for close pairs of nearly equal magnitude. In none of the close pairs observed spectroscopically was there any evidence on the spectrograms of duplicity or widening of either absorption or emission lines, but at 10 Å/mm these are not very sensitive criteria.

We shall now discuss the results for the several systems individually and summarize all of them at the end of the paper. In the following, the quantity W_0 is the measured H-K emission width in km/sec, corrected for instrumental widening, as defined in a paper by the writer (WILSON, 1959) which discusses also the derivation of the relationship between W_0 and M_v used here.

The latter is expressed by the equation

(4) $$M_v = -14.94 \log W_0 + 27.59.$$

Probable errors for W_0 and M_v are computed from the scatter of the measured values in the usual manner.

1. ADS 755 = 36 And.

V = 5.42 (EGGEN, 1955); 5.51 (SPINRAD); 5.46 adopted.

B — V = 1.04 (EGGEN, 1955); 0.96 (SPINRAD); 1.00 adopted.

Δm = 0.44 (WALLENQUIST, 1954).

From 10 spectrograms: $W_0 = 38.7 \pm 0.84$ km/sec; $M_v = +3.87 \pm 0.14$. Orbital data: $a = 1''006$; P = 155.58 yr. (RABE, 1958).

From the adopted m_v for the system and the value of Δm, the apparent magnitudes of the two stars are

$V_A = +6.03$; $V_B = +6.46$, and the corresponding values of the total mass: $\mathfrak{M} = 0.85$; $\mathfrak{M} = 1.5$.

Thus the mass of each component is probably less than that of the sun although, since the mass ratio is unknown, more precise values cannot be given. As we shall see, these objects lie on the lower boundary of the subgiant region in the color-magnitude diagram, and must be extremely old.

2. ADS 7724 = γ Leo.

V = 1.95, B — V = 1.12 (EGGEN, 1955). Δm = 1.24 (WALLENQUIST, 1954). From V and Δm, $V_A = 2.25$, $V_B = 3.50$.

This is the only pair for which spectroscopic observations of the members could be made separately. From five spectrograms of the brighter component and four of the fainter, we find:

$$(W_0)_A = 65.8 \text{ km/sec}, (M_v)_A = + 0.44$$
$$(W_0)_B = 55.2 \text{ km/sec}, (M_v)_B = + 1.54$$

Because of the small numbers of observations, probable errors have not been computed, but we note that the derived value of ΔM differs by only 0.14 mag. from the Δm of WALLENQUIST.

There are two recent orbits:

$$a = 2''742 \qquad P = 701.4 \text{ yr. (GÜNTZEL-LINGNER, 1956)},$$
$$a = 2''505 \qquad P = 618.56 \text{ yr. (RABE, 1958)},$$

which differ by only 0.01 in the logarithm of a^3/P^2.

Masses, computed from the measures of each component separately, are

From component A, $\mathfrak{M} = 0.51$
From component B, $\mathfrak{M} = 0.61$

These total masses appear to be absurdly low, but the reason for this result is not clear. If it be assumed that approximately one solar mass is a reasonable value of each component, then the computed total masses above are too small by a factor of 4. If this deficiency is to be attributed entirely to the derived luminosities, it follows that the H-K width method is in error by a whole magnitude for the components of γ Leo. This is perhaps conceivable, but there is no other evidence for discrepancies as large as this. On the other hand, the very long period of this system suggests that observations may not yet suffice to provide reliable orbital elements.

3. ADS 8035 = α UMa.

$V = 1.79$, $B - V = 1.06$ (JOHNSON and MORGAN, 1953); $V = 1.82$, $B - V = 1.07$ (EGGEN, 1955); $V = 1.80$ adopted.
$\Delta m = 2.90$ (EGGEN, 1955).
From 9 spectrograms: $W_0 = 71.83 \pm 0.68$ km/sec; $M_v = - 0.16 \pm 0.06$.
Orbital data: $a = 0''769$; $P = 44.66$ yr. (COUTEAU, 1959).

From the adopted m_v and Δm the apparent magnitudes of the two stars are

$$V_A = + 1.87; V_B = + 4.79,$$

and the total mass, computed from the magnitudes of the brighter component is

$$\mathfrak{M} = 4.0.$$

In the case of α UMa, the ratio mass-of-faint star/total mass is known from the work of SPENCER JONES and FURNER [1937] to be 0.309. Hence the masses of components A and B are:

$$\mathfrak{M}_A = 2.76; \ \mathfrak{M}_B = 1.24.$$

With reasonable allowances for uncertainties, these masses, together with the absolute magnitudes, are not inconsistent with the interpretation that the secondary is a main-sequence star of spectral type F 0 to F 5, while the primary began existence on the main sequence somewhere near type A 0 and has subsequently evolved to the right in the color-magnitude diagram.

4. ADS 8695 = 35 Com.

$V = 4.96$ (SPINRAD); $B - V = 0.86$ (SPINRAD); $\Delta m = 2.2$ (FRANZ, 1956). From 10 spectrograms: $W_0 = 64.1 \pm 1.23$ km/sec; $M_v = +0.59 \pm 0.13$. Orbital data: $a = 1''897$; $P = 674.23$ yr. (SCHMEIDLER, 1938).

The apparent magnitudes are

$$(m_v)_A = 5.09; \ (\mathfrak{M}_v)_B = 7.29,$$

and the resultant value of the total mass, $\mathfrak{M} = 7.6$. For a pair whose brighter member has an absolute visual magnitude of $+0.6$, this mass appears considerably too large. As with γ Leo, the long period of 35 Com suggests that the orbital parameters are not yet known with sufficient precision.

5. λ 179 = $-38°8592$.

I have been unable to find photoelectric observations of this object in the literature. KNIPE [1961] gives the values

$$(m_v)_A = 4.6; \ (m_v)_B = 4.8,$$

and the HR magnitude is 4.04, (*Harvard Ann.* **44**.). One might reasonably expect these magnitudes to be within about 0.2 mag. of their values on the V system, but the uncertainty introduced by the lack of accurate photometry should be borne in mind.

From 8 spectrograms: $W_0 = 108.70 \pm 1.78$; $M_v = -2.83 \pm 0.11$. Orbital data: $a = 0''1492$; $P = 61.8$ yr. (KNIPE, 1961).

For this pair we compute two values of the total mass, corresponding to the apparent magnitudes of the components as explained earlier. We find:

$$m_v = 4.6, \ \mathfrak{M} = 23.5$$
$$m_v = 4.8, \ \mathfrak{M} = 30.9$$

The spectral type from my spectrograms is about K 0 and the luminosity class approximately II, in agreement with the H-K absolute magnitude.

For such stars the value of B − V would be expected to be about 1.2.

Evidently the mass of each star is about 12 to 15 times that of the sun. On the current evolutionary picture, therefore, these objects have evolved to the right in the color-magnitude diagram from a main-sequence position near spectral type B 0.

6. ADS 11468.

m_v = 5.39 (SPINRAD); B − V = 1.07 (SPINRAD); Δm = 0.0 (FRANZ, 1956). From 9 spectrograms: W_0 = 71.0 ± 1.0; M_v = −0.11 ± 0.09.

There are two recent orbits: a = 0″255; P = 184.6 yr. (WILSON, 1950)
a = 0″36; P = 338.0 yr. (BAIZE, 1958),

which yield, respectively, the masses

$$\mathfrak{M} = 3.0, \quad \mathfrak{M} = 2.3.$$

The mass of each star, therefore, is between 1.15 and 1.5.

7. ADS 11479.

m_v = 5.64 (SPINRAD); B−V = 1.05 (SPINRAD); Δm = 0.09 (FRANZ, 1956). Nine spectrograms give W_0 = 54.20 ± 0.8, M_v = + 1.69 ± 0.10. Orbital data: a = 0″418; P = 190.8 yrs. (AREND, 1951). We neglect the small magnitude difference and assume m_v = 6.40 for each star, hence,

$$\mathfrak{M} = 1.35,$$

and the mass of each star is approximately 0.7.

8. ADS 16538 = π Cep.

m_v = 4.37 (EGGEN, 1955), 4.37 (SPINRAD); B − V = 0.72 (SPINRAD); Δm = 3.5 (EGGEN, 1955). Measures of 8 spectrograms yield W_0 = 61.4 ± 0.5 km/sec, M_v = + 0.89 ± 0.05. Orbital data: a = 0″86, P = 150 yr. (MULLER, 1951). With the Δm given by EGGEN, the apparent magnitudes are

$$(m_v)_A = 4.41, (m_v)_B = 7.92,$$

and the total mass is found to be

$$\mathfrak{M} = 3.4.$$

There is a serious difficulty in this system since the bright star is itself a spectroscopic binary of period 556 d. If EGGEN's Δm is correct, the absolute magnitude of the faint member of the wide pair is about + 4.4 and it should, therefore, lie on the main sequence and have a mass approximately equal to that of the sun. But nothing is known about the faint member of the close pair except that it is probably at least one magnitude fainter than the bright component, since lines of the secondary were not observed (HARPER, 1925). If we take the mass of the close pair as 2.4, then certainly a lower limit to the mass of the brighter, evolved component is 1.2. Perhaps it would be reasonable to suppose that the mass of the faint member of the close pair is not less than 0.5. Then we would have for the brighter member of the close pair

$$1.2 < \mathfrak{M} \leqslant 1.9,$$

but I cannot see how to improve this result.

9. ADS 16836 = 72 Peg.

$m_v = 5.05$ (SPINRAD); $B - V = 1.28$ (SPINRAD); $\Delta m = 0.0$ (FRANZ, 1956).
Measures of 10 spectrograms give $W_0 = 70.6 \pm 0.7$ km/sec;
$M_v = -0.01 \pm 0.07$.

Orbital data: $a = 0''40$; $P = 218$ yr. (WIDORN, 1954), from which

$$\mathfrak{M} = 4.2,$$

and the mass of each member, therefore, is $\mathfrak{M} = 2.1$.

TABLE I

Summary of Results

Star	(M_v)K	B−V	$\mathfrak{M}$ (☉)
ADS 755	+3.9	1.00	0.6
7724 A	+0.4	1.12	<0.3
7724 B	+1.5	1.12	<0.3
8035	−0.2	1.07	2.8
8695	+0.6	0.86	~6
λ179	−2.8	~1.2	12
ADS 11468	−0.1	1.07	1.3
11479	+1.7	1.05	0.7
16538	+0.9	0.72	~1.5
16836	0.0	1.28	2.1

The results are now summarized in table I. Here I have attempted to provide values of absolute magnitudes and masses for individual stars by taking what seem to be reasonable mean values where necessary. As the preceding discussion of the various systems indicates abundantly, there are many uncertainties and these figures can, at best, be considered as only approximate.

Finally, it is of interest to illustrate the outcome of the investigation by means of a color-magnitude diagram. From the tables given by ALLEN [1955], the derived masses are transferred to spectral types on the main sequence, and the latter are then transformed to B − V by means of the standard spectral type −(B−V) relationship as given in ARP [1958].

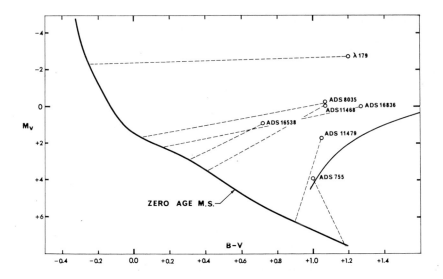

Fig. 1 — Location of components of binaries in color-magnitude diagram, and mean evolutionary paths from main sequence.

The present absolute magnitudes, $(M_v)_K$, and observed (B−V) values locate the stars in the color-magnitude diagram, and these points have been connected by dotted lines with the corresponding points on the zero-age main sequence (BLAAUW, 1963). Each dotted line, therefore, represents a kind of average evolutionary trajectory. They appear to be reasonably consistent with the predictions of evolutionary theory. The curved line on the right in the diagram is the lower boundary of the giant-subgiant region as determined by H-K observations of numerous field stars. Points for γ Leonis and ADS 8695 have not been plotted for reasons stated above.

REFERENCES

ALLEN, C.W., 1955, *Astrophysical Quantities* (Athlone Press, University of London).
AREND, S., 1951, *Ann. Roy. Obs. Belg.*, **5**, 161.
ARP, H.C., 1958, *Handbuch der Physik*, **LI**, (Springer), p. 75.
BAIZE, P., 1958, *J.O.*, **41**, 163.
BLAAUW, A., 1963, *Stars and Stellar Systems*, **III**, *Basic Astron. Data* (ed. K. Aa. Strand, University of Chicago Press, Chicago), p. 383.
COUTEAU, P., 1959, *J.O.*, **42**, 30.
EGGEN, O.J., 1955, *A.J.*, **60**, 65.
FRANZ, O., 1956, *Mitt. Wien Sternwarte*, **8**, 1.
GÜNTZEL-LINGNER, U., 1956, *A.N.*, **283**, 73.
HARPER, W.E., 1925, *Pub. D. A.O.*, **3**, 204.
HARRIS, D.L., STRAND, K. Aa., and WORLEY, C.E., 1963, *Stars and Stellar Systems*, **III**, *Basic Astron. Data* (ed. K. Aa. Strand, University of Ch cago Press, Ch cago), p. 273.
JOHNSON, H.L. and MORGAN, W.W., 1953, *Ap.J.*, **117**, 313.
KNIPE, G.F.G., 1961, *Union Obs. Circ.*, **6**, 375.
MULLER, P., 1951, *Bull. Astron.*, **16**, 210.
RABE, W., 1958, *A.N.*, **284**, 97.
SCHMEIDLER, F., 1938, *A.N.*, **268**, 151.
SPENCER JONES, H. and FURNER, H.H., 1937, *M.N.R.A.S.*, **98**, 92.
SPINRAD, H., *private communication*.
WALLENQUIST, A., 1954, *Ann. Uppsala Obs.*, **4**, No. 2.
WIDORN, T., 1954, *Mitt. Wien Sternwarte*, **7**, No. 8.
WILSON, O.C., 1959, *Ap. J.*, **130**, 499.
WILSON, JR., R.H., 1950, *A. J.*, **55**, 159.
WORLEY, C.E., 1963, *Pub. U.S. Naval Obs.*, Sd series, **XVIII** — Part III.

The machine computation of spectroscopic binary elements

R. H. WOLFE, JR., HENRY G. HORAK, N. WYMAN STORER
University of Kansas

1 — Abstract

A Fortran II program is given for calculating the elements of a spectroscopic binary orbit. The method is that of Wilsing-Russell followed by a differential correction, but modified to apply to high as well as low eccentricities. A preliminary value for the period is required, which can, if desired, be improved by the differential correction.

2 — Introduction

There are several advantages to using an electronic computer to evaluate the orbital elements of a spectroscopic binary: each radial velocity measurement can be treated as an individual observation rather than averaging to form normal points; it is possible to make use of the method of harmonic analysis, which would be considered too laborious for desk-calculator work; finally, a least-squares' solution can always be carried out, giving the probable errors of the various quantities and elements.

The harmonic method adopted is that of Wilsing-Russell (WILSING, 1893; RUSSELL, 1902) followed by a differential correction, and modified to apply to high as well as low eccentricities.

The program presented herein is written in Fortran II especially for the IBM 1620 computer. The computer at Kansas University has four tape units and 60,000 digits of core storage. There should be little trouble in modifying the program for other similar computers.

The orbital elements are designated by the following symbols:

V_0 : the radial velocity of the center of mass of the system relative to the sun;
P : the period of revolution;
T : the time of periastron passage;
ω : the argument of periastron (the angle from the ascending node to periastron, measured in the plane of the orbit);
e : the eccentricity;
$a \sin i$: the projection of the semi-major axis of the orbit onto the line from the sun to the center of mass of the system; a is the semi-major axis, i the inclination;
K : the semi-amplitude of the radial velocity curve.

There are two values of $a \sin i$ and K, one for each component of the system.

Gauthiers-Villars, Paris - Modern Astrophysics - 1967.

3 — The harmonic analysis

The basic equation for the radial velocity of one component of a spectroscopic binary is the following (BINNENDIJK, 1960; AITKEN, 1964)

$$(1) \qquad V = V_0 + \sin \omega \sin i \frac{d}{dt} (r \cos \theta) + \cos \omega \sin i \frac{d}{dt} (r \sin \theta),$$

where V is the radial velocity of the component relative to the sun, r the length of the radius vector relative to the center of mass, and θ the true anomaly. The time, t, is introduced by series derivable from the theory of elliptic motion, viz. (BROUWER and CLEMENCE 1961):

$$(2) \qquad r \cos \theta = -\frac{3}{2} ae + a X_1 \cos \mu (t - T) + \frac{1}{2} ae X_2 \cos 2\mu (t - T) + \dots,$$

$$r \sin \theta = \qquad a Y_1 \sin \mu (t - T) + \frac{1}{2} ae Y_2 \sin 2\mu (t - T) + \dots,$$

where

$$X_1 = 1 - \frac{3}{8} e^2 + \frac{5}{192} e^4 - \dots,$$

$$X_2 = 1 - \frac{2}{3} e^2 + \frac{1}{8} e^4 - \dots,$$

$$(3)$$

$$Y_1 = 1 - \frac{5}{8} e^2 - \frac{11}{192} e^4 - \dots,$$

$$Y_2 = 1 - \frac{5}{6} e^2 + \frac{1}{12} e^4 - \dots,$$

and $\mu = 2\pi/P$. Differentiating (2) with respect to t and substituting in (1) gives:

$$V = V_0 - \mu a \sin \omega \sin i X_1 \sin M - \mu ae \sin \omega \sin i X_2 \sin 2M +$$
$$(4) \qquad + \mu a \cos \omega \sin i Y_1 \cos M + \mu ae \cos \omega \sin i Y_2 \cos 2M + \dots,$$

where $M = \mu(t - T)$ is the mean anomaly. Since T is not known, M cannot as yet be determined, therefore we introduce the argument M' reckoned from an arbitrary epoch t_0, thus

$$(5) \qquad M = \mu(t - t_0) + \mu(t_0 - T) = M' + M_0,$$

where $M' = \mu(t - t_0)$ and $M_0 = \mu(t_0 - T)$.

Substituting (5) into (4), expanding and collecting terms, gives the fundamental harmonic equation

$$(6) \qquad V = V_0 + S_1 \sin M' + S_2 \sin 2M' + C_1 \cos M' + C_2 \cos 2M' + \dots,$$

where

$$S_1 = -\mu a \sin i (X_1 \sin \omega \cos M_0 + Y_1 \cos \omega \sin M_0),$$
$$(7) \qquad S_2 = -\mu ae \sin i (X_2 \sin \omega \cos 2 M_0 + Y_2 \cos \omega \sin 2M_0),$$
$$C_1 = \mu a \sin i (Y_1 \cos \omega \cos M_0 - X_1 \sin \omega \sin M_0),$$
$$C_2 = \mu ae \sin i (Y_2 \cos \omega \cos 2 M_0 - X_2 \sin \omega \sin 2M_0).$$

Observed values of V and M' can be substituted into (6), giving a set of simultaneous equations of condition with unknowns V_0, S_1, S_2, C_1, C_2. The normal equations are then formed and solved in accordance with the method of least squares.

4 — Determination of the elements

It remains to solve for the orbital elements (other than V_0) as functions of S_1, S_2, C_1, C_2. This can be done as follows (RUSSELL, 1902): Let

(8)
$$b_1 \cos \beta_1 = Y_1 \cos \omega, \qquad \alpha_1 = M_0 + \beta_1,$$
$$b_1 \sin \beta_1 = X_1 \sin \omega, \qquad \alpha_2 = 2M_0 + \beta_2,$$
$$b_2 \cos \beta_2 = Y_2 \cos \omega, \qquad A_1 = b_1 \, \mu a \sin i,$$
$$b_2 \sin \beta_2 = X_2 \sin \omega, \qquad A_2 = b_2 \, \mu a e \sin i.$$

Since X_1, X_2, Y_1, Y_2 are positive, we can choose b_1, b_2 and hence A_1, A_2 to be also positive.

Substituting these relations into (6) and (7) gives

$$V = V_0 - A_1 \sin \alpha_1 \sin M' - A_2 \sin \alpha_2 \sin 2M'$$

(9)
$$+ A_1 \cos \alpha_1 \cos M' + A_2 \cos \alpha_2 \cos 2M'.$$

Comparing with (6), we obtain

(10)
$$S_1 = - A_1 \sin \alpha_1, \qquad C_1 = A_1 \cos \alpha_1,$$
$$S_2 = - A_2 \sin \alpha_2, \qquad C_2 = A_2 \cos \alpha_2,$$

from which

(11)
$$\tan \alpha_1 = - S_1/C_1, \qquad A_1^2 = C_1^2 + S_1^2,$$
$$\tan \alpha_2 = - S_2/C_2, \qquad A_2^2 = C_2^2 + S_2^2,$$

Equations (10) and (11) determine A_1, A_2, α_1, α_2.

The quantities b_1, b_2, β_1, β_2 are computed by iteration, beginning with the following initial values for ω and e:

(12)
$$\omega^{(0)} = 2\alpha_1 - \alpha_2, \qquad e^{(0)} = A_2/A_1.$$

The preliminary $b_1^{(0)}$, $b_2^{(0)}$, $\beta_1^{(0)}$, $\beta_2^{(0)}$ are computed from:

(13)
$$b_1^{(0)2} = Y_1^{(0)2} \cos^2 \omega^{(0)} + X_1^{(0)2} \sin^2 \omega^{(0)}, \qquad \tan \beta_1^{(0)} = X_1^{(0)} \tan \omega^{(0)}/Y_1^{(0)},$$
$$b_2^{(0)2} = Y_2^{(0)2} \cos^2 \omega^{(0)} + X_2^{(0)2} \sin^2 \omega^{(0)}, \qquad \tan \beta_2^{(0)} = X_2^{(0)} \tan \omega^{(0)}/Y_2^{(0)}.$$

The improved values, $\omega^{(1)}$, $e^{(1)}$, are then found from

$$\omega^{(1)} = 2\,\alpha_1 - \alpha_2 - 2(\beta_1^{(0)} - \omega^{(0)}) + (\beta_2^{(0)} - \omega^{(0)}),$$

(14)
$$e^{(1)} = b_1^{(0)} A_2/b_2^{(0)} A_1 .$$

The process can be repeated, using $\omega^{(1)}$, $e^{(1)}$ in place of $\omega^{(0)}$, $e^{(0)}$. Once the final values of ω, e, b_1, b_2, β_1, β_2 are found, a sin i can be computed from

$$(15) \qquad\qquad a \sin i = A_1/b_1 \, \mu,$$

and M_0 from

$$(16) \qquad\qquad M_0 = \alpha_2 - \alpha_1 + \beta_1 - \beta_2.$$

The time of periastron is obtained from

$$(17) \qquad\qquad T = t_0 - \frac{M_0}{\mu}.$$

Finally, K is given by

$$(18) \qquad\qquad K = \frac{\mu a \sin i}{\sqrt{1 - e^2}}.$$

The method is very accurate for small eccentricities, but can be used for moderate and high eccentricities provided that the series (6) is carried out further; this means that in the least squares solution more unknowns than just V_0, S_1, S_2, C_1, C_2 are involved. The only reason for including these additional values of S and C is to obtain more accurate values for the first five from which the elements are obtained. For eccentricities greater than about 0.6 the series (6) diverges. If, however, enough C's and S's are evaluated from the observations by least squares, the resulting curve will pass through every point. The problem associated with high eccentricities, then, is that the elements are being determined from a set of converging coefficients by a method based on a diverging series. It was found that reasonable values of the elements could be obtained for eccentricities as high as 0.83 by solving for five or six S's and C's. Although the accuracy of such results is difficult to judge, these elements can nevertheless be used as the basis for a differential correction.

5 — The probable errors

The probable error, $r(C)$, of any particular harmonic coefficient, C, is related to the probable error of one observation, $r(1)$, by

$$(19) \qquad\qquad r(C) = \frac{r(1)}{\sqrt{p(C)}} , p(C) = \frac{D}{D_c} ,$$

where $p(C)$ is the weight of C, D is the determinant of the coefficients of the normal equations formed from (6), and D_c is the corresponding minor of the coefficient of the particular S or C in question. It then follows that

$$r^2(A_i) = \frac{1}{A_i^2} \, [C_i^2 r^2(C_i) + S_i^2 r^2(S_i)],$$

$$r^2(\alpha_i) = \frac{1}{A_i^4} \, [S_i^2 r^2(C_i) + C_i^2 r^2(S_i)] \qquad (i = 1, 2),$$

(20)
$$r^2(e) = \frac{1}{A_1^2} [e^2 r^2(A_1) + r^2(A_2)], \quad r^2(M_0) = r^2(\alpha_1) + r^2(\alpha_2),$$

$$r^2(\omega) = 4 r^2(\alpha_1) + r^2(\alpha_2), \qquad r(K) = r(A_1),$$

$$r(a \sin i) = r(A_1)/\mu, \qquad r(T) = r(M_0)/\mu.$$

If the observations are equally spaced in time, it can be shown that the probable errors of all the harmonic coefficients are equal.

6 — The differential correction

For the case of moderate and high eccentricities it is necessary to use the method of differential correction to improve the preliminary orbit. The equation is well known (SCHLESINGER, 1908, STERNE, 1941):[1]

$$dV = dV_0 + [e \cos \omega + \cos (\theta + \omega)] dK$$
$$- K [e \sin \omega + \sin (\theta + \omega)] d\omega$$
$$+ K [\cos \omega - (1 - e^2)^{-1} \sin \theta \sin (\theta + \omega) (2 + e \cos \theta)] de$$
(21)
$$- K (t - T) (1 - e^2)^{-\frac{3}{2}} \sin (\theta + \omega) (1 + e \cos \theta)^2 d\mu$$
$$+ K\mu (1 - e^2)^{-\frac{3}{2}} \sin (\theta + \omega) (1 + e \cos \theta)^2 dT,$$

where dV is the residual in radial velocity, and dK, dω, de, dμ, dT are corrections to the elements. The probable errors of the elements are simply those of the corrections. If the corrections are large, it is necessary to carry out the correction procedure again.

7 — Description of the program

The program presented here is written in Fortran II (MCCRACKEN, 1961) especially for the IBM 1620. The data is entered by means of punched cards, and the results are obtained in the same form. There are four console switches addressable by the program which are used to alter the course of the program execution.

The program is divided into four parts: (1) the calculation of the preliminary elements (and probable errors) by the method of harmonic analysis; (2) the differential correction of the preliminary elements, including probable errors; (3) the computation of theoretical radial velocities; (4) punching a set of cards which prints a theoretical radial velocity curve when tabulated on the IBM 407 Accounting Machine. There is a short transition section between parts (1) and (2) to test the eccentricity in order to choose between correcting the elements or finishing the computation by computing the residuals. If $e \leqslant 0.03$, or if the probable error of the eccentricity is larger than $\frac{1}{2} e$, then the preliminary elements are punched as the final values, and the residuals are computed. If the eccentricity is more accurate, and greater than 0.03, the preliminary elements are differentially corrected as many times as needed until the correction to K is smaller than one-third of its probable error after which the residuals are computed and punched.

The first data entered for the elements' program is a card with a number punched in the second column. This number specifies how many C and S coefficients are to be calculated and may be as large as seven. If the number is zero, the program will transfer control to the differential correction part; therefore a set of elements can be corrected without first

---

[1] Schlesinger credits this equation to LEHMANN-FILHES.

computing preliminary values. The next set of cards entered is one with the period, number of observations, and an arbitrary reference date such as that of the last observation. This card is followed by the observation cards each of which contains the date, the radial velocity and the weight of the observation.

The machine next computes the mean anomaly, M', for each observation based on the arbitrary "last date", t_0 [eq. (5)]. The sines and cosines of the various multiples of M' are then computed as coefficients for the observational equation [eq. (6)], and the normal equations are formed. The quantities V_0, C_1, ..., S_1, ... are determined by a least squares' subroutine based on the square root method (STORER, 1960). The elements and probable errors follow [eqs. (14)-(18), and (20)]. The necessity for using the differential correction is checked as previously explained.

The differential correction starts by recomputing the phases based upon the time of periastron given by the preliminary orbit. The coefficients in the basic equation (21) are evaluated, and the least squares' subroutine again called, which gives the corrections to the elements and the probable errors. Afterwards the corrections are added to the elements, and the correction of K and its probable error checked to see if a satisfactory degree of convergence has resulted; if not the process is repeated. Finally the computation returns to the part of the program which calculates the residuals, dV, but this time they are punched along with the radial velocity and other information.

Now if the first card entered has a zero in the second column, the control bypasses the harmonic section, accepts four cards with the elements on them and transfers directly to the differential correction routine. The first of these four cards may be anything such as a card reading *Final Elements*, and the other three must contain the elements in the same form as would have been punched from the harmonic analysis.

In case the orbit is fairly close to being circular the time of periastron is not determined very accurately; for this reason the time, $TV0$, at which the radial velocity is equal to that of the center of mass is computed.

The uses of the console switches will now be explained. Switch 1 is turned on when it is desired to correct the period, otherwise the term involving $d\mu$ is set equal to zero. Switch 2 is turned on to have occasional results typed out. Turning it on during either the harmonic analysis or differential correction causes the number of the observation being worked on to be typed. If it is on while e and ω are being found from the C's and S's, the value of e will be typed each time around the iteration. Finally if it is on when the correction and error of K are checked, these two values will be typed. Switch 3, however, is used solely to change the course of the program. It may be desirable to change the number of C's and S's used in the harmonic analysis; this can be done by putting switch 3 on, and reading a new first card. Also if the value of e computed from the A's and α's ever exceeds unity in the iteration, its value is typed and the machine stops. Another card can be entered specifying a different number of C's and S's to be solved for, switch 3 turned on, and the machine started again. During the differential correction switch 3 may be turned on to cause the correction cycle in progress to be the last one. Such a use for the switch here would be to end the computation if the differential correction were converging too slowly or not at all.

In order to give the operator an idea of the progress of the computation several messages are typed out during the execution of the program. The first gives the identification placed in the second to seventh columns of the second card entered, and the number of C's or S's being solved for. Once the computation has reached the differential correction the message *Diff Corrn* is typed. At the end of each correction cycle the message *Elements Corrected* is typed, preceded by *Period Corrected* if switch 1 is on. Finally *End of Computation* is typed when the program is finished.

The fourth part of the program is really independent of the first three parts. It computes a set of theoretical radial velocities and punches a set of cards which prints a theoretical velocity curve with the observations, when tabulated on the IBM 407 Accounting Machine.

It is necessary to enter the observations and elements to perform these operations. The velocity is computed for each hundredth of the period throughout one cycle; the observations are sorted by phases and when the phase of such an observation is close to that of the theoretical value being computed, the two are punched in a card in the form of a zero and asterisk respectively. If no observation falls at the phase of a particular theoretical value, only the asterisk is punched; on the other hand, if an asterisk and a zero fall in the same place, the zero is preferred. After the cards for the curve are punched the message *End Graph* is typed. Turning switch 1 on causes only the theoretical velocities to be computed and the theoretical curve to be plotted, in which case only the elements cards are entered. If switch 2 is turned on, only the observational curve is plotted, so that the elements cards are not needed. In place of them, however, a card with a value of K must follow the observations, where K is placed in the same position on the card as it would be on the elements cards. A suitable value of K may be obtained by dividing the difference between the largest and smallest radial velocities by two.

The detailed description of the program is of course best given by the program listing itself which is presented in the next section. Comments have been added to aid interpretation of the routines: a slash, /, represents an apostrophe in these comments.

8 — Program listing

```
*  8 6
C     A PROGRAM TO DETERMINE THE ELEMENTS OF A SPECTROSCOPIC BINARY
C
      DIMENSIONZ(18,18),V(350),FJD(350),WT(350),Q(17)
      DIMENSIONC(2),S(2),C2(2),S2(2),A2(2)
      DIMENSIONA(2),ALPH(2),RC(2),RS(2),RC2(2),RS2(2),RA(2),RAL2(2)
      DIMENSIONRA2(2),B(2),BETA(2)
C  ASSIGNMENT OF THE SAME AREA FOR THE Z MATRIX AS USED BY THE
C  LEAST SQUARES SUBROUTINE
      COMMONZ
C  DEFINING FREQUENTLY USED CONSTANTS
      PI2=6.2831853
      PIO2=1.5707963
      PI=3.1415927
      PI3O2=4.7123889
      RADEG=57.29578
      ASI=86400.
      Q(1)=1.
C
C         THE APPROXIMATE ELEMENTS
C
C         NORMAL EQUATIONS FOR THE HARMONIC ANALYSIS
C
C  ENTERING ALL INPUT FOR HARMONIC ANALYSIS
   64 READ991,M
  991 FORMAT(I2)
C  BYPASS   READING   OF   OBSERVATIONS IF SWITCH 3 IS   ON
      IF(SENSESWITCH3)700,888
C  OTHERWISE READ OBSERVATIONS
  888 READ4,ID1,ID2,P,N,FJDL
      READ3,(FJD(I),V(I),WT(I),I=1,N)
C  DEFINING PRELIMINARY VALUES= SUM OF P(O-C)2
      IX=5
      SV2=0.
```

```
C   GIVE FLOATING POINT VALUE TO NUMBER OF OBSERVATIONS
       FFN=N
C   MEAN DAILY MOTION
       FMU=PI2/P
   502 TYPE59,ID1,ID2,M
    59 FORMAT(2A3,I3,1HM)
C   IF THE NUMBER OF C AND S COEFFICIENTS IS ZERO READ ELEMENTS
       IF(M)700,701,700
   701 READ1
     1 FORMAT(80X)
       READ339,ID1,ID2,V0,FK,E,W,T0
   339 FORMAT(1X,2A3,5X,F8.3,13X,F8.3/11X,F8.6,14X,F8.5/11X,F10.3)
C   AND GO TO THE DIFFERENTIAL CORRECTION
       GOTO300
C   OTHERWISE CONTINUE WITH HARMONIC ANALYSIS
C   BRANCH FROM SWITCH 3 ON JOINS HERE
   700 M2=2*M
       M21=M2+1
       M22=M2+2
       M23=M2+3
C   SET THE Z MATRIX EQUAL TO ZERO
       DO60I=1,M23
       DO60J=1,M23
    60 Z(I,J)=0.
C   FROM HERE ON EACH OBSERVATION IS DEALT WITH ONE AT A TIME
       DO2I=1,N
C   FINDING THE PHASE BY EXTRACTING THE DECIMAL PART OF THE TIME
C   INTERVAL DIVIDED BY THE PERIOD
       EPPH=(FJDL−FJD(I))/P
       IEP=EPPH+1.
       EP=IEP
       PH=EP−EPPH
       FM=PH*PI2
C   FINDING THE COEFFICIENTS OF C1 AND S1
       Q(2)=COSF(FM)
       Q(3)=SINF(FM)
C   AND THOSE OF C2, S2 TO CM, SM
       DO989J=4,M2,2
       J1=J−1
       J2=J1−1
C   BY THE SINE AND COSINE OF SUMS OF ANGLES
       Q(J)=Q(J2)*Q(2)−Q(J1)*Q(3)
   989 Q(J+1)=Q(J1)*Q(2)+Q(J2)*Q(3)
       Q(M22)=V(I)
C   NUMBER OF OBSERVATIONS IS TYPED IF SWITCH 2 IS ON
       IF(SENSESWITCH2)781,780
   781 TYPE362,I
   362 FORMAT(I3)
C   SETTING UP NORMAL EQUATIONS FOR LEAST SQUARES SOLUTION
   780 DO2J=1,M22
       DO2K=J,M22
     2 Z(J,K+1)=WT(I)*Q(J)*Q(K)+Z(J,K+1)
C
C       SOLUTION FOR THE COEFFICIENTS BY LEAST SQUARES
```

```
C
          CALLLSTSQ(M21,FFN)
C   AT THIS POINT CONTROL TRANSFERS TO LEAST SQUARES SUBPROGRAM
C   LISTED AT THE END OF THIS PROGRAM. THEN CONTROL RETURNS HERE
C       DETERMINATION OF THE APPROXIMATE ELEMENTS
C   EVALUATION OF A1 AND A2 FROM (11)
          DO20J=1,2
          C(J)=Z(M22,2*J)
          S(J)=Z(M22,2*J+1)
          C2(J)=C(J)*C(J)
          S2(J)=S(J)*S(J)
          A2(J)=C2(J)+S2(J)
      20 A(J)=SQRTF(A2(J))
C   EVALUATION OF E FROM (12)
          E=A(2)/A(1)
C   EVALUATION OF ALPHA1 AND ALPHA2 FROM (11)
          DO27J=1,2
          IF(C(J)) 21,22,23
      23 ALPH(J)=ATANF(-S(J)/C(J))
          GOTO26
      21 ALPH(J)=ATANF(-S(J)/C(J))+PI
          GOTO26
      22 IF(S(J))24,24,25
      24 ALPH(J)=PIO2
          GOTO26
      25 ALPH(J)=PI3O2
C   TRANSFER OF C AND S ERRORS TO DIFFERENT LOCATION
      26 RC(J)=Z(M23,2*J)
          RS(J)=Z(M23,2*J+1)
          RC2(J)=RC(J)*RC(J)
          RS2(J)=RS(J)*RS(J)
C   EVALUATION OF THE ERRORS FOR THE A/S FROM (20)
          RA2(J)=(C2(J)*RC2(J)+S2(J)*RS2(J))/A2(J)
C   AND FOR THE ALPHA/S
          RAL2(J)=(C2(J)*RS2(J)+S2(J)*RC2(J))/(A2(J)*A2(J))
C   IF E IS ZERO STATE THAT W AND T ARE INDETERMINANT
          IF(E-5.E-7)100,100,27
      27 CONTINUE
C   EVALUATION OF W FROM (12)
          W=2.*ALPH(1)-ALPH(2)
          WP=W
C   BEGINNING OF ITERATION FOR IMPROVED VALUES OF E AND W
      31 E2=E*E
          E1=E
C   EVALUATION OF X/S AND Y/S FROM (3)
          C(1)=1.-E2*(3./8.-5.*E2/192.)
          S(1)=1.-E2*(5./8.+11.*E2/192.)
          C(2)=1.-E2*(.66666667-.125*E2)
          S(2)=1.-E2*(5./6.-E2/12.)
C   ROUTINE TO FIND BETA
          COSW=COSF(W)
          SINW=SINF(W)
          IF(COSW)32,33,32
      32 C2W=COSW*COSW
          S2W=SINW*SINW
```

```
C    EVALUATION OF BETA/S FROM (13)
        DO34J=1,2
        BETA(J)=ATANF(C(J)*SINW/(S(J)*COSW))
        IF(COSW)35,34,34
     35 BETA(J)=BETA(J)+PI
C    EVALUATION OF B/S FROM (13)
     34 B(J)=SQRTF(C(J)*C(J)*S2W+S(J)*S(J)*C2W)
        GOTO39
     33 IF(SINW)37,36,36
     36 BETA(1)=PIO2
        BETA(2)=PIO2
        GOTO38
     37 BETA(1)=PI3O2
        BETA(2)=PI3O2
     38 B(1)=C(1)
        B(2)=C(2)
CORRECTION OF W FROM (14)
     39 W=WP-2.*BETA(1)+BETA(2)+W
C
C    REEVALUATION OF E FROM (14)
        E=A(2)*B(1)/(A(1)*B(2))
        IF(SENSESWITCH2)406,405
    406 TYPE984,E
C    IF E IS ONE OR GREATER ANOTHER GUESS AT THE SERIES LENGTH
C    CAN BE ENTERED
    405 IF(1.-E)982,981,981
    982 TYPE984,E
        PAUSE
        IF(SENSESWITCH3)501,64
    501 READ991,M
        GOTO502
    981 E1=E1-E
CHECK FOR CONVERGENCE
        IF(E1*E1-2.5E-13)6,6,31
C    EVALUATE A SIN I FROM (15),
      6 ASINI=ASI*A(1)/(B(1)*FMU)
C    T FROM (16) AND (17),
        TO=FJDL-(ALPH(2)-ALPH(1)+BETA(1)-BETA(2))/FMU
C    K FROM (18),
        FK=FMU*ASINI/(ASI*SQRTF(1.-E2))
C    AND THE ERROR FOR E FROM (20)
        RE=SQRTF((E2*RA2(1)+RA2(2))/A2(1))
CHECK TO SEE WHETHER OR NOT ELEMENTS MUST BE CORRECTED
        IF(E/2.-RE)7,7,121
    121 IF(E-.03)7,7,50
C    IF SO, PUNCH APPROXIMATE VALUES AND GO TO THE DIFF CORRN ROUTINE
     50 IDEN=2
        PUNCH42
     42 FORMAT(30X,15HAPPROX ELEMENTS)
        GOTO109
C    IF NOT, PUNCH VALUES AS FINAL ELEMENTS
      7 IDEN=1
        PUNCH88
     88 FORMAT(1H0,29X,14HFINAL ELEMENTS)
```

```
C   EVALUATION OF THE ERRORS OF W FROM (20),
    109 RW=SQRTF(4.*RAL2(1)+RAL2(2))
C   OF K FROM (20),
        RK=SQRTF(RA2(1))
C   OF A SIN I FROM (20),
        RASI=ASI*RK/FMU
C   AND OF T FROM (20)
        RT0=SQRTF(RAL2(1)+RAL2(2))/FMU
C   EVALUATE ERROR OF W IN DEGREES
        RWV=RADEG*RW
C   REDUCTION OF W TO PRINCIPAL VALUES
    200 IF(W)51,52,53
     51 W=W+PI2
        GOTO200
     53 WX=W-PI2
        IF(WX)52,52,54
     54 W=WX
        GOTO53
C
CONVERSION OF W TO DEGREES
     52 WV=RADEG*W
    125 PUNCH43,ID1,ID2,IDEN,Z(M22,1),Z(M23,1),FK,RK,ASINI,RASI
        VO=Z(M22,1)
        PUNCH44,ID1,ID2,IDEN,E,RE,W,RW,WV,RWV
        PUNCH40,ID1,ID2,IDEN,T0,RT0,P,FMU,Z(M23,M23)
        IF(IDEN-1)201,201,300
C   EVALUATION OF TIME OF V0 AND ITS ERROR
    201 TV0=FJDL+(PI+ALPH(1))/FMU
        RTV0=SQRTF(RAL2(1))/FMU
        PUNCH46,ID1,ID2,IDEN,TV0,RTV0
     46 FORMAT(1H0,2A3,I2,4HTV0=,F10.3,2H R,F9.4)
        IF=1
        GOTO305
C   ROUTINE FOR WHEN E IS ZERO
C   EVALUATION OF K
    100 FK=A(1)
C   SETTING INDETERMINANT VALUES EQUAL TO ZERO
        W=0.
        WV=0.
C   EVALUATION OF A SIN I
        ASINI=ASI*FK/FMU
        T0=0.
        RT0=0.
C   EVALUATION OF THE ERRORS OF K AND A SIN I
        RK=SQRTF(RA2(1))
        RASI=ASI*RK/FMU
        IDEN=0
        RW=0.
        RWV=0.
        PUNCH98
     98 FORMAT(30X,17HCIRCULAR ELEMENTS)
        GOTO125
```

```
C
C        THE DIFFERENTIAL CORRECTION
C
   300 TYPE123
   123 FORMAT(10HDIFF CORRN)
       IDEN=1
       IF=0
COMPUTATION OF PRELIMINARY VALUES TO FIND THE RADIAL VELOCITY
   305 SINW=SINF(W)
       FMU2=FMU* FMU
       ESINW=E*SINW
       COSW=COSF(W)
       ECOSW=E*COSW
       VKECW=V0+FK*ECOSW
       E2M=1.-E*E
       RT=SQRTF(E2M)
       DE2M=RT*RT*RT
       EOR2=E/1.414
       FTAN=SQRTF((1.+E)/(1.-E))
       DO777J=1,8
       DO777K=1,8
   777 Z(J,K)=0.
       IF(IF)334,333,334
C   ROUTINE FOR IF=1
   334 PUNCH335
   335 FORMAT(14H0OBSERVATIONS/,4X,2HJD,8X,5HEPOCH,5X,5HPHASE,8X,1HV,11X.
      13HO-C,8X,2HWT)
C
C        NORMAL EQUATIONS FOR THE CORRECTIONS
C
   333 DO330I=1,N
       IF(SENSESWITCH2)783,782
   783 TYPE362,I
CALCULATION FOR PHASE(AS BEFORE)
   782 EPPH=(T0-FJD(I))/P
       IEP=EPPH+1.
       EP=IEP
       PHA=EP-EPPH
C   FOR MEAN ANOMALY
       FMA=PHA*PI2
C   FIRST GUESS AT ECCENTRIC ANOMALY
       EA=FMA*EOR2
C   DIFFERENTIAL CORRECTION FOR ECCENTRIC ANOMALY
   400 SINE=SINF(EA)
       FNUM=EA-E*SINE
       DENOM=1.-E*COSF(EA)
       DISC=FMA-FNUM
       IF(DISC*DISC-2.5E-13)401,401,402
   402 EA=EA+DISC/DENOM
       GOTO400
   401 EA=EA/2.
       COSE=COSF(EA)
       IF(COSE)102,103,102
   103 TA=PI
       GOTO 104
```

```
    102 SINE=SINF(EA)
C    EVALUATION OF TRUE ANOMALY
        TA=2.*ATANF(FTAN*SINE/COSE)
    104 COSV=COSF(TA)
        SINV=SINF(TA)
        COSVW=COSV*COSW-SINV*SINW
C    EVALUATION OF VELOCITY RESIDUAL
        OC=V(I)-VKECW-FK*COSVW
        IF(IF)604,603,604
C    PUNCH RESIDUAL AND OTHER VALUES FOR IF=1
    604 PUNCH331,ID1,ID2,FJD(I),IEP,PHA,V(I),OC,WT(I)
    331 FORMAT(1X,2A3,7X,F10.3,4X,I5,2X,F9.6,5X,F7.2,4X,F8.3,4X,F5.2)
C    ACCUMULATION OF SUM OF P(O-C)2
        SV2=SV2+WT(I)*OC*OC
        GOTO330
CONTINUE WITH CORRECTION FOR IF=0
    603 SINVW=SINV*COSW+COSV*SINW
        ECOSV=E*COSV
        FACT1=1.+ECOSV
        FACT2=SINVW/DE2M
COEFFICIENT FOR DK
        Q(2)=ECOSW+COSVW
C    FOR DE
        Q(3)=FK*(COSW-SINV*SINVW*(2.+ECOSV)/E2M))
C    FOR DW
        Q(4)=-FK*(ESINW+SINVW)
C    FOR DT
        Q(5)= FK*FMU*FACT1*FACT1*FACT2
        IF(SENSESWITCH1)321,322
    321 IX=6
C    FOR D MU IF SWITCH 1 IS ON
        Q(6)=Q(5)*(T0-FJD(I))/FMU
        Q(7)=OC
        GOTO323
    322 IX=5
        Q(6)=OC
    323 IX2=IX+2
        IX1=IX+1
C    SETTING UP NORMAL EQUATIONS
        DO101J=1,IX1
        DO101K=J,IX1
    101 Z(J,K+1)=WT(I)*Q(J)*Q(K)+Z(J,K+1)
    330 CONTINUE
        IF(IF)337,336,337
C    EVALUATION OF PROBABLE ERROR FOR IF=1
    337 FX=IX
        R1=.6745*SQRTF(SV2/(FFN-FX))
        PUNCH338,ID1,ID2,R1
    338 FORMAT(1H0,2A3,2X,3HR1=,F9.4)
        TYPE340
    340 FORMAT(18HEND OF COMPUTATION)
        GOTO64
C    FOR IF=0 CONTROL AGAIN TRANSFERS TO LEAST SQUARES SUBPROGRAM
```

```
C
C        SOLUTION FOR THE CORRECTIONS BY LEAST SQUARES
C
  336 CALLLSTSQ(IX,FFN)
CONTROL RETURNS HERE
CORRECTION OF ELEMENTS
        V0=V0+Z(IX1,1)
        FK=FK+Z(IX1,2)
        E=E+Z(IX1,3)
        W=W+Z(IX1,4)
        T0=T0+Z(IX1,5)
        IF(SENSESWITCH1)324,410
  324 FMU=FMU+Z(7,6)
        P=PI2/FMU
        TYPE327
  327 FORMAT(16HPERIOD CORRECTED)
  410 TYPE370
  370 FORMAT(18HELEMENTS CORRECTED)
        IF(SENSESWITCH2)785,784
  785 TYPE786,Z(IX1,2),Z(IX2,2)
  786 FORMAT(2(E14.8,2X))
  784 IF(SENSESWITCH3)306,787
CORRECTION STOPS IF SWITCH 3 IS ON
C   OTHERWISE CHECK FOR CONVERGENCE
  787 IF(Z(IX1,2)*Z(IX1,2)−Z(IX2,2)*Z(IX2,2)/9.)306,306,305
C
C          THE FINAL ELEMENTS
C
  306 IF=1
C   EVALUATION OF W IN DEGREES
        WV=RADEG*W
        RWV=RADEG*Z(IX2,4)
        E2=E*E
        IF(SENSESWITCH1)411,325
C   PROBABLE ERROR OF P (IF SWITCH 1 IS ON)
  411 RP=P/FMU*Z(8,6)
        PUNCH326,ID1,ID2,P,N,FJDL,RP
  326 FORMAT(1H0,2A3,5X,2HP=,E13.7,5X,2HN=,I3,8X,4HLJD=,F10.3,4X,3HER=,E
     19.2)
  325 PUNCH88
C   EVALUATION OF A SIN I AND ITS ERROR
        ASINI=ASI*RT*FK/FMU
        RASI=ASI*RT/FMU*SQRTF(Z(IX2,2)**2+EZ*(FK*Z(IX2,3)/E2M)**2)
        PUNCH43,ID1,ID2,IDEN,V0,Z(IX2,1),FK,Z(IX2,2),ASINI,RASI
        PUNCH44,ID1,ID2,IDEN,E,Z(IX2,3),W,Z(IX2,4),WV,RWV
        PUNCH 40,ID1,ID2,IDEN,T0,Z(IX2,5),P,FMU,Z(IX2,IX2)
        GOTO305
CONTROL RETURNS TO READ MORE DATA
   40 FORMAT(1H0,2A3,I2,2HT=,F10.3,2H R,F9.4,2X,2HP=,E14.7,2X,3HMU=,F10.
     17,2X,3HR1=,F9.4)
     2X,3HR1=,F9.4)
   43 FORMAT(1H0,2A3,I2,3HVO=,F8.3,2H R,F7.3,2X,2HK=,F8.3,2H R,F7.3,2X,6
     1HASINI=,E12.5,1HR,E9.2)
   44 FORMAT(1H0,2A3,I2,2HE=,F8.6,2H R,F8.6,2X,2HW=,F8.5,2H R,F8.5,6HRAD
     1 W=,F9.4,2H R,F9.4,3HDEG)
    3 FORMAT(22X,F9.3,7X,F7.2,9X,F5.3)
```

```
  984 FORMAT(F9.6)
    4 FORMAT(1X,2A3,7X,EI3.7,7X,I3,13X,F9.3)
      END


*  8 6
C                          LEAST SQUARES SUBROUTINE
C
      SUBROUTINELSTSQ(N,FNO)
      DIMENSIONZ(18,18)
      COMMONZ
CONTROL FROM MAIN PROGRAM TRANSFERRED TO HERE
      M=N+1
      M1=M+1
      FN=N
      DO14I=1,M
      L=I+1
COMPUTATION OF DIAGONAL MATRIX ELEMENTS
      DO11K=1,I
      IF(I−K)12,12,11
   11 Z(I,L)=Z(I,L)−Z(K,L)*Z(K,L)
   12 IF(M−I)65,65,66
   66 Z(I,L)=SQRTF(Z(I,L))
      L1=L+1
      DO10J=L1,M1
COMPUTATION OF ELEMENTS TO RIGHT OF DIAGONAL
      DO13K=1,I
      IF(I−K)10,10,13
   13 Z(I,J)=Z(I,J)−Z(K,L)*Z(K,J)
   10 Z(I,J)=Z(I,J)/Z(I,L)
      Z(I,I)=1./Z(I,L)
      DO15J=1,I
      IF(I−J)14,14,16
   16 PP=0.
      L1=I−1
COMPUTATION OF ELEMENTS TO LEFT OF DIAGONAL
      DO17K=J,L1
   17 PP=PP+Z(K,L)*Z(K,J)
   15 Z(I,J)=−Z(I,I)*PP
   14 CONTINUE
C    EVALUATION OF R1
   65 Z(M1,M1)=.6745*SQRTF(Z(M,M1)/(FNO−FN))
      DO18I=1,N
      Z(M,I)=0.
      PP=0.
      DO19J=I,N
C    EVALUATION OF UNKNOWNS
      Z(M,I)=Z(M,I)+Z(J,I)*Z(J,M1)
C    EVALUATION OF RECIPROCAL WEIGHTS
   19 PP=PP+Z(J,I)*Z(J,I)
C    EVALUATION OF PROBABLE ERRORS OF UNKNOWNS
   18 Z(M1,I)=Z(M1,M1)*SQRTF(PP)
C    RETURN CONTROL TO MAIN PROGRAM
      RETURN
      END
```

```
*  8 6
C    A PROGRAM TO COMPUTE AND PLOT A THEORETICAL AND OBSERVATIONAL RADIAL
                         VELOCITY CURVE
C
     DIMENSIONPH(350),V(350),NV(27),VL(350)
C    DEFINING SEVERAL CONSTANTS
     PI2=6.2831853
     PI=3.1415927
   3 IF(SENSESWITCH1)51,50
C    READING OF OBSERVATIONS FOR OBSERVATIONAL CURVE
  50 READ4,ID1,ID2,P,N,TO
     READ2,(PH(I),V(I),I=1,N)
  51 IF(SENSESWITCH2)53,52
C    READING A VALUE OF K WHEN ONLY AN OBSERVATIONAL CURVE IS DESIRED
  53 READ55,FK
  55 FORMAT(33X,F8.3)
     GOTO84
C    READING OF ELEMENTS FOR THEORETICAL CURVE
  52 READ1
   1 FORMAT(80X)
     READ339,ID1,ID2,V0,FK,E,W,TO
  84 IF(SENSESWITCH1)87,85
COMPUTATION OF PHASES (AS IN ELEMENTS PROGRAM)
  85 DO70I=1,N
     EPPH=(TO-PH(I))/P
     IEP=EPPH+1.
     EP=IEP
  70 PH(I)=EP-EPPH
C    SORTING OF OBSERVATIONS INTO ORDER OF ASCENDING PHASE
     DO600I=1,N
     DO600J=I,N
     IF(PH(I)-PH(J))600,600,601
 601 PP=PH(J)
     PH(J)=PH(I)
     PH(I)=PP
     PP=V(J)
     V(J)=V(I)
     V(I)=PP
 600 CONTINUE
C
C              CALCULATIONS FOR THEORETICAL CURVE
C
  87 IF(SENSESWITCH2)54,305
C    EVALUATION OF PRELIMINARY VALUES FOR FINDING THEORETICAL VELOCITY
 305 SINW=SINF(W)
     FMU=PI2/P
     FMU2=FMU*FMU
     ESINW=E*SINW
     COSW=COSF(W)
     ECOSW=E*COSW
     VKECW=V0+FK*ECOSW
     E2M=1.-E*E
     RT=SQRTF(E2M)
     DE2M=RT*RT*RT
```

```
      EOR2=E/1.414
      FTAN=SQRTF((1.+E)/(1.-E))
      VMP=70.*(V0/FK+ECOSW)-80.5
   54 FINCR=0.
      M2=1
C   BEGINNING OF LOOP TO PUNCH CURVE PLOTTING CARDS
      DO10KK=1,101
C   ZEROING PUNCH AREA TO GIVE BLANKS ON THE CARDS
      DO635L=1,27
  635 NV(L)=0
      IF(SENSESWITCH2)57,56
COMPUTATION OF THE ECCENTRIC ANOMALY BY DIFFERENTIAL CORRECTION
   56 FMA=FINCR*PI2
  602 EA=FMA*EOR2
  400 SINE=SINF(EA)
      FNUM=EA-E*SINE
      DENOM=1.-E*COSF(EA)
      DISC=FMA-FNUM
      IF(DISC*DISC-2.5E-13)401,401,402
  402 EA=EA+DISC/DENOM
      GOTO400
CALCULATION OF TRUE ANOMALY
  401 EA=EA/2.
      COSE=COSF(EA)
      IF(COSE)102,103,102
  103 TA=PI
      GOTO104
  102 SINE=SINF(EA)
      TA=2.*ATANF(FTAN*SINE/COSE)
CALCULATION OF THEORETICAL RADIAL VELOCITY
  104 COSV=COSF(TA)
      SINV=SINF(TA)
      COSVW=COSV*COSW-SINV*SINW
      VL(KK)=VKECW+FK*COSVW
   57 IF(SENSESWITCH1)619,700
C
C       SEARCHING AND PLOTTING OF OBSERVATIONAL VALUES
C
  700 DO608M=M2,N
C   SEARCHING FOR PHASES
      M2=M
      DPH=PH(M2)-FINCR
      IF(DPH*DPH-.25E-4)610,610,611
  611 IF(DPH)608,608,619
CONVERSION OF VELOCITY TO INTEGER FORM
  610 IV=70.*V(M2)/FK-VMP
C   AND SELECTION OF PROPER STORAGE LOCATION
      J1=IV/6
      K1=(IV-6*J1)/2
      J1=J1+1
      IF(K1-1)614,613,612
CHECK TO SEE WHICH NUMBER TO PLACE IN CHOSEN LOCATION
  614 MC=10000
```

```
C
CHECK ON HIGH 2 DIGITS
      IF(NV(J1)/10000-50)615,616,617
  613 MC=100
CHECK ON MIDDLE 2 DIGITS
      IF((NV(J1)-NV(J1)/10000*10000)/100-50)615,616,617
  612 MC=1
CHECK ON LOW 2 DIGITS
      IF(NV(J1)-NV(J1)/100*100-50)615,616,617
CHOOSE 50 TO PUNCH 0
  615 MD=50
      GOTO650
CHOOSE 22+50=72 TO PUNCH 2
  616 MD=22
      GOTO650
CHOOSE 1+7N TO PUNCH N+1
  617 MD=1
C   EXECUTION OF ABOVE CHOICE
  650 NV(J1)=NV(J1)+MC*MD
  608 CONTINUE
C
C                        PLOTTING OF THEORETICAL VALUES
C
  619 IF(SENSESWITCH2)623,58
C   EVALUATION OF VELOCITY IN INTEGER FORM
  58 IVLP=70.*COSVW+80.5
C   THIS PART IS THE SAME AS THE PLOTTING PART ABOVE EXCEPT
C   A CHECK IS MADE FOR NON-ZERO NUMBERS ONLY
      J=IVLP/6
      K=(IVLP-6*J)/2
      J=J+1
      IF(K-1)622,621,620
C   HIGH 2 DIGITS
  620 MC=1
      IF(NV(J)-NV(J)/100*100)623,624,623
C   MIDDLE 2 DIGITS
  621 MC=100
      IF((NV(J)-NV(J)/10000*10000)/100)623,624,623   ,
C   LOW 2 DIGITS
  622 MC=10000
      IF(NV(J)/10000)623,624,623
C   PLACEMENT OF 14 FOR ASTERISK
  624 NV(J)=NV(J)+14*MC
C   PUNCHING OF ASTERISK AND ZEROS
  623 PUNCH627,(NV(J),J=1,27)
  627 FORMAT(26A3,A2)
  10 FINCR=FINCR+.01
C   END OF CURVE PLOTTING LOOP
      TYPE704
  704 FORMAT(9HEND GRAPH)
      IF(SENSESWITCH2)3,11
  11 FINCR=0.
      PUNCH60
  60  FORMAT(27X,17HTHEORETICAL CURVE/1H0,10X,5HPHASE,7X,7HPH DAYS,10X,
      11HV)
```

```
C   LOOP TO PUNCH THEORETICAL VELOCITY VALUES
        DO705 I =1,101
C   PHASE IN DAYS
        PHD=FINCR*P
        PUNCH706,ID1,ID2,FINCR,PHD,VL(I)
   705 FINCR=FINCR+.01
        GOTO3
C   RETURN TO READ DATA
   706 FORMAT(1X,2A3,5X,F5.2,4X,F10.3,7X,F7.2)
     2 FORMAT(22X,F9.3,7X,F7.2)
   339 FORMAT(1X,2A3,5X,F8.3,13X,F8.3/11X,F8.6,14X,F8.5/11X,F10.3)
     4 FORMAT(1X,2A3,7X,E13.7,7X,I3,13X,F9.3)
        END
```

9 — A computation example

The orbits of several binaries were computed in order to test the effectiveness of the program and to check for programming mistakes; however, only one example is presented here, viz.: 26 Aquilae (Franklin, 1952). Since the eccentricity is high (0.83), the approximate elements were obtained with the harmonic series carried out to C_5 and S_5 (a series carried out to C_6 and S_6 also gave suitable elements). The final elements were determined by the method of differential correction based on these approximate elements.

An "R" is placed between a quantity and its probable error, and can be transliterated "$\pm$". "W" represents ω (given both in radians and degrees), "V0" the velocity of the center of mass, "N" the number of observations, "LJD" the harmonic analysis reference date, "ER" the probable error of the period, "R 1" the probable error of one observation (two values are given, the one which appears with the elements is based on the solution of the normal equations; the other which directly follows the table of observations is computed directly from the residuals, "O-C"). The other symbols have their usual meanings.

26 AQUILAE — FRANKLIN
APPROX ELEMENTS

```
V0= −17.626 R    .978 K=    19.151 R  1.436  ASINI= 5.30580E+07R 5.26E+06
E= .654716 R .153597  W= 2.40610 R   .33711RAD W= 137.8598 R   19.3155DEG
T= 33676.547 R 10.9818  P= 2.6654400E+02  MU=   .0235727  R1=    4.8931
         P= .2665441E+03    N= 51        LJD= 33474.890      ER= 1.53E−02
```

FINAL ELEMENTS

```
V0= −17.941 R    .095 K=    29.884 R   .198  ASINI= 6.11182E+07R 4.06E+05
E= .831208 R .000992  W= 2.66294 R   .00696RAD W= 152.5757 R   .3989DEG
T= 33686.746 R   .0486  P=2.6654411E+02  MU=  .0235727  R1=   .5169
```

OBS/ JD	EPOCH	PHASE	V	O-C	WT
22584.665	42	.348054	−17.10	−1.010	.50
22951.695	41	.725049	−11.10	−.278	.50
25435.861	31	.044955	−38.92	−.216	.50
22531.832	42	.149839	−25.40	−2.270	.50
30538.891	12	.190117	−20.70	.231	1.00
30555.820	12	.253630	−18.11	.407	1.00
30575.732	12	.328334	−15.72	.803	1.00
30597.810	12	.411164	−15.17	−.299	1.00

30648.639	12	.601861	−12.00	.133	1.00
30908.668	11	.577418	−10.03	2.400	1.00
31276.865	10	.958792	−15.73	−.056	1.00
31294.817	9	.026142	−47.09	1.632	.50
31341.671	9	.201925	−20.21	.196	.50
31355.658	9	.254400	−19.14	−.647	1.00
31614.966	8	.227252	−18.57	.839	1.00
31637.857	8	.313133	−14.98	1.900	.50
31658.886	8	.392028	−15.50	−.283	1.00
31677.815	8	.463044	−13.83	.184	1.00
31691.749	8	.515321	−13.00	.247	.50
32015.821	7	.731150	−10.74	.025	1.00
32036.833	7	.809981	−9.07	1.125	1.00
32065.778	7	.918575	−11.30	−.112	1.00
32404.770	5	.190379	−20.27	.649	1.00
32410.765	5	.212871	−20.42	−.463	1.00
32413.813	5	.224306	−19.04	.477	1.00
32432.705	5	.295184	−17.91	−.579	1.00
33167.743	2	.052843	−35.31	.762	1.00
33171.677	2	.067603	−32.63	−.213	1.00
33177.735	2	.090331	−29.58	−.953	1.00
33182.662	2	.108815	−26.56	−.105	1.00
33189.655	2	.135051	−24.36	−.201	1.00
33195.640	2	.157505	−22.63	.021	1.00
33215.619	2	.232461	−18.78	.443	1.00
33372.024	2	.819249	−10.87	−.713	.50
33384.015	2	.864236	−11.77	−1.622	1.00
33390.995	2	.890423	−11.37	−.970	1.00
33397.984	2	.916644	−10.72	.384	1.00
33414.008	2	.976762	−23.09	.572	1.00
33416.916	2	.987672	−36.65	.452	1.00
33418.974	2	.995393	−55.98	−.312	1.00
33420.976	1	.002904	−69.21	.415	1.00
33422.940	1	.010272	−65.10	.033	1.00
33423.968	1	.014129	−60.55	−.088	1.00
33424.940	1	.017776	−57.05	−.743	1.00
33426.974	1	.025407	−48.71	.575	1.00
33428.990	1	.032970	−43.79	.450	1.00
33430.952	1	.040331	−39.88	.691	1.00
33432.986	1	.047962	−37.22	.407	1.00
33438.873	1	.070048	−31.75	.172	1.00
33451.839	1	.118693	−26.42	−.916	1.00
33474.890	1	.205174	−21.18	−.910	1.00

R1 =   .5205

26 AQUILAE − FRANKLIN
THEORETICAL CURVE

	PHASE	PH DAYS	V
26 AQL	0.00	0.000	−50.00
26 AQL	.01	2.665	−66.23
26 AQL	.02	5.330	−53.68
26 AQL	.03	7.996	−45.50

26 AQL	.04	10.661	−40.04
26 AQL	.05	13.327	−36.17
26 AQL	.06	15.992	−33.28
26 AQL	.07	18.658	−31.03
26 AQL	.08	21.323	−29.21
26 AQL	.09	23.988	−27.70
26 AQL	.10	26.654	−26.42
26 AQL	.11	29.319	−25.32
26 AQL	.12	31.985	−24.36
26 AQL	.13	34.650	−23.51
26 AQL	.14	37.316	−22.75
26 AQL	.15	39.981	−22.07
26 AQL	.16	42.647	−21.44
26 AQL	.17	45.312	−20.88
26 AQL	.18	47.977	−20.35
26 AQL	.19	50.643	−19.87
26 AQL	.20	53.308	−19.42
26 AQL	.21	55.974	−19.00
26 AQL	.22	58.639	−18.61
26 AQL	.23	61.305	−18.24
26 AQL	.24	63.970	−17.89
26 AQL	.25	66.636	−17.56
26 AQL	.26	69.301	−17.25
26 AQL	.27	71.966	−16.96
26 AQL	.28	74.632	−16.67
26 AQL	.29	77.297	−16.40
26 AQL	.30	79.963	−16.15
26 AQL	.31	82.628	−15.90
26 AQL	.32	85.294	−15.66
26 AQL	.33	87.959	−15.43
26 AQL	.34	90.624	−15.21
26 AQL	.35	93.290	−15.00
26 AQL	.36	95.955	−14.80
26 AQL	.37	98.621	−14.60
26 AQL	.38	101.286	−14.41
26 AQL	.39	103.952	−14.22
26 AQL	.40	106.617	−14.04
26 AQL	.41	109.283	−13.87
26 AQL	.42	111.948	−13.70
26 AQL	.43	114.613	−13.53
26 AQL	.44	117.279	−13.37
26 AQL	.45	119.944	−13.21
26 AQL	.46	122.610	−13.06
26 AQL	.47	125.275	−12.91
26 AQL	.48	127.941	−12.77
26 AQL	.49	130.606	−12.62
26 AQL	.50	133.272	−12.48
26 AQL	.51	135.937	−12.35
26 AQL	.52	138.602	−12.21
26 AQL	.53	141.268	−12.08
26 AQL	.54	143.933	−11.95
26 AQL	.55	146.599	−11.83
26 AQL	.56	149.264	−11.71
26 AQL	.57	151.930	−11.59

26 AQL	.58	154.595	−11.47
26 AQL	.59	157.260	−11.35
26 AQL	.60	159.926	−11.24
26 AQL	.61	162.591	−11.13
26 AQL	.62	165.257	−11.02
26 AQL	.63	167.922	−10.91
26 AQL	.64	170.588	−10.81
26 AQL	.65	173.253	−10.71
26 AQL	.66	175.919	−10.61
26 AQL	.67	178.584	−10.51
26 AQL	.68	181.249	−10.42
26 AQL	.69	183.915	−10.33
26 AQL	.70	186.580	−10.24
26 AQL	.71	189.246	−10.15
26 AQL	.72	191.911	−10.07
26 AQL	.73	194.577	−9.99
26 AQL	.74	197.242	−9.91
26 AQL	.75	199.908	−9.84
26 AQL	.76	202.573	−9.78
26 AQL	.77	205.238	−9.72
26 AQL	.78	207.904	−9.66
26 AQL	.79	210.569	−9.62
26 AQL	.80	213.235	−9.58
26 AQL	.81	215.900	−9.55
26 AQL	.82	218.566	−9.53
26 AQL	.83	221.231	−9.52
26 AQL	.84	223.896	−9.53
26 AQL	.85	226.562	−9.57
26 AQL	.86	229.227	−9.62
26 AQL	.87	231.893	−9.71
26 AQL	.88	234.558	−9.84
26 AQL	.89	237.224	−10.01
26 AQL	.90	239.889	−10.26
26 AQL	.91	242.555	−10.60
26 AQL	.92	245.220	−11.08
26 AQL	.93	247.885	−11.74
26 AQL	.94	250.551	−12.70
26 AQL	.95	253.216	−14.14
26 AQL	.96	255.882	−16.41
26 AQL	.97	258.547	−20.28
26 AQL	.98	261.213	−27.66
26 AQL	.99	263.878	−43.31
26 AQL	1.00	266.544	−66.76

REFERENCES

AITKEN, R., 1964, *The Binary stars*, (Dover reprint, New York), Chapt. VI.

BINNENDIJK, L., 1960, *Properties of Double Stars*, (Press, Philadelphia. Univ. of Pennsylvania), p. 164.

BROUWER, D. and CLEMENCE, M.G., 1961, *Methods of Celestial Mechanics* (Academic Press, New York), pp. 79, 80.

FRANKLIN, K., 1952, *Ap. J.*, **116**, 383.

MCCRACKEN, D., 1961, *A Guide to FORTRAN Programming* (Wiley, New York).

RUSSELL, H. N., 1902, *Ap. J.*, **15**, 252.

SCHLESINGER, F., 1908, *Publ. Allegheny Obs.*, **1**, 35.

STERNE, T., 1941, *Proc. Nat. Acad. Sc.*, **27**, 175.

STORER, N., 1960, *Least Squares for Physical Scientists* (private distribution).

WILSING, J., 1893, *A. N.*, **134**, 89.

Initiation à la théorie générale du transfert des particules

V. KOURGANOFF

Faculté des Sciences d'Orsay de l'Université de Paris.

Préface

La profonde originalité d'Otto STRUVE ne se manifeste pas seulement dans ses travaux de recherche et dans ses découvertes. Dans ses manuels, ses monographies, ses conférences, ses articles du *Sky and Telescope*, il a su porter à la perfection un « style d'exposition » très original, tendant à dépouiller les problèmes des complications purement mathématiques, et à faire ressortir, par d'*audacieuses approximations physiques*, l'essence des phénomènes.

La leçon introductive du cours* que je professe à la Faculté des Sciences d'Orsay de l'Université de Paris, sur *La théorie générale du transfert des particules*, s'inspire tout particulièrement du « style de STRUVE ».

Aussi, suis-je heureux d'offrir ce modeste hommage à la mémoire de celui qui exerça une influence profonde et décisive sur mon enseignement et sur l'ensemble de mon attitude envers la science.

Introduction

L'étude d'un champ de neutrons dans un réacteur nucléaire et l'étude d'un champ de photons dans une étoile, conduisent aux raisonnements physiques (et aux équations mathématiques) de même type.

La diversité des notations et des terminologies employées en « neutronique » et en astrophysique cache souvent ce parallélisme fondamental.

Aussi, y a-t-il intérêt à étudier la *diffusion des neutrons* et le *transfert du rayonnement* (photons) sous la forme d'une THÉORIE GÉNÉRALE DU TRANSFERT DE PARTICULES ayant pour objet l'étude des effets macroscopiques d'interaction entre particules mobiles (neutrons, photons) et particules d'un milieu fixe (noyaux, atomes, ions...).

Nous présenterons ici une introduction à une telle théorie générale, au moyen d'un modèle simple, en insistant sur la *signification physique* des principales équations par lesquelles s'exprime ce «transfert».**

---

* Ce cours est sous presse aux éditions Gordon and Breach, New York (dépositaire en France : Editions Dunod), sous le titre «Introduction à la théorie générale du transfert des particules». La version en anglais sera publiée par Gordon and Breach en 1967.

** Les méthodes *mathématiques* de résolution de ces équations ont déjà été exposées dans notre ouvrage «Basic Methods in Transfer Problems» publié en 1964 aux éditions Dover, U.S.A., en 2e édition.

Présentation de la nature physique du problème sur un « modèle » simple

a) Définition du « modèle »

Considérons une plaque homogène horizontale constituée de noyaux très massifs, non susceptibles ni de fissions ni de « captures stériles » de neutrons. Envoyons sur cette plaque un faisceau vertical de neutrons de même énergie. Certains neutrons passeront sans interaction avec le milieu, tandis que d'autres entreront en interaction; mais, en absence de fissions et de captures stériles, celle-ci se réduira aux « diffusions » (déviations) par chocs, avec conservation du nombre de neutrons (autant de neutrons avant et après le choc).

Une situation analogue existerait pour une « nappe de brouillard » éclairée par un phare puissant; ou pour un «modèle simple» d'atmosphère stellaire.

Des noyaux très massifs seront peu accélérés par les chocs et l'énergie de chaque neutron sera très sensiblement la même avant et après le choc. (Les astrophysiciens reconnaîtront ici la « diffusion de résonance »!)

Physiquement, on peut concevoir les chocs entre un « champ » de neutrons (mobiles) et les noyaux d'un milieu (fixe) comme une succession de deux *phases* distinctes, séparées par un intervalle de temps très court :

1° *Le prélèvement*, par le milieu, d'un des neutrons du faisceau incident. Ce prélèvement représente, pour le champ des neutrons une *perte provisoire*.

2° *La restitution*, par le milieu, du neutron prélevé, au champ de neutrons. Nous dirons que cette restitution constitue une *ré-émission* (dans une certaine direction); le préfixe « *ré* » rappelant le caractère *secondaire* de cette émission, consécutive à un prélèvement.

Pour les noyaux très massifs la *ré-émission* est *isotrope* : les neutrons prélevés sur un faisceau d'une certaine direction sont ré-émis en proportion égale dans *toutes* les directions de l'espace.

Or, vis-à-vis de la propagation verticale des neutrons, on peut partager l'ensemble des directions de ré-émission en « directions montantes » et « directions descendantes », et envisager des *moyennes* sur chacun de ces deux groupes. Dans le cas isotrope, envisagé ici, ces deux moyennes seront égales, (fig. 1).

On ne sera donc pas très éloigné de la situation physique réelle, en supposant, en première approximation, que déjà la diffusion «*individuelle*» par chaque noyau se réduit à *deux ré-émissions uniquement verticales* (en proportion égales vers le haut et vers le bas).

Un tel schéma physique (« modèle ») est très instructif : il est suffisamment réaliste pour mettre en évidence le phénomène essentiel de *la variation de la densité du faisceau de neutrons avec l'altitude malgré l'isotropie des ré-émissions*, sans compliquer l'analyse par des détails d'une importance secondaire (effet des neutrons « latéraux »)!

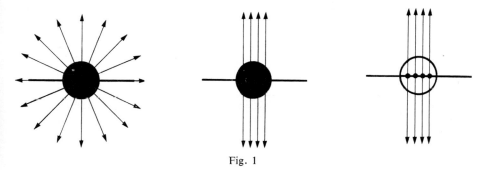

Fig. 1

b) *Notations*

Considérons maintenant la figure 2, qui définit les notations du point de vue du *niveau* auquel se rapportent les différents «courants de neutrons» montants (M) ou descendants (D), en nombre de neutrons, d'une certaine énergie, par cm² et par seconde. S désigne la « surface supérieure »; F désigne le « fond » de la plaque (surface inférieure).

Introduisons, pour plus de clarté physique, deux axes, Ox et $O'x'$, dirigés respectivement vers le bas et vers le haut, et envisageons une tranche horizontale mince (i, s) de la plaque (i = face « inférieure »; s = face « supérieure » de la tranche). Convenons de désigner par x la coordonnée de (s) sur l'axe Ox; et par x' la coordonnée de (i) sur l'axe $O'x'$. Ainsi un même niveau physique, tel que (i), sera décrit soit par x' soit par $(x + \Delta x)$. Mais contrairement à ce que mettrait un lecteur étourdi, les valeurs numériques (« mathématiques »!) de (x') et de $(x + \Delta x)$ seront différentes. Sur la figure 2, par exemple, le niveau (i) est décrit soit par $x' = 13$ soit par $(x + \Delta x) = 8$.

Dans le même ordre d'idées nous poserons :

$M = M_x$ pour le courant de rayonnement montant au niveau x;
$M(x)$ pour l'expression mathématique de M en fonction de x;
$D = D_x$ pour le courant du rayonnement descendant au niveau x;
$D(x)$ pour l'expression mathématique de D en fonction de x.

Ces conventions nous permettront d'introduire la quantité M′ définie comme le courant du rayonnement montant au niveau x' (niveau i) et la quantité D′ définie comme le courant du rayonnement descendant au niveau x' (niveau i).

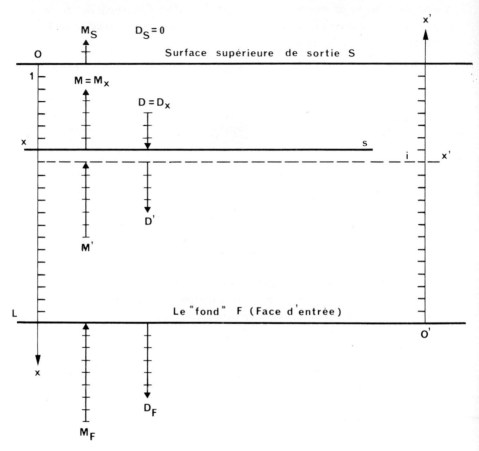

Fig. 2

On aura donc :

$$M' = M_{(x+\varDelta x)}; \; D' = D_{(x+\varDelta x)}$$

et par conséquent aussi :

$$M' = M(x + \varDelta x); \; D' = D(x + \varDelta x).$$

On notera cependant que

$$M' \neq M(x') \text{ puisque } x' \neq (x + \varDelta x).$$

On suppose, comme « conditions aux limites », que

(C$_F$) $M(L) = M_F \neq 0$ (Rayonnement « incident » sur le fond F non nul).

(C$_S$) $D(0) = D_S = 0$ (Rayonnement « incident » sur la face S, nul).

Un premier problème physique intéressant est le suivant : *l'existence de* $D_x \neq 0$, postulée sur la figure 2, *est-elle compatible avec la condition* $\overline{D}_S = 0$?

c) Première étude (globale) du problème

Considérons une portion de la tranche (i, s) de un cm^2 de section et évaluons le *bilan* en nombre de particules (neutrons) « entrant » dans (i, s) et « sortant » de (i, s) par seconde :

$$\text{« entrant »} = M' + D; \quad \text{« sortant »} = M + D'.$$

L'hypothèse de l'absence de fissions et de captures s'exprime par la relation :

(1) $\boxed{M + D' = M' + D}$; ou $\boxed{M - D = M' - D'}$.

Nous découvrons l'intérêt de la grandeur physique $J = J_x$ définie, au niveau x, par

(2) $$J = M - D; \quad J_x = M_x - D_x.$$

En effet, si l'on pose

(3) $$J_x = J(x)$$

on aura

(3*bis*) $$J_{x+\Delta x} = M' - D';$$

et la relation prendra la forme :

(4) $$J(x) = J(x + \Delta x) = C^{te},$$

valable même quand (Δx) n'est pas infiniment petit.

La quantité J définie par (2) s'appelle «courant net» en «neutronique»; J/π s'appelle le «flux net» en astrophysique.

La relation (4) nous apprend que J_x *est indépendant de* x. (N.B. — Attention! Cette propriété est liée à l'hypothèse de l'absence de fissions et de captures stériles; elles n'est pas générale!)

En particulier, l'indépendance de J_x par rapport au niveau x, permet d'écrire :

(4*bis*) $J_S = J_F = J_0$ où $J_0 = C^{te}$.

Mais d'après la définition de J, la relation (4*bis*) s'écrit aussi :

(5) $(M_S - D_S) = (M_F - D_F) = J_0$;

et comme D_S est nul (condition à la frontière S), il résulte de (5) que

(6) $D_F = M_F - J_0 = M_F - M_S$ ou $\boxed{M_S = M_F - D_F}$,

et

(7) $J_0 = M_S = M(0) =$ Débit du rayonnement qui émerge par la face S.

En appliquant une fois de plus la définition de J nous aurons :

(8) $M - D = J_0 = M_S$

ou, plus explicitement :

(8*bis*) $M(x) - D(x) = J_0 = M(0)$.

Conclusion

L'étude « globale » à laquelle nous venons de nous livrer montre, par la relation (6), que le rayonnement qui émerge par la face S, donné par M_S, sera d'autant plus « affaibli » par la traversée de (FS), par rapport au rayonnement incident, donné par M_F, que le rayonnement « diffusé vers l'arrière », par la face F, donné par D_F, sera plus important. Mais elle ne nous apprend rien sur la valeur de D_F. Elle ne nous apprend même pas si D_F est différent de zéro. Pour trouver la valeur de D_F nous devons approfondir notre analyse. C'est ce que nous allons faire au paragraphe suivant.

d) Étude détaillée, faisant intervenir les propriétés diffusantes du milieu vis-à-vis des particules mobiles considérées

1° Le «*coefficient de prélèvement*» et la «*section efficace macroscopique*». Pour prouver que pour un milieu réellement «diffusant» $D_F \neq 0$, et plus généralement que $D_x \neq 0$ (sauf pour $x = 0$), il convient de se rappeler que, comme nous l'avons signalé ci-dessus, sur l'ensemble des particules traversant la tranche (*is*), *une partie seulement subit des chocs* (et pénètre dans des noyaux du milieu avant d'être ré-émise), le reste étant «transmis» sans interaction.

On peut dire, aussi, que la partie non transmise est « *prélevée* » par le milieu (en vue de la ré-émission). Seule cette partie prélevée participe à la diffusion.

Désignons par $(\delta M'/M')$, (et non dM'/M', qui aura une autre signification), la fraction qui représente la «perte relative par prélèvement» subie par M' lors de la traversée de (*is*), d'épaisseur infinitésimale (*dx*), par le faisceau montant. (Ici, et dans tout ce qui suit, *dx* sera *une quantité essentiellement positive*).

Il est évident que pour un milieu *homogène* cette perte par prélèvement est la même pour deux couches (*is*) successives de même épaisseur (*dx*). Cela signifie que le prélèvement est double pour une épaisseur (2 *dx*) et que, plus généralement, $(\delta M'/M')$ est *une fraction proportionnelle à* (*dx*).

Cela reste vrai pour un milieu continu *non homogène*, stratifié en couches planes perpendiculaircs à O*x*, à condition de se restreindre aux épaisseurs (*dx*) *infiniment petites*.

En neutronique on désigne le rapport $(\delta M'/M')/(dx)$ par le symbole Σ ce qui donne la formule (définition de Σ) :

$$(9) \qquad \qquad \delta M' = (dx)\, M'\Sigma.$$

Σ caractérise le « pouvoir de prélèvement » du milieu d'une certaine *nature* et *état physique* vis-à-vis des particules mobiles d'une certaine *nature et énergie*.

En neutronique Σ est appelé « *section efficace macrocopique* (totale) du milieu vis-à-vis des neutrons considérés». Nous préférons l'appeler «*coefficient de prélèvement*». C'est une propriété du milieu vis-à-vis des neutrons d'une certaine «espèce» (énergétique) et non une propriété intrinsèque du milieu ou des noyaux qui le composent. En astrophysique Σ est désigné par κ et on l'appelle «coefficient général d'absorption du milieu vis-à-vis des photons d'une certaine fréquence».*

Dans un milieu *non homogène*, Σ serait une fonction des coordonnées du point considéré. Si le milieu était stratifié en couches planes perpendiculaires à O*x*, Σ ne dépendrait que de *x*, et l'on aurait à tenir compte de la fonction donnée $\Sigma(x)$. Dans notre problème $\Sigma(x) = C^{te}$.

Naturellement, si le « pouvoir de prélèvement » du milieu ne dépend pas du *sens* des particules mobiles (ce que nous supposerons ici) nous aurons

---

* Ce qui est fort ambigu car le mot «absorption» suggère à la fois un prélèvement et une «capture» (cette dernière non suivie de ré-émission).

pour le prélèvement δD opéré par le milieu sur D, dans la traversée de (dx) :

(10) $$\delta D = (dx)\,D\,\Sigma$$

avec la même valeur de Σ que dans (9).

2° *Établissement de « l'équation de transfert».* — On se rappelle que d'après l'étude globale, l'hypothèse de l'absence de fission et de l'absence de « captures stériles » se traduit par la relation (1) :

$$M' + D = D' + M.$$

Mais, au lieu de faire apparaître $J = M - D = M' - D'$, comme au paragraphe (c) nous allons transcrire cette relation sous la forme :

(11) $$M' - M = D' - D.$$

On voit ainsi que le calcul de la différence $(M' - M)$ se ramène au calcul de la différence $(D' - D)$. Or, l'analyse de cette dernière est plus commode que celle de la différence $(M' - M)$ parce que

(12) $$D' - D = D_{x'} - D_x = D(x + dx) - D(x) = \Delta D$$

représente à la fois (en grandeur et en signe) « l'accroissement de la fonction D au voisinage de x, pour un accroissement dx de la variable » et la « variation physique de la grandeur D au cours de la traversée de la tranche d'épaisseur dx par le faisceau descendant ». (On pourrait dire encore qu'il est plus facile de raisonner sur la fonction $D(x)$ que sur la fonction $M(x)$, parce que nous utilisons une variable x qui croît vers le bas, ce qui correspond *au sens de propagation* du faisceau décrit par D).

Essayons de voir de quoi se compose *physiquement* la différence (ΔD) définie par (12).

D'après la définition de Σ, les prélèvements $\delta M'$ et δD opérés respectivement sur M' et D par la tranche (is) s'élèvent à $(dx)\,M'\Sigma$ et $(dx)\,D\Sigma$, ce qui donne un prélèvement total p égal à :

(13) $$p = \delta M' + \delta D = (dx)\,M'\Sigma + (dx)\,D\Sigma = (dx)\,(M' + D)\Sigma.$$

Or, n'oublions pas que dans notre problème *tous* les prélèvements (et par conséquent aussi le prélèvement total) sont intégralement restitués (ré-émis) mais de manière isotrope : moitié vers le haut, moitié vers le bas.

Cela signifie que la restitution vers le bas, comme celle vers le haut, s'élève à $p/2$.

Ainsi, au cours de la traversée de (*is*) le faisceau descendant *s'appauvrit* du prélèvement (δD) et *s'enrichit* de l'ensemble ($p/2$) des ré-émissions vers le bas [en provenance de (δM$'$) et de (δD)].

Autrement dit, le raisonnement physique montre que :

$$D' = D - \delta D + p/2 = D - (dx)\,D\Sigma + \tfrac{1}{2}(dx)\,(M' + D)\Sigma$$

et cela se traduit mathématiquement, en vertu de (12), par

(14) $$(\varDelta D) = -(dx)D\Sigma + \tfrac{1}{2}(dx)\,(M' + D)\,\Sigma,$$

et par

(15) $$\frac{(dD)}{(dx)} = -D\Sigma + \tfrac{1}{2}(M' + D)\,\Sigma\,.$$

Ici (dD) et (dx) sont mis entre parenthèses pour ne pas confondre le quotient (dD)/(dx) des accroissements de D et de x, avec la dérivée (dD/dx). Pour que ce quotient prenne une signification de dérivée, il faut naturellement faire tendre (dx) vers zéro. Mais alors M$'$ tend vers M et l'équation (15) se transforme en équation :

(16) $$\boxed{\frac{dD}{dx} = (-D\Sigma) + \tfrac{1}{2}(M + D)\,\Sigma\,.}$$

On dit que cette équation représente « *l'équation de transfert* » pour le rayonnement descendant D, dans le cas du modèle considéré.

On constate que cette équation est *une* équation différentielle linéaire du premier ordre, faisant intervenir *deux* fonctions inconnues D(x) et M(x).

Nous aurions pu, naturellement, compléter cette équation par une équation analogue exprimant (dM/dx) en fonction de M et D (voir la Remarque ci-dessous). Mais il est plus simple d'utiliser « l'intégrale première » fournie par la constance de J(x).

En effet, la relation (8*bis*) :

$$M - D = J_0 = C^{te}$$

nous permet d'éliminer M, ce qui donne :

$$\frac{dD}{dx} = -D\Sigma + \tfrac{1}{2}(D + J_0 + D)\Sigma$$

c'est-à-dire

(17) $$\frac{dD}{dx} = \tfrac{1}{2}\,J_0\,\Sigma\,.$$

Certes, nous ne connaissons pas encore la valeur de la constante J_0 en fonction de la donnée M_F, mais la constance de J_0 nous permet d'intégrer quand même l'équation (17) en remettant à plus tard la détermination de J_0 :

$$(18) \qquad D(x) = \tfrac{1}{2} J_0 x \Sigma + D(0);$$

ce qui, compte tenu de la condition à la frontière S : $D_S = D(0) = 0$ donne :

$$(19) \qquad D(x) = \tfrac{1}{2} J_0 x \Sigma.$$

Remarque : En dérivant $(M - D) = J_0 = C^{te}$ par rapport à x, il vient : $dM/dx = dD/dx$. Il en résulte que (17) peut se mettre sous la forme :

$$(17bis) \qquad \frac{dM}{dx} = \tfrac{1}{2} J_0 \Sigma = \tfrac{1}{2} (M-D) \Sigma,$$

ce qui, à son tour, peut se mettre sous la forme :

$$(16bis) \qquad -\frac{dM}{dx} = -M\Sigma + \tfrac{1}{2} (M+D) \Sigma$$

qui représente l'équation de transfert pour le rayonnement montant. Nous aurions pu l'établir directement par le raisonnement physique, mais en rencontrant quelques complications de signe, évitées par l'usage de $D(x)$ comme intermédiaire de calcul.

3° *Allusion aux généralisations possibles.* — Quand on considère des problèmes plus généraux que le problème que nous venons de traiter, on rencontre, au lieu des fonctions $M(x)$ et $D(x)$, des grandeurs $I(P, \omega)$ qui décrivent «l'intensité» du rayonnement au point P suivant une direction $\vec{\omega}$ *quelconque* par rapport aux axes de coordonnées (x, y, z).

Les dérivées (dD/dx) et (dM/dx) sont alors remplacées par des « dérivées de la fonction scalaire $I(P, \vec{\omega})$ suivant une certaine direction » ce qui introduit la fonction vectorielle *grad* I et par conséquent les dérivées partielles de I par rapport à x, y et z (ω restant invariable).

Quant aux quantités telles que $(-D\Sigma)$ ou $(-M\Sigma)$ elles sont remplacées naturellement par $(-I\Sigma)$; tandis que les sommes $(M+D)$, introduites par le calcul du prélèvement total p, sont remplacées, dans le cas d'une ré-émission isotrope, par des intégrales de la forme :

$$\int_{\Omega} I(P, \vec{\omega}) \, d\omega$$

relatives aux différents faisceaux obliques d'angle solide ($d\omega$) autour de la direction $\overleftarrow{\omega}$.

Une ré-émission *non isotrope* introduirait des intégrales de la forme :

$$\int_\Omega I(P, \vec{\omega}) f(\vec{\omega}, \vec{\omega}') \, d\omega,$$

où les fonctions $f(\vec{\omega}, \vec{\omega}')$, dites « fonctions de phase », décrivent l'anisotropie de la ré-émission.

Les équations de transfert ainsi obtenues sont du type « intégrodifférentiel », comportant des dérivées partielles de $I(P, \vec{\omega})$ par rapport aux variables de position, telles que (x, y, z), et des intégrales, telles que celles écrites ci-dessus, de $I(P, \vec{\omega})$ par rapport aux variables de direction $(\vec{\omega}, d\omega)$.

Le « problème de transfert » consiste à résoudre de telles équations en tenant compte des « conditions aux limites » et de certaines conditions de liaison (telles que $J = J_0 = C^{te}$ dans le problème que nous venons d'étudier).

4° *La solution définitive.* Revenons, après cette brève digression, à notre solution (19), que nous rappelons ci-dessous :

$$(20) \qquad\qquad D(x) = \tfrac{1}{2} J_0 \, x \, \Sigma.$$

Elle n'est pas encore entièrement satisfaisante, car elle donne $D(x)$ en fonction de J_0 et non de la véritable donnée du problème fournie par la condition à la frontière F, c'est-à-dire par la valeur non nulle de M_F .

Physiquement, notre donnée est :

$$(21) \qquad\qquad M(L) = M_F$$

avec

$$(22) \qquad\qquad x_F = L,$$

et nous devons exprimer toutes les grandeurs intéressantes : $D(x)$; $M(x)$; D_F; M_S; J_0; ... en fonction des paramètres géométriques (x, L), de la caractéristique physique Σ générale de notre système, et de M_F qui précise les conditions particulières de l'expérience considérée.

Or, J_0 s'exprime, en partie, en fonction de M_F par (5), c'est-à-dire par

$$(23) \qquad\qquad J_0 = M_F - D_F$$

(qui n'est autre chose que la définition de J appliquée au niveau F).

Nous nous rapprocherons donc de la solution en écrivant (20) sous la forme :

$$(24) \qquad\qquad D(x) = \tfrac{1}{2} (M_F - D_F) \, x \, \Sigma.$$

On voit maintenant que pour exprimer D_F en fonction de M_F, il suffit d'appliquer (24) au niveau F où $x = L$, ce qui donne :

$$(25) \qquad\qquad D(L) = D_F = \tfrac{1}{2} (M_F - D_F) L \, \Sigma,$$

d'où l'on tire immédiatement l'expression de D_F en fonction de M_F :

$$(26) \qquad\qquad D_F = \frac{\tfrac{1}{2} M_F L \, \Sigma}{1 + \tfrac{1}{2} L \, \Sigma}$$

Nous découvrons ainsi que la rapport D_F/M_F ne dépend pas séparément de L et de Σ, mais seulement de leur produit $(L\Sigma)$.

Aussi posera-t-on de manière générale :

$$(27) \qquad\qquad \tau = x\Sigma \qquad \text{dans le } cas\ homogène,$$

et

$$(27bis) \qquad d\tau = dx \,.\, \Sigma(x) \qquad \text{dans le } cas\ «\ stratifié\ »,$$

la grandeur $(d\tau)$ représentant une sorte « *d'épaisseur physique* » associée à « l'épaisseur géométrique » (dx). En astrophysique $(d\tau)$ s'appelle : « épaisseur optique »; et τ représente la « profondeur optique » comptée vers le bas à partir de la surface supérieure S.

Et, en désignant par

$$(28) \qquad\qquad \tau_{tot} = L \, \Sigma = \int_0^L \Sigma(x) \, dx$$

l'épaisseur physique totale de la plaque, il vient :

$$(29) \qquad\qquad D_F = \frac{M_F \, (\tau_{tot}/2)}{1 + (\tau_{tot}/2)} \,.$$

Mais nous savons déjà que la conservation globale du rayonnement s'exprime par $M_S = M_F - D_F$ de sorte que :

$$(30) \qquad\qquad M_S = M_F \left(1 - \frac{D_F}{M_F}\right) = \frac{M_F}{1 + \dfrac{\tau_{tot}}{2}} \,.$$

Comme, d'autre part, l'application de la définition de J au niveau S, donne $J = M_S - D_S = M_S - 0 = M_S$ on voit que J_0 est également donné par la formule (30) :

$$(30bis) \qquad\qquad J_0 = M_S = \frac{M_F}{1 + \dfrac{\tau_{tot}}{2}} \,.$$

On vérifie que J_0 est bien indépendant de τ, comme il était indépendant de x.

Cherchons maintenant les fonctions $D(\tau)$ et $M(\tau)$ donnant les variations de $D = D_x = D_\tau$ et de $M = M_x = M_\tau$ avec la profondeur physique τ.

En divisant l'expression (24) de $D(x)$ par l'expression (25) de $D(L)$ le facteur $(M_F - D_F)$ s'élimine et l'on trouve :

$$\frac{D(x)}{D(L)} = \frac{D}{D_F} = \frac{D_\tau}{D_F} = \frac{x}{L} = \frac{\tau}{\tau_{tot}}$$

d'où l'on tire, compte tenu de l'expression (29) de D_F :

$$(31) \qquad D = D_\tau = \frac{(\tau/2)\,M_F}{1+(\tau_{tot}/2)}.$$

Enfin, compte tenu de la définition de J, nous avons :

$$M = M_\tau = D_\tau + J_0$$

de sorte que, en ajoutant les expressions de J_0 et de D données par les formules (30*bis*) et (31), on obtient immédiatement :

$$(32) \qquad M = M_\tau = \frac{\left[1+\dfrac{\tau}{2}\right]M_F}{1+\dfrac{\tau_{tot}}{2}}$$

5° *Discussion.* Notre problème ne présente d'intérêt physique que si la plaque possède une certaine épaisseur géométrique L, non nulle, et s'il y a une certaine intéraction entre le milieu et les particules mobiles, c'est-à-dire si Σ est non nul (plaque non « transparente »).

Dans ces conditions l'épaisseur physique totale de la plaque, τ_{tot}, présentera une certaine valeur *non nulle* et *positive*.

La formule (31), qui donne $D = D_\tau$, montre alors que « le courant descendant » de particules mobiles (neutrons ou photons), nul par hypothèse au niveau S $(\tau = 0)$, *croît proportionnellement à la profondeur physique* τ et atteint sa valeur maximale D_F au niveau F $(\tau_F = \tau_{tot})$. Cette valeur maximale est donnée par la formule (29).

Comme D_F est ainsi toujours différent de zéro (et positif), on peut considérer que le faisceau incident M_F subit une sorte de reflexion partielle, ou *réflexion diffuse*, sur la face d'entrée F de la plaque.

Comme, d'autre part, le transfert considéré est «conservatif», le rayonnement qui émerge par la face supérieure de la plaque, M_S, représente le rayonnement incident diminué du rayonnement D_F renvoyé vers le bas par diffusion : $M_S = M_F - D_F$. Ainsi M_S est toujours inférieur à M_F dans un rapport donné par la formule (30). Il y a donc *extinction partielle* du faisceau incident par le milieu diffusant.

[N. B. — En astrophysique on a pris l'habitude regrettable de désigner cette *extinction partielle* par le mot « absorption » (tout court), par opposition au mot « absorption vraie » désignant les « captures stériles » de photons, non ré-émis, mais convertis en chaleur par des chocs dits de « deuxième espèce ». Dans cette terminologie on dira que notre plaque produit sur le rayonnement une « absorption par diffusion ». Il est vrai, d'ailleurs, que pour un observateur situé au-dessus de S, tout se passe comme si une partie des photons incidents était réellement « absorbée » (au sens vulgaire du mot) par le milieu].

Remarquons enfin que la fonction mathématique qui, d'après la formule (32), décrit la variation du rayonnement montant $M = M_\tau$ avec τ, est *une fonction croissante* de τ, mais comme au cours de la propagation du rayonnement montant, de F à S, la profondeur physique τ *diminue*, à la croissance mathématique de $M(\tau)$ correspond une *décroissance linéaire* du rayonnement montant M, avec la distance physique $(\tau_{tot} - \tau)$ à *la face d'entrée* F. De son côté, la valeur de l'intensité du rayonnement descendant qu'un observateur se propageant avec M rencontre en allant de F vers S, *diminue* aussi suivant une loi linéaire en $(\tau_{tot} - \tau)$.

C'est ce qui explique la constance de la différence entre M et D, c'est-à-dire la constance du « courant net » $J = J_0$ donné par la formule (30*bis*).

On cosmic ray astrophysics

V. L. GINZBURG

P. N. Lebedev Physical Institute, Academy of Sciences of the USSR, Moscow

The emergence of essentially new methods of investigation, or in other words, the branching-out of new fields, has been perhaps the major characteristic of the development of astronomy in these two decades. We are referring, of course, to radio and radar astronomy, gamma- and X-ray astronomy, primary cosmic ray research, etc.

The results obtained with the new means (in combination with the classic optical method, of course) are many and varied. One of the most important of these results is the elucidation of the outstanding role of cosmic rays in the universe. Not so long ago stars, interstellar gas and the solid phase (planets, dust, etc.) would be indicated as the only constituents of the Galaxy and Metagalaxy. Today cosmic rays must certainly be listed among the basic astronomical components.

The entire set of problems involved in cosmic ray research can be called cosmic ray astrophysics (though traditionally, the field is usually confined to the origin of cosmic rays). The present paper is a short survey of the contemporary status of this field. A more elaborate treatment of these problems will be found in refs. by GINZBURG and SYROVATSKIJ [1964a, 1964b], (apart from these sources containing quite extensive bibliographies, we refer to comparatively few papers, including those by the present author and his collaborators, which by no means implies that the papers referred to are more important than many other papers concerned with the same subjects).

1 — Primary Cosmic Rays in the Vicinity of the Earth

Cosmic rays were discovered some fifty years ago as a result of establishing the fact that there exists an ionizing radiation whose intensity increases with the distance from the Earth's surface. Since it is not the primary cosmic rays reaching the Earth but their secondary products that are mainly observed in the atmosphere, the nature of the primary cosmic rays was an open problem for several decades. At first they were considered to be hard

γ-rays, then electrons and only in the '40s the primary cosmic rays were found to consist mainly of protons; the nuclei of various elements were detected in cosmic rays in 1948. Electrons were first traced in the primary cosmic rays (EARL, 1961, MEYER and VOGT, 1961) and positrons (DE SHONG, HILDEBRAND and MEYER, 1964).[1] As for the cosmic γ-rays, it is only (if the Sun is excluded) their upper flux cutoff that has so far been indicated (KRAUSHAAR and CLARK, 1962 and 1963).

Thus the investigation of the primary cosmic rays which started under way with the advent of high-altitude balloons, rockets and satellites is, essentially, a comparatively recent development. If it is recalled, moreover, that the corresponding experiments are often highly complicated, it will become obvious why quite a few problems still want clarification. Thus, within the accuracy of measurement attained (about 1%) no spatial aniso-tropy of cosmic ray intensity has been detected. Yet there is every ground to believe (GINZBURG and SYROVATSKIJ, 1964a) that the cosmic ray intensity anisotropy will be detected if the accuracy is raised by one order or two and its investigation will yield interesting results. The energy spectrum of primary electrons, let alone positrons, observed in the vicinity of the Earth is another moot point. The chemical composition of cosmic rays at $\mathscr{E} \geqslant 10^{12}$ eV/nucleon, and especially at 10^{15} eV/nucleon, the shape of the energy spectrum of cosmic rays in the energy range $E > 10^{15}$ to 10^{16} eV and some other problems still await elucidation. At the same time much important evidence has already been obtained and we shall briefly deal with it here.

The chemical composition of cosmic rays with kinetic energies $\mathscr{E}_k \geqslant 5.10^8$ eV/nucleon and up to $\mathscr{E} \sim 10^{12}$ to 10^{12} eV/nucleon[2] is known sufficiently well. Though sometimes it is not separate elements that are investigated but rather the intensities of groups of nuclei are determined (e.g., the group of L nuclei includes Li, Be and B nuclei). The corresponding data are listed in table I (for more details and comments to the table see GINZBURG and SYROVATSKIJ 1964a); here we shall merely note that the concentration of cosmic ray particles N is connected by virtue of their isotropy with the intensity I by the simple relation $N = (4 \pi I)/v$ where the speed of the particles v at $\mathscr{E}_k \geqslant 10^9$ eV/nucleon can well be replaced by the velocity of light c).

The investigation of the chemical composition warrants two essential conclusions.

---

[1] The results of this paper became known late in 1963. However, to avoid confusion we refer everywhere to the year of publication of the papers and not of the appearance of the preprints.

[2] It is relevant that a large part of cosmic ray particles occurs within the energy interval indicated (see below).

TABLE I

Chemical composition of cosmic rays

Group of nuclei	Atomic number Z	Averaged atomic weight $\bar{A}$ for the nuclei of each group	Intensity of cosmic rays I, $m^{-1} sr^{-1} sec^{-1}$	Number of nucleons in flux	$I/I_H = N/N_H$	Average abundances of elements in the universe	
						(Suess and Urey, 1956)	(Cameron, 1959, 1960)
p	1	1	1 300	1 300	680	3 360	6 830
α	2	4	88	352	46	2 584	1 040
L	3 to 5	10	1.9	19	1.0	10^{-5}	10^{-5}
M	6 to 9	14	5.7	80	3.0	2.64	10.1
H	≥ 10	31	1.9	59	1.0	1	1
VH	≥ 20	51	0.53	28	0.28	0.06	0.05

(the nuclei VH enter into the group of H-nuclei)

(1) The presence in the primary cosmic rays of a considerable number of L-nuclei which are very scarce in the universe is almost conclusive evidence of the secondary origin of these nuclei. This means that nuclei of the group L (i.e., Li, Be and B) have originated from the fragmentation of heavier cosmic ray nuclei in collisions with interstellar gas nuclei (i.e., practically with protons). Hence it follows that the cosmic rays have passed gas volumes of several g/cm^2 on the average before reaching the Earth. With an interstellar gas concentration $n \sim 10^{-2}$ cm^{-3} and density $\rho \sim 10^{-26}$g/cm^3 (such are the average values for the area filled by cosmic rays in the Galaxy) the path of 3 g/cm^2 corresponds to the distance $l_0 \sim 3.10^{26}$ cm $\simeq 100$ Mps and the time T $\simeq l_0/c \sim 3.10^8$ y. For this time cosmic rays may still be obtained within the Galaxy (including its halo, of course) taking into account their wandering in the interstellar magnetic fields.

(2) From the fragmentation and observed composition it can be inferred that it is the heavy and medium nuclei (the M and H groups) that must mainly be accelerated in the cosmic ray sources. A considerable part of cosmic ray protons and α-particles observed in the vicinity of the Earth are thus secondary in origin.

The total cosmic ray intensity in the vicinity of the Earth (at minimum solar activity) is

(1) $I_n \simeq 0.4$ nucleons/cm^2. sec. sr, $I_p \simeq 0.20$ protons/cm^2. sec. sr .

Here I_n is the intensity of all nucleons including free protons, and I_p is the intensity of the proton component. In other words, the number of nucleons in the nuclei roughly equals the number of protons making up the proton component.

From equation (1) it follows, taking into account the energy spectrum, that the total concentration of cosmic ray nucleons in the vicinity of the Earth is

(2) $\mathcal{N}_n \simeq 2.10^{-10}$ nucleons/cm^3, $\mathcal{N}_p \simeq 1.0 \times 10^{-10}$ protons/cm^3 .

The kinetic energy density and pressure of cosmic rays are

(3) $w_{cr} \simeq 0.9$ eV/cm$^3 \simeq 1.4 \times 10^{-12}$ erg/cm^3, $p \simeq \dfrac{w_{cr}}{3} \simeq 4.10^{-12}$ dyne/cm^2

For reasons which are not yet sufficiently clear the cosmic ray intensity as a function of kinetic energy has a maximum at $E_K \simeq 1.2$ GeV for protons and $\mathscr{E}_k \simeq 0.5$ GeV/nucleon for nuclei with A $\simeq 2$ Z. The main contribution to the energy density w_{cr} comes from the cosmic rays with energies higher than that corresponding to the maximum. In the energy range $10 > E > 10^6$ GeV the energy spectrum of cosmic rays can be expressed with good accuracy as

(4) $\qquad I_n(E)dE = 1.8 \times E^{-2.6}$ nucleons/cm^2. sec. sr. GeV.

Here it is assumed that the chemical composition of cosmic rays remains throughout the interval the same as at low energies. In the superhigh energy region $E > 10^6$ GeV $= 10^{15}$ eV the character of the spectrum changes and the question of the chemical composition remains open. In the first order approximation in the region $10^6 < E < 10^{11}$ GeV we can put $I(E) = KE^{-\gamma}$ with $\gamma \simeq 3$. The highest energy of cosmic ray particles ever observed is 10^{20} eV ~ 10 joules.

The energy and pressure of cosmic rays (EARL, 1961) are the same as those of interstellar gas with a concentration $n \sim 1$ atom/cm^3 at $T \sim 10^4$ °K. If the energy density and pressure of cosmic rays and magnetic field are compared, we obtain for the field an estimate $H \sim \sqrt{8\pi w_{cr}} \sim 5.10^{-6}$ Oe. Thus we can see that even the data on cosmic rays in the vicinity of the Earth point to the essential role which the energy and pressure of cosmic rays may play in the Galaxy. However, since cosmic rays are practically completely isotropic, observational evidence in the vicinity of the Earth leaves open the problem of the sources of cosmic rays and, strictly speaking, of their spatial distribution. In this sense cosmic ray astrophysics began in fact to develop only after the establishment early in the '50s of the connection between cosmic rays and non-thermal radio emission[3].

2 — Cosmic Rays and Magnetobremsstrahlung (Synchrotron) Cosmic Emission

The characteristics of magnetobremsstrahlung electromagnetic emission originating in the motion of relativistic charged particles in a magnetic field were revealed more than fifty years ago (SCHOTT, 1912). However, the magnetobremsstrahlung mechanism was neglected for sometime even after the discovery of cosmic radio emission, and it was only in 1950 to 1953 (ALFVEN and HERLEFSON, 1950; KIEPENHEUER, 1950; GINZBURG, 1951, 1953, 1954, 1956; GETMANTSEV, 1952) that the magnetobremsstrahlung nature of the non-thermal radio emission of the Galaxy and discrete sources (the envelopes of supernovae and radiogalaxies) was disclosed. The magneto-

---

[3] The important and interesting field of solar cosmic rays and cosmic rays intensity variations (DORMAN, 1963a and 1963b) is left out of this paper altogether.

bremsstrahlung mechanism was then used to account for the optical continuous spectrum emission (GORDON, 1954; SHKLOVSKY, 1953) occurring
in the case of large solar bursts, in the Crab nebula and for some galaxies.
The fact that magnetobremsstrahlung emission may be strongly polarized
(GINZBURG, 1953, 1954, 1956; GORDON 1954) proved essential in its identification.

Cosmic magnetobremsstrahlung emission is practically produced by electrons alone and thus yields information on the spatial distribution and
energy spectrum of cosmic ray electrons in the universe[4].

Without going into detail (GINZBURG and SYROVATSKY, 1964a; 1965),
we give several principal formulae of the magnetobremsstrahlung theory.

The total power of magnetobremsstrahlung emission originating in the
motion of an electron of total energy $E \gg mc^2$ is

(5)

$$P_n(E) = \int_0^\infty p(v)\,dv = \tfrac{2}{3}\left(\frac{e^2}{mc}\right)^2 \cdot cH_\perp^2 \left(\frac{E}{mc^2}\right)^2 = 1.57 \cdot 10^{-15}\, H_\perp^2 \left(\frac{E}{mc^2}\right)^2 \frac{\text{erg}}{\text{sec}}$$

where $H_\perp$ is the component, normal to the electron velocity, of the magnetic
field $\vec{H}$ in which the electron moves (the field H is henceforth measured in
Oe). The spectral density of the total emission power per electron($Hz \equiv c/sec$)

(6) $$p(v) = \frac{\sqrt{3}\,e^3\, H_\perp}{mc^2}\, F\left(\frac{v}{v_c}\right) = 2.37.10^{-22}\, H_\perp\, F\left(\frac{v}{v_c}\right) \frac{\text{erg}}{\text{sec Hz}}$$

where v is the frequency,

$$v_c = \frac{3e\, H_\perp}{4\,\pi\, mc}(E/mc^2)^2$$

and the function $F(v/v_c)$ is plotted in the figure.

The spectral density $p(v)$ has the maximum

(7) $$p(v_m) = 1.6\, \frac{e^3\, H_\perp}{mc_{\perp}^2} = 2.16 \cdot 10^{-22}\, H_\perp\, \frac{\text{erg}}{\text{sec Hz}}$$

at the frequency

(8) $$v_m \simeq 0.29\, v_c = 1.2.10^6\, H_\perp \left(\frac{E}{mc^2}\right)^2 = 4.6.10^{-6}\, H_\perp\,(E_{ev})^2\, \text{Hz}$$

---

[4] Both electrons and positrons are meant by electrons unless a special reservation is
made.

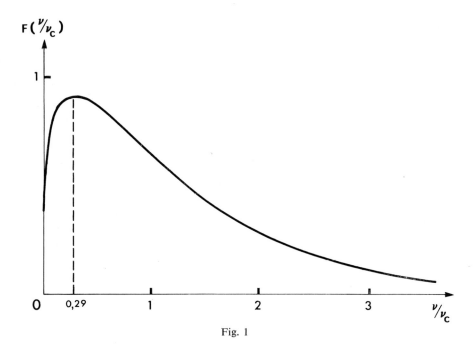

Fig. 1

The energy of the electron for which the emission maximum occurs at the frequency $v = v_m$ is

$$(9) \qquad E_m = 7.5 \cdot 10^{-10} \left(\frac{v_m}{H_\perp}\right)^{\frac{1}{2}} \text{erg} = 4.7 \cdot 10^2 \left(\frac{v}{H_\perp}\right)^{\frac{1}{2}} ev$$

Let us assume that electrons of energy E in a homogeneous field (mono-energetic spectrum) are distributed isotropically over all the directions, the concentrations of electrons N_e being constant along the line of sight and the electrons occupying an area L long. Then the emission intensity is $I_v = (p(v) N_e L)/4\pi$ and its maximum value is (Suess and Urey, 1956 and Cameron, 1959, 1960).

$$(10) \qquad I_{v,m} = 1,7.10^{-23} \, H_\perp N_e L \, \frac{\text{erg}}{\text{cm}^2.\text{sr. sec. Hz}}$$

If the concentration of relativistic electrons varies along the line of sight, $N_e L$ must obviously be replaced by the integral $\int_0^L N_e(\vec{r})) \, dr$ taken along the line of sight. If the field along the line of sight H = const is isotropic on the average in all directions, we have $H_\perp^2 = \frac{2}{3} H^2$. Then we obtain under the assumption that for all electrons the maximum in the emission spectrum occurs at the observed frequency v [i.e., their energy is given by equation (9)]

$$(11) \qquad I_v = 1.4.10^{-23} \, H \, N_e L \frac{erg}{cm^2 \, sr. \, sec. \, Hz}$$

For relativistic power spectrum electrons $N_e(E) = KE^{-\gamma}$ (total concentration $N_e = \int N_e(E) \, dE$) occupying an area measuring L along the line of sight we obtain under the assumption that the field in this area is on the average random

$$(12) \qquad I_v = 1.35.10^{-22} \, a(\gamma) \, KLH^{(\gamma+1)/2} \left(\frac{6.26.10^{18}}{v}\right)^{(\gamma-1)/2} \frac{erg}{cm^2 \, sr \, sec \, Hz}$$

where $a(\gamma)$ is a coefficient changing comparatively slowly ($a(1) = 0.283$, $a(1.5) = 0.147$, $a(2) = 0.103$ and $a(4) = 0.0725$).

The flux $\phi_v = \int I_v \, d\Omega$ from a discrete source with a volume V at a distance R is

$$(13) \qquad \phi_v = 1.35.10^{-22} \, a(\gamma) \frac{KVH^{(\gamma+1)/2}}{R^2} \left(\frac{6.26.10^{18}}{v}\right)^{(\gamma-1)/2} \frac{erg}{cm^2 \, sec. \, Hz}$$

where the same assumptions as in the derivation of equation (12) are also used.

From the above expressions two essential circumstances are obvious: (1) if magnetobremsstrahlung emission has the power spectrum, as is often the case, the spectral index α is connected with the exponent in the electron spectrum γ by a relation independent of other quantities

$$(14) \qquad I_v \sim v^{-\alpha}, \alpha = \frac{\gamma-1}{2}$$

and (2) by measuring the intensity or flux we also obtain information on the number of relativistic electrons in the line of sight or throughout the discrete source. In this case we must, of course, know the area length L or the distance to the source R and, which is less trivial and more essential, the strength of the field H. Additional considerations must be brought into play to estimate the field H. For example, in some cases it is natural to assume that the magnetic energy density $H^2/8\pi$ roughly equals the energy density of all cosmic rays w_{cr}. Sometimes we can use the relation, following under certain assumptions from magnetic hydrodynamics $H^2/8\pi \sim (\rho u^2)/2$ where $(\rho u^2)/2$ is the kinetic energy density of the gas. Finally, there are methods of estimating the field H by data on stellar light polarization, Zeeman splitting of the neutral hydrogen radio line, various dynamic considerations, etc. For example, all estimates for the Galaxy yield field values between 10^{-6} and 10^{-5} Oe, and the larger of these values should rather be accepted in the arms of the spiral.

The magnetobremsstrahlung of non-thermal radio emission appeared at once highly probable just because for the field H $\sim 10^{-5}$ and characteristic galactic dimensions L ~ 10 kps the observed intensity I_ν in the meter band could be explained if there are in the Galaxy relativistic electrons with concentration

$$N_e \, (E > 1 \, \text{Gev}) = \int_{1 \, Gev}^{\infty} N_e \, (E) \, dE \sim 10^{-12} \, \text{cm}^{-3}$$

It is clear from the above concentration of all cosmic rays at the Earth (GINZBURG and SYROVATSKIJ, (1964b), that to account for radio emission it is sufficient for the electron concentration to come up to no more than $\sim 1\%$ of the total cosmic ray concentration. Now, this amount of electrons in cosmic rays did not contradict the observations and estimates available at that time (KIEPENHEUER, 1950; GINZBURG, 1951) and later was confirmed by direct measurements (EARL, 1961; MEYER and VOGT, 1961; AGRINIER, 1964).

The evidence available now does not make anyone (as far as we know) doubt the magnetobremsstrahlung nature of non-thermal cosmic radio emission (with the exception of some types of sporadic solar radio emission and other "compact sources; see GINZBURG and OZERNOY, 1966). Therefore, we shall not dwell on the relevant evidence in more detail and will give below some results concerning cosmic rays in the universe obtained with the aid of the magnetobremsstrahlung formulae. However, we first discuss another method making it possible in principle to obtain information on cosmic rays far from the Earth, viz., gamma astronomy.

3 — Cosmic Rays and Gamma Astronomy

Gamma astronomy is still in the nascent stage and there is no certainty that this field will prove especially fruitful. Nevertheless, and in a sense just because of the dimness of actual prospects in this field, we want to dwell on it (for more detail see the survey of GINZBURG and SYROVATSKIJ [1964b]; the papers by KRAUSHAAR and CLARK [1962; 1963], HAYAKAWA [1952] and MORRISSON [1958] may in particular be called pioneering efforts in gamma astronomy).

Cosmic gamma rays must mainly be generated by cosmic rays under which we conventionally class all charged particles with kinetic energies larger than 10^8 eV. The following processes are primarily responsible for the generation of cosmic gamma rays.

(1) Decays of π^0-mesons ($\pi^0 \to \gamma + \gamma$ process) produced by cosmic rays in interstellar gas.

(2) Bremsstrahlung γ-radiation caused by electrons (and positrons) of the cosmic ray electron component in their collisions with nuclei and electrons of the interstellar medium.

(3) Compton scattering of relativistic electrons on optical photons emitted by stars and nebulae.

Some other processes may also be indicated: annihilation γ-radiation ($e^+ + e^- \to \gamma + \gamma$ process), γ-radiation of excited nuclei (of interstellar gas or of cosmic rays) and some others.

The intensity of γ-rays $I_\gamma(E_\gamma)$ measured in photons/cm^2. sec. sr is proportional to the intensity of the cosmic rays generating the γ-radiation $I(E)$, the gas density ρ or the optical photon energy density w_{ph} along the line of sight and finally the size of the generation region L along the line of sight. Thus, by measuring the intensity of γ-rays and knowing ρ or w_{ph} and L we can find the intensity of cosmic rays or their electron component. As an example, it can be indicated that cosmic rays with the intensity (4) generate in the Galaxy as a result of the production and subsequent decay of π^0-mesons γ-rays with the intensity

$$(15) \quad I_{\gamma,\pi^0}(> E_\gamma) = \int_{E_\gamma}^{\infty} I_{\gamma,\pi^0}(E_\gamma)\, dE_\gamma = 3 \cdot 10^{-4}\, M(L) E_\gamma^{-1,8}\, \frac{\text{photon}}{\text{cm}^2\,\text{sr}\,\text{sec}}.$$

where E_γ is measured in GeV and $M(L)$ is the mass of the gas in the Galaxy along the line of sight; in the direction at the galactic center $M(L) \simeq 6.10^{-2}$ g/cm^2, in the direction at the pole $M(L) \simeq 6.10^{-4}$ g/cm^2 and on the average in all directions $M(L) \simeq 1.6 \times 10^{-3}$ g/cm^2. Hence it is clear, for example, that for the Galaxy we have

$$I_{\gamma,\pi^0}(E_\gamma > 1\,\text{Gev}) \lesssim 2.10^{-5}\, \frac{\text{photon}}{\text{cm}^2\,\text{sr. sec}}$$

At lower energies equation (15) is inaccurate; a more elaborate calculation shows that even in the direction at the galactic center we have $I_{\gamma,\pi^0}(E_\gamma > 50\,\text{MeV}) \simeq 3.10^{-4}$ and on the average in all directions for the Galaxy $I_{\gamma,\pi^0}(E_\gamma > 50\,\text{MeV}) \simeq 8.10^{-6}$. Taking into account all other processes we have on the average for the Galaxy $I_\gamma(E_\gamma > 50\,\text{MeV}) \simeq 2.10^{-5}$. At the same time, according to measurements (KRAUSHAAR and CLARK, 1963), we have on the average in all directions

$$(16) \quad I_\gamma(E_\gamma > 50\,\text{Mev}) \leqslant (3.3 + 1.3)\, 10^{-4}\, \frac{\text{photon}}{\text{cm}^2. \text{st. sec}}$$

Therefore: if the intensity $I_\gamma (E_\gamma > 50 \text{ MeV}) \simeq 3.10^{-4}$ proved to be real and not simply an upper limit for the measurements made, the corresponding γ-emission must most likely be metagalactic in origin. However, the result (16) is quite significant even now. The fact is that in metagalactic space there are certainly quite numerous optical photons with energies $h\nu_{ph} \sim 1 \text{ eV}$ so that the density of optical emission energy $w_{ph,mg} \geq 2.10^{-3} \text{ eV/cm}^3 \sim$ $\approx 3.10^{-15} \text{ erg/cm}^3$. Therefore, the production of γ photons as a result of scattering of relativistic electrons on optical photons must be especially effective if there are relativistic electrons in metagalactic space.

It is noteworthy that for electrons with energies

$$E \ll [(mc^2)^2/h\nu_{ph}] \sim 2.10^{11} \text{ eV}$$

(it is assumed here that the energy of optical photons $h\nu_{ph} \sim 1 \text{ eV}$) this process is very similar to magnetobremsstrahlung emission. The condition $E \ll [(mc^2)^2/h\nu_{ph}]$ means that in the electron rest system the photon energy $h\nu'_{ph} \sim (h\nu_{ph}E)/(mc^2) \ll mc^2$ and the process of scattering can be treated classically. This implies that the electron is accelerated by the wave field and emits scattered waves as a result; these waves are similar to magnetobremsstrahlung emission originating in the acceleration of an electron moving in a magnetic field. The fact that this is not the question of a mere analogy becomes evident if the magnetobremsstrahlung emission power (5) and γ-radiation power or, which amounts to the same, magneto-bremsstrahlung and Compton energy losses of a relativistic electron are compared. It appears that the Compton losses are $\{$if $E \ll [(mc^2)^2/h\nu_{ph}]\}$

$$P_k(E) = \frac{32\pi}{9} \left(\frac{e^2}{mc^2}\right)^2 c\, w_{ph}(E/mc^2)^2 \tag{17}$$

i.e., are precisely equal to magnetobremsstrahlung losses (5) in a magnetic field isotropically on the average with the energy density

$$H^2/(8\pi) = \tfrac{3}{2}[H_\perp^2/8\pi] = w_{ph}.$$

On the other hand, both radiations under discussion differ in the spectrum: the average energy of γ-rays is $E_\gamma \sim h\nu_{ph}(E/mc^2)^2$ and the characteristic energy of magnetobremsstrahlung photons

$$E_\nu = h\nu \sim \frac{e\, H_\perp\, h}{mc}(E/mc^2)^2\,.$$

Since the frequency of light ν_{ph} is considerably higher than the cosmic gyrofrequency[5] eH/mc the magnetobremsstrahlung spectrum (at the given energy E) is much softer than the spectrum of scattered photons.

Returning to metagalactic space, the total power of γ-rays from relativistic electrons is here the same as the power of their magnetobremsstrahlung emission in the field H $\sim \sqrt{8 \pi w_{\mathrm{ph}}} \sim 3.10^{-7}$ Oe. Actually, however, the metagalactic field appears to be much weaker, and anyway, has not been determined by any direct method. Therefore, it is γ-astronomy and not radio astronomy that yields estimates of the intensity of the cosmic ray electron component in metagalactic space. Thus, using the value (16), it can readily be seen that the concentration of relativistic electrons in Metagalaxy is $1/30$ of their concentration in the Galaxy if not less.

The problem of γ-radiation of discrete sources also has a fairly long record. However, the expected γ-ray fluxes are rather small, though quasistars and especially 3 C 273 B may prove exceptions. If quasars emit magnetobremsstrahlung radiation and the size of the radiating area is less than a light year, quasars will yield a relatively large γ-ray flux owing to Compton scattering (GINZBURG and SYROVATSKIJ, 1964b; GINZBURG, OZERNOY and SYROVATSKIJ, 1964). Let us note, moreover, that γ-astronomy dovetails with X-ray astronomy where several interesting results have been obtained (we mean above all the discovery of discrete sources of X-rays in the Crab nebula and Scorpio). We cannot, however, discuss within the scope of this paper this range of problems in any greater detail (GINZBURG and SYROVATSKIJ [1964b] and its bibliography).

4 — Cosmic Rays in the Universe

As indicated above, the information obtained on the primary cosmic rays in the vicinity of the Earth gave in itself grounds to believe that the dynamic and energetical role of cosmic rays in the Galaxy is quite essential. Apart from fully confirming this conjecture, radio evidence warranted even further reaching conclusions. Viz. it transpired that cosmic rays are omnipresent in the universe, and there are especially many cosmic rays in non-stationary

---

[5] The electron revolution frequency in a magnetic field $\omega_{\mathrm{H}} = eH/mc \cdot mc^2/E$ and at first glance it seems that it is this frequency and not the frequency $eH_{\perp}/mc$ that must be the analogue of the frequency of light ν_{ph}. However, the fact is that a relativistic electron moving in a magnetic field radiates in the direction of the observer only for a time $t \sim mc/eH_{\perp}$ Therefore, the characteristic magnetobremsstrahlung radiation frequency is $\omega \sim \left(\dfrac{eH_{\perp}}{mc} \right) \cdot (E/mc^2)^2$ where the factor $(E/mc^2)^2$ results from taking into account the Doppler effect. For more detail GINZBURG and SYROVSATKIJ (1964a, 1965).

explosive areas such as the envelopes of supernovae, radiogalaxies and quasars.

This connection between non-stationary systems and cosmic rays is in general quite comprehensible in the current terms of plasma physics and magnetic hydrodynamics. A plasma state with intense motions (whether streams or waves of different types is immaterial), but without magnetic field and rapid particles is unstable in general. Therefore, even if an outburst (say, of a supernova) can be regarded in its earlier stage without taking into account the magnetic field and cosmic rays, the field and cosmic rays would come inevitably into play some time later. The problem as to the level to which the energy of the field and cosmic rays may come up, can have no universal solution: the answer depends on several factors and in particular the time of development of the process. However, in many cases a certain quasi-equilibrium can be expected with the densities of different energies approximately equal, i.e.,

$$(18) \qquad \frac{\rho \mu'}{2} \sim \frac{H^2}{8\pi} \sim w_{cr}.$$

The magnetic field becomes stronger because of the « entanglement of the lines of force » as well as because of the compression of the gas owing to the « freezing-in » of these lines (the latter effect is especially strong in the gravitational collapse (GINZBURG, 1964; GINZBURG and OZERNOY, 1964).

Since astronomical objects in the phase of an outburst (or intense development in general) are certainly of great interest and at the same time it is in such objects that many cosmic rays must be generated and are in fact generated, the intimate connection between cosmic ray astrophysics and the investigation of supernovae, radio galaxies and quasars is evident. However, cosmic rays are also of primary importance in such relatively tranquil regions as the Galaxy as a whole or metagalactic medium.

Both radio evidence and considerations based on different estimates and the current concepts of the structure of the spiral and the Galaxy as a whole suggest that cosmic rays fill on the average rather uniformly the entire Galaxy including the halo, i.e., the quasi-spherical region with a radius $R \sim 3.10^{22}$ cm and volume $V \sim 10^{68}$ cm^3. The energy density of cosmic rays and their energy spectrum are close to those observed in the vicinity of the Earth at minimum solar activity (GINZBURG and SYROVATSKIJ, 1964a, 1964b; EARL, 1961; MEYER and VOGT, 1961). Hence it follows that the total energy of cosmic rays in the Galaxy $w_{cr} \sim w_{cr} \cdot V \sim 10^{56}$ erg. The lifetime of cosmic rays is probably determined by their exit from the system (i.e., into metagalactic space) and is $T_{cr} \sim 3.10^8$ y. Therefore, to maintain the intensity of cosmic rays at the present-day level cosmic rays must be injected with the power

$$(19) \qquad U \sim \frac{w_{cr}}{T_{cr}} \sim 10^{40} \text{ erg/sec.}$$

This injected power can be ensured by the flares of supernovae which are just the main sources of cosmic rays in the Galaxy in the stationary galactic model (GINZBURG and SYROVATSKIJ, 1964a); in the non-stationary model (BURBIDGE and HOYLE, 1963) by the bursts of the galactic nucleus. However, the existence of such bursts has not yet been proved and it appears (GINZBURG and SYROVATSKIJ, 1963a, 1964a, 1964c) that even if they do occur they play a lesser or approximately equal role as the flares of supernovae in the generation of cosmic rays. This means in particular that each burst of the nucleus generates only a comparatively small part of cosmic rays in the Galaxy and thus the picture is quasi-stationary. It should be emphasized, however, that the question of the role of bursts of the galactic nucleus remains rather obscure (some ways of promising the elucidation of the effectiveness of nucleus bursts as generators of cosmic rays are indicated in refs. GINZBURG and SYROVATSKIJ, 1963a, 1964a).

Radio evidence warrants the conclusion that in the radio band the Galaxy radiates $L_r \sim 4.10^{38}$ erg/sec while its luminosity in the optical range is $L_{opt} \approx 4.10^{43}$ erg/sec. Elaborate calculations (GINZBURG and SYROVATSKIJ, 1963a, 1964c) show that the observed non-thermal galactic radio emission cannot be created by secondary electrons produced from the $\mu^{\pm} \to e^{\pm}$-decay of $\pi^{\pm}$-mesons generated by cosmic rays in the interstellar medium. This inference is confirmed by measurements (DE SHONG, HILDEBRAND and MEYER, 1964) which show that the electron component of cosmic rays at the Earth contains many more electrons than positrons (the $\pi^{\pm} \to \mu^{\pm} \to e^{\pm}$ decay products contain on the contrary more positrons since the generating component is charged positively and hence more π^{+}-mesons than π^{-}-mesons are generated). Both radio evidence and observations at the Earth (AGRINIER et al., 1964) in general agree with such a spectrum of electrons in the energy range $5.10^8 < E < 10^{10}$ eV (GINZBURG and SYROVATSKIJ, 1964b)

$$(20) \qquad I_e(E) = 5.10^{-3} E^{-2} \frac{\text{electron}}{\text{cm}^2 \text{sr. sec. Gev}}$$

The role of cosmic rays in the envelopes of supernovae is highly essential. Suffice to say that the total energy of cosmic rays in the envelope of Cassiopeia A comes to 10^{49} to 10^{50} erg and in the Crab nebula 10^{48} to 10^{49} erg.

Besides, a considerable number of relativistic particles may have escaped from the envelopes. Thus less energy perhaps passes in the outburst of a supernova into cosmic rays than into the emission of light and the kinetic energy of the envelope. In the case of the Crab nebula relativistic electrons are also responsible for a considerable part of optical radiation and perhaps X-ray radiation (GINZBURG and SYROVATSKIJ, 1964b). Besides, there are grounds to suppose that the generation of cosmic rays continues at present in the Crab nebula (perhaps the magnetosphere of the collapsed star is involved here (GINZBURG, 1964; GINZBURG and OZERNOY, 1964).

Above we mentioned supernovae and possible outbursts of the galactic nucleus as sources of cosmic rays in the Galaxy. Thus the metagalactic theories of the origin of cosmic rays in the Galaxy were left out of consideration. The fact is that metagalactic theories imply[6] that throughout the Metagalaxy or in the areas adjacent to the Galaxy the energy density of cosmic rays $w_{cr,mg}$ is roughly the same as in the Galaxy (EARL, 1961). If this were the case, however, the energy of cosmic rays in metagalactic space would exceed by two or three orders the kinetic energy of intergalactic gas and the energy of the magnetic field. For this reason as well as on the grounds of the data of γ-astronomy discussed above we believe (GINZBURG and SYROVATSKIJ, 1963b 1964a) that the energy density of cosmic rays in the Metagalaxy $w_{cr,mg} \ll w_{cr,G} \sim 10^{-12}$ erg/cm^3 and perhaps

$$(21) \qquad w_{cr,mg} \lesssim 10^{-15} \text{ erg/sec}$$

It should be emphasized, however, that the inequality $w_{cr,mg} \ll w_{cr,G}$ cannot as yet be regarded as rigorously proved and the hypothesis that $w_{cr,mg} \sim w_{cr,G} \sim 10^{-12}$ erg/cm^2 has its advocates (BURBIDGE and HOYLE, 1964) (we refer to the latest paper known to us; some criticisms can be found in the paper by GINZBURG and SYROVATSKIJ, in press). It can be hoped that with the development of γ-astronomy the question of the role of cosmic rays in the Metagalaxy will be answered quite definitely. Let us also note that even if $w_{cr,mg} \ll w_{cr,G}$, in the superhigh energy region ($\mathscr{E} \geqslant 10^{16}$ to 10^{17} eV/nucleon) the Metagalactic cosmic rays may predominate even in our Galaxy. This possibility is quite realistic, taking into account the fact that in the Galaxy it is difficult to create as well as retain particles with energies $\mathscr{E} \geqslant 10^{17}$ eV/nucleon. At the same time such particles might be accelerated in powerful radiogalaxies.

---

[6] It is assumed that cosmic rays in metagalactic space are distributed isotropically in all directions.

Our Galaxy is known to be one of the galaxies which are «normal» in the radio band. The ratio between radio and optical emission may vary considerably from one radiogalaxy to another. Thus, for Cygnus A we have $L_r \sim 7.10^{44}$ erg/sec and $L_{opt} \sim 10^{44}$ erg/sec, i.e., the ratio is roughly 10^6 times larger than for our Galaxy. The energy of cosmic rays in Cygnus A is estimated to be $w_{cr} \sim 3$ to 10×10^{60} erg. In most other radiogalaxies and quasars the energy of cosmic rays is smaller, but on the whole it can be contended that the creation of radiogalaxies and quasars involves energy releases coming to 10^{61} and perhaps even 10^{62} erg. Since the Sun's energy $M_\odot c^2 \sim 10^{54}$ erg the origin of powerful radiogalaxies can hardly be associated with supernova outbursts and the implosion of nuclear energy. Rather the source of outbursts in radiogalaxies is directly the gravitation energy. (GINZBURG, 1961; HOYLE, FOWLER, BURBIDGE and BURBIDGE, 1964); less substantiated though more concrete perhaps is the hypothesis according to which quasars are newly originating galaxies in which cosmic rays are generated owing to the gravitation energy decreasing in the compression of gas (GINZBURG, 1961; FIELD, 1964).

In the case of radiogalaxies and quasars, just as in the case of supernova envelopes, the pressure and energy of cosmic rays are among the decisive factors. It is sufficient to recall the spread of radio emitting clouds in Cygnus A and the luminous ejections in Virgo A and some other sources.

We must confine ourselves to the above remarks[7]. Our purpose has been achieved if we have shown that cosmic rays have come into their own in astronomy. Since the astronomical study of cosmic rays is a comparatively recent development which has yet yielded results and inferences of primary importance, there is every reason to believe that the development of cosmic ray astrophysics holds out attractive prospects. This conclusion also takes into account, of course, the numerous possibilities resulting from the application of several new methods of investigation.

The author of this paper has unfortunately been unable to establish personal contacts with the late Otto STRUVE. He has all the more reasons to have accepted the Editors' proposal to write a paper for this collection and thus to pay a tribute at least in this form to the memory of the man whose name is inseparably linked with the development of astronomy in this century.

---

[7] *Note added in proof.* The reader can find some new data, results and references in the last papers by Ginzburg and Syrovatskij published in The Proc. of the IXth intern. conf. on cosmic rays (London, 1965) and prepared for the IAU Symposium N 31 (Noordwijk, 1966; to be published).

REFERENCES

AGRINIER, B. et al., 1964, Phys. Rev. Lett., 13, 377.
ALFVEN, H. and HERLEFSON, N., 1950, Phys. Rev., 78, 616.
BURBIDGE, G. R. and HOYLE, F., 1963, Ap. J., 138, 57.
BURBIDGE, G. R. and HOYLE, F., 1964, Proc. Phys. Soc., 84, 141.
CAMERON, G. W., 1959, Ap. J., 129, 676.
CAMERON, G. W., 1960, Ap. J., 131, 519.
DE SHONG, J. A., HILDEBRAND, R. H., and MEYER, P., 1964, Phys. Rev. Lett., 12, 3.
DORMAN, L. I., 1963a, Cosmic Ray Variations and Space Research (Akad. Nauk SSSR).
DORMAN, L. I., 1963b, Progress in Elementary Particle and Cosmic Ray Physics, 7 (Amsterdam).
EARL, J. A., 1961, Phys. Rev. Lett., 6, 125.
FIELD, G. B., 1964, Nature 202, 786.,
GETMANTSEV, G. G., 1952, Dokl. Akad. Nauk SSSR, 83, 557.
GINZBURG, V. L., 1951, Dokl. Akad. Nauk SSSR, 76, 377.
GINZBURG, V. L., 1953, Usp. Fiz. Nauk, 62, 37.
GINZBURG, V. L., 1954, Fortschritte der Physik, 1, 659.
GINZBURG, V. L., 1956, Nuovo Cimento Suppl., 3, 38.
GINZBURG, V. L., 1961, Astr. Zh. 38, 380; Soviet Astron., 5, 282.
GINZBURG, V. L., 1964, Dokl. Akad., Nauk SSSR., 156, 43.
GINZBURG, V. L. and OZERNOY, L. M., 1964, J. E. T. P., 47, 1030. Sov. Phys. — J. E. T. P., 20, 689.
GINZBURG, V. L. and OZERNOY, L. M., 1966, Ap. J., 144, 599.
GINZBURG, V. L., OZERNOY, L. M., and SYROVATSKIJ, S. I., 1964, Dokl. Akad. Nauk SSSR, 157, 557.
GINZBURG, V. L. and SYROVATSKIJ, S. I., 1963a, Proc. Intern. Conf. Cosmic Rays (Jaipur, India).
GINZBURG, V. L. and SYROVATSKIJ, S. I., 1963b, Astr. Zh. 40, 466; Soviet Astron. 7, 356.
GINZBURG, V. L., and SYROVATSKIJ, S. I., 1964a, The Origin of Cosmic Rays (Pergamon Press, London).
GINZBURG, V. L. and SYROVATSKIJ, S. I., 1964b, Some Questions of γ- and X-Ray Astronomy, Usp. Fiz. Nauk, 84, 201 (see also Space Sci. Rev. 1965, 4, 267).
GINZBURG, V. L. and SYROVATSKIJ, S. I., 1964c, Astr. Zh., 41, 430; Soviet Astron. 8,3 42.
GINZBURG, V. L. and SYROVATSKIJ, S. I., 1965, Ann. Rev. of Astron. and Astroph., 3.
GINZBURG, V. L. and SYROVATSKIJ, S. I., On the Problems of the Astroph. of Cosmic Rays, Izv. Akad. Nauk SSSR (ser. fiz.) 1965, 29, 819.
GORDON, I. M., 1954, Dokl. Akad. Nauk. SSSR, 94, 813.
HAYAKAWA, S., 1952, Progr. Theor. Phys., 8, 517.
HOYLE, F., FOWLER, W. A., BURBIDGE, G. R., and BURBIDGE, E. M., 1964, Ap. J., 139, 909.
KIEPENHEUER, K. O., 1950, Phys. Rev., 79, 738.
KRAUSHAAR, W. L. and CLARK, G. W., 1962, Phys. Rev. Lett., 8, 106.
KRAUSHAAR, W. L. and CLARK, G. W., 1963, Proc. Intern. Conf. Cosmic Rays (Jaipur, India).
MEYER, P. and VOGT, R., 1961, Phys. Rev. Lett., 6, 193.
MORRISON, P., 1958, Nuovo Cimento, 7, 858.
SCHOTT, G. A., 1912, Electromagnetic Radiation (Cambridge University Press, Cambridge).
SHKLOVSKIJ, I. S., 1953, Dokl. Akad. Nauk SSSR, 90, 983.
SUESS, H. E. and UREY, H. C., 1956, Rev. Mod. Phys., 28, 53.

Structure of galaxies and formation of spiral arms

S. B. PIKELNER

Sternberg Astronomical Institute, Moscow

Professor Otto STRUVE gave much attention to problems of stellar evolution and formation of stars and stellar systems. His famous book, *Stellar Evolution*, had great influence on the development of this important branch of science in its early stages. Later his reviews in *Sky and Telescope* summarized new results and helped clarify and complete the harmonious picture of today. Now the center of gravity of investigations moves to the problem of the formation of galaxies.

The modern ideas on the formation of galaxies, which are the results of papers by J. H. OORT, F. HOYLE, W. BAUM and other scientists may be summarized as follows. The original matter condensed into clouds with mass $M \approx 10^{13} M\odot$. These clouds condensed approximately in an isothermal way and divided into several smaller clouds which gave birth to big galaxies or groups of galaxies.

Evolution of galaxies which had an angular momentum followed such a pattern (see, for example, the lecture by Professor OORT at the 12th meeting of the IAU in Hamburg, [1964]). In the beginning the clouds were large and the angular velocity low. The gas mainly contracted and at this time were formed the oldest stars which moved in very elongated trajectories. Stars formed at this time maintained their original distribution in space, but the gas lost its energy and gradually became concentrated on the main plain. At the same time galaxies contracted towards their axes until the gas began to move in circular orbits which correspond to the specific angular momentum of each element of gas. In the process of the flattening of the system, clusters and stars more and more rich in heavy elements were formed because at this time there appeared many massive stars having a fast evolution. After this flattening, the stars of a disc or intermediate subsystems which comprise a main part of the general mass of a galaxy, were formed, and only a small part of the matter—less than 2%—remained as a gas. This gas and the stars that were born from it became a flat subsystem. Flat subsystems usually form spiral arms. Sometimes they are two regular symmetrical spirals, sometimes several loosely wound branches. Roughly half of all spiral galaxies are barred spirals with a straight bar transforming at the ends into spiral arms.

Gauthier-Villars, Paris - Modern Astrophysics - 1967.

Many SB have a ring passing over the ends of a bar. Sometimes spiral arms are tangent to the little inner ring.

Spiral arms are connected with a magnetic field. In our Galaxy the presence of a magnetic field can be proved by many methods: directly from the Zeeman effect in the 21 cm line, from polarization of stellar light, from nonthermal radioemission, from the shape of the elongated dark and emission nebulae and filaments, and from the rotation of the plane of linear polarization of radio sources. Polarization of stellar light, nonthermal radioemission and some other effects are observed in other galaxies too.

Magnetic lines are directed approximately along spiral arms. This can be inferred from the observations and moreover it is necessary for the arms to be stable. Otherwise they would be disintegrated into separate bits which could not become reconnected soon. Generally speaking spiral arms often appear broken, consisting of many pieces. However, this is only an illusion. We do not observe the whole arm but only associations of hot stars and dark complexes in it. Condensations of gas in spiral arms have some angular momentum relative to the center of the condensations. During the compression this gives some rotation relative to the neighboring regions, and a part of the arm turns until it is stopped by the tension of the magnetic lines. In this case the arm has a irregular broken structure, separate parts of which are connected with the invisible parts of the magnetic tubes which have no stellar associations.

The suggestion that arms are continued tubes of magnetic lines is based upon the following points. Arms cannot exist for a long time without a longitudinal field; in many spiral galaxies we can see continuous arms; there are no principal differences between the composition of regular and irregular spirals; a magnetic tube, the diameter of which is many parsecs, cannot break in several billion years since the conductivity of the gas is rather high. For these reasons we can assume that arms are really magnetic tubes even though they may be twisted a little.

Moreover magnetic lines may be antiparallel as well as parallel. Statistical investigations of the rotation of the planes of polarization of radiosources have shown that in the vicinity of the sun the field has a different direction on both sides of the galactic plane. The thickness of the southern part is greater than that of the northern part of the field.

A magnetic field not only keeps the continuity of the arm but fulfills a still more important role. It prevents the condensation of the arm, the contraction of it to the axis and transformation of its gas into stars. The thickness of the arm is conditioned by the equilibrium of magnetic forces and gravitation. The gravitational force is dependent upon the density of the gas and upon the stellar density. Therefore, in the central parts of the Galaxy where stellar density is very high, the arms are much thinner than those in the outer parts of the Galaxy where the gravitational contraction is determined only by the gas. The similar effect may explain the difference between spiral arms in Sa, Sb and Sc galaxies.

The formation of spiral arms is connected with gravitational condensation of the gas. Moreover, the magnetic field should play an important part. For the formation of arms it is necessary to compress the gas into a tube with longitudinal magnetic lines. Such a compression takes place primarily in the center of a galaxy where the gas with a low angular momentum is concentrated. High stellar density of spherical and intermediate subsystems in the central region show that there existed a great deal of gas with a low momentum. Compression of the gas to the center is followed by a flattening of the system, by compression of the gas to the galactic plane. Magnetic lines in this stage should have a shape like that in figure 1; they are compressed in the center and diverged on the whole disc. As the magnetic lines try to unbend, magnetic forces are directed as shown in figure 1. Before

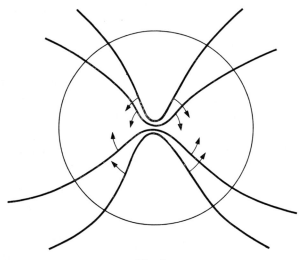

Fig. 1

compression of the tube, magnetic forces are insignificant in comparison with the gravitation and with the gradient of thermal and turbulent pressure. These important forces are in quasi equilibrium, but motions dissipate and gravitational condensations begin. Magnetic forces are little disturbances which develop and form two new condensations on the same magnetic tube. These condensations are situated in the vicinity of the central condensation. The magnetic tube is compressed in these condensations but is sharply diverged at the end. The process is repeated—magnetic forces stimulate formation of the next condensations on the same magnetic lines. The process of condensation is propagated along the magnetic field. This phenomenon may be called a magneto-gravitational wave.

Propagation of the wave is facilitated by the following circumstance. During the flattening the disc is unstable relative to tangential motions. Deviation from the axial symmetry cause the movements of the gas to the radii where the density is greater. Therefore the formation of several first condensations in the magnetic tube evoke a general movement of the gas towards the diameter, and the whole tube returns quickly to equilibrium.

Formation of spiral arms is connected, according to this hypothesis, with the central condensation. Therefore, galaxies without the central condensation are irregular, and have no spiral structure.

As Prof. B. J. Bok told the writer, this conclusion is supported by the following fact. The Large Magellanic Cloud has no condensation in its dynamical center and it has no spiral arms with population I. The Small Magellanic Cloud has little condensation in its center and it has a slim, subtle arm which is barely visible.

Sometimes spiral arms are split into several thin filaments. Such phenomena are observed in M 81, M 101 and some other galaxies, and may be easily explained. The gas in the magnetic tube may condense as a whole. But it is possible for it to divide into several different contracting masses. Each of these masses condenses separate parts of the magnetic tubes and originates a separate magneto-gravitational wave forming a thin filament which begins from a given point and goes in an outward direction.

Magneto-gravitational waves can be the cause of the formation not only of spiral arms but of other similar features. When there is gravitational condensation in a magnetic field, the central condensation must stimulate the condensation of the gas in the same magnetic lines. In such a way chains of young Herbig-Haro objects in stellar associations or bridges and tails which join interacting galaxies may be formed. The formation of a galaxy in a big cloud makes a wave of condensation which propagates along magnetic lines. It creates a gas cylinder (bridge) with the magnetic field which is similar to a spiral arm. If there is some fluctuation of density of the gas on the same magnetic lines, the wave stimulates the formation of the second, smaller galaxy which is connected to the first. The wave can go farther and form a tail on the other side of the little galaxy. Such bridges and tails were investigated by F. Zwicky and by B.A. Vorontzov-Veljaminov.

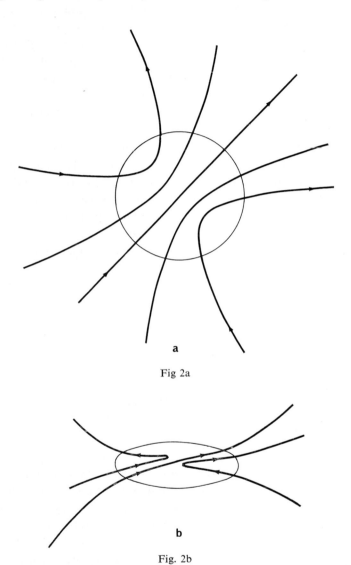

a

Fig 2a

b

Fig. 2b

J.H. Piddington found that the angle between the metagalactic magnetic field and the axis of rotation is important. He showed that if this angle, $\alpha \approx 90°$, the magnetic field strongly increased in the process of disc formation. The process which has been discussed in this paper has to do with approximately such a case, namely forming an arm as a tube of magnetic lines with similar direction. Let us now discuss the case when $0 < \alpha < 90°$. In the beginning the contraction is quite isotropical and a field such as is shown in figure 2a is formed. In the second stage the gas is condensed into the disc and the field now consists of a tube which passes through both arms and of two folded separated tubes which are held by a central condensation (fig. 2b). Each arm has a neutral surface which separates the fields of opposite direction. This may explain the observations of Faraday rotation of radio-emission. According to these observations the surface of change of polarity in our arm is situated above the galactic plane.

In the vicinity of the neutral surface the magnetic pressure gradient is directed quite the opposite to the normal direction; it does not support the gas against the gravitation but promotes contraction. Moreover, in this region the field is slowly annihilated. Magnetic lines of opposite direction slowly drift to the neutral surface and destroy one another. In this region the gas which is not supported by magnetic pressure must condense and form inter-stellar clouds. Formation of hot stars, H II regions, supernovae explosions, instabilities of various kinds, push out the condensed gas into magnetic fields of spiral arms. The external field penetrates into the gas, which has no field, due to a riffle instability. The clouds become divided into thin parallel filaments along the magnetic field. This explains the filamentary structure of many obscure nebulae and reflection field.

Fig. 3

We have a special case when the rotational axis and the external magnetic field are parallel. After contraction and flattening of the system takes place, magnetic lines go to the center and come back (see fig. 3). Now there are no lines which cross the center and no preferential direction for spiral arms; all radii of the disc are equivalent. However, although the disc during the contractions is unstable, it would be divided into pieces due to random fluctuations. Each condensation gives a magneto-gravitational wave which forms an arm. These arms do not cross the very center. It is possible that multiarm galaxies are formed in such cases. This hypothesis is supported by the fact that arms of multiarm galaxies usually do not run up to the very center. They often exist as tangents of a little ring around the center. This ring may be formed by differential rotation which is especially high in the central region. Displacement of the ends of the arms may give a composed ring as is shown in figure 4.

Fig. 4

The problem of differential rotation is so far unsolved. The rotation of our Galaxy established from the 21 cm line is such that the arms should essentially change their shape in a time less than 10^9 years. This was discussed in many papers. The problem is connected neither with the origin of arms nor with the nature of forces which determine their motions. If arms exist for a long time and if their rotation is in accordance with radio observations, they should be tangled. This contradiction is especially important in multiarm galaxies where angles between arms and radii are considerably less than 90°. However, the differential rotation of these galaxies has not been sufficiently studied.

A characteristic and very common type of spiral galaxies is the barred spiral, SB. A typical barred spiral has a straight bar which at the ends transforms abruptly into spiral arms.

In many SB the transition from bar to arms is very sharp. The composition of a bar is similar to that of the usual spiral arms; it consists of gas and young stars. It should also have a longitudinal magnetic field, otherwise it will be unstable. Conservation of the straight shape of the bar is possible only if its rotation is like that of a rigid body, i.e. if acceleration of gravity toward the center is proportional to the radial distance.

The mass of a bar like that of the spiral arms is a small part of the whole mass of a galaxy. The mass is concentrated in the old stars of low luminosity which form in our Galaxy the intermediate and spherical subsystems. In order to have rigid body rotation it is necessary for these subsystems to form a sphere with uniform density or a spheroid with a low concentration of mass at the center. Therefore barred spirals are different from common spiral galaxies in the following way. The latter have a strong concentration of old stars at the center while in SB the density is nearly uniform to a given distance. At this distance where the ends of the bar are, the density diminishes sharply and farther out it decreases in the usual way. The density jump is necessary to explain a sharp transition from a straight bar to the tightly wound spiral arms.

We cannot avoid the conclusion that during the period of formation of the old stars in SB some cause removed the gas from the central region out to a definite given radius. Such a cause may be only an explosion similar to explosions in M 82 and in several extragalactic radiosources. The nature of the explosion here is not essential. If the explosion takes place when the gas of the galaxy was already contracted into a disc, the jet would be thrown out only along the minor axis of the galaxy. In the plane of the disk there will be motion similar to the expansion of the 3 kps arm in our Galaxy. It cannot become a uniform spheroid which would be necessary to explain the rigid body rotation of a bar. Therefore, we suppose that the explosion takes place when the gas of the galaxy was still spherical. A shock wave would sweep gas from the central region and concentrate it into a thin layer behind the front. At a given distance, which depends upon the energy of the explosion and upon the density of the gas, the wave stops. Its energy is transferred into heating and into the gravitational energy of a shell. A thin spherical shell with a density of more than 10^{-24} g cm^{-3} is formed. It is quite motionless for about 5×10^7 years. In this time the gas, heated by shock, would cool to several thousand degrees Kelvin. The layer of a gas of such a temperature is gravitationally unstable, and would divide into parts which would shrink and divide again to give birth to clusters and stars.

Let us digress a little. Stars usually formed in clusters and the less the density of a gas, the greater the mass of a cluster which can be shrunk by gravitation. Therefore, globular clusters which were formed in rarefied gas of an early stage of a galaxy are much more massive than galactic clusters which were formed in denser gas of a flat subsystem. In a later stage the main part of clusters are disintegrated by external disturbances, or dissipated, and a background of single and double stars and of small groups appeared. In a dense spherical shell of a SB rather small clusters similar to galactic ones would be formed, and there would be no globular clusters in the inner part of these galaxies.

Stars which were formed in the shell have a rather low angular momentum because the gas was ejected from inner regions of the galaxy. However, they have a rather large energy obtained from an explosion and therefore must move along very elongated trajectories inside the sphere. One can calculate their average density in space if the distribution of angular momentum is known. Let us suppose that the distribution of momentum in the gas before an explosion was the same as that in an intermediate subsystems in our Galaxy, and that this distribution is conserved, i.e. that viscosity in the shell is negligible. In a first approximation we say that stars are moving in a field of a uniform sphere. Calculations give us the second approximation (see fig. 5) which is really not very different from uniform distribution. However, there are some concentrations in the center and in the shell where stars were formed. Outside this shell, $(R > R_{sp})$, stars appeared in the usual way and should form a common disc.

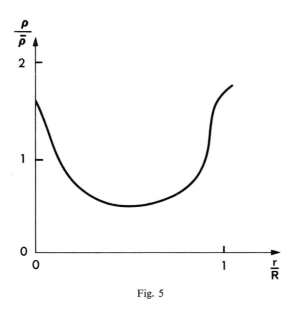

Fig. 5

Remnants of the gas in the shell which did not turn into stars, gradually lost their energy and travelled in circular orbits in the disc. The radius of their orbits is dependent upon the initial momentum. The gas which was removed by the exposition from the central region or from the region near the rotational axis, returns to the center and the magnetic lines are dragged to the center with it. The central concentration creates a magneto-gravitational wave which propagates (from the center) along the magnetic tube.

The wave stimulates the condensation of the gas in the tube. This condensation takes place simultaneously with the flattening of the system, and is facilitated by the fact that the unsymmetrical disc is not at all in equilibrium. In this way a bar might be formed. More massive condensations may be formed at the ends of a bar since the density in the shell was higher and more gas may have remained. After passing the shell, the wave propagates farther and forms spiral arms.

Differential rotation outside the shell folded up the magnetic tubes into spiral arms. Inside the sphere the density is quite uniform and differential rotation is low, but it should also bend the bar. A still more important effect, also resulting in a bending of the bar, is a tension of magnetic lines of the spiral arms. This tension is directed perpendicularly to the bar at its end, and should transform a straight bar into a S-shape in about 10^8 years. In order to maintain a sharp break at the ends, a lot of mass, about $10^8 M_\odot$, must be concentrated there. However, with a gas of such a mass there should be many hot stars making the ends of the bar very bright. Apparently, at the ends of bars having sharp breaks there are clusters of old stars—remnants of a shell. In these clusters magnetic lines are fixed by the gas, the mass of which must be no less than $10^6 M_\odot$. In this case tension of magnetic lines cannot drag the gas out of the cluster.

Tension of the magnetic field between the center and the clusters at the ends straighten the bar, forcing it to rotate as a rigid body. However, the velocity of a circular rotation in a nonuniform sphere is a little different from the velocity of rotation of the bar. Therefore centrifugal force and force of gravity are not in equilibrium, and the gas in the bar moves preferentially from the center. In the inner part of the bar the gas must move to the center. If the distribution of density is as shown in figure 5, the velocity of the streams at the ends of the bar must be about 24 km/sec and the velocity of the streams to the center, about 4 km/sec. This explains the observed streaming of gas along the bar and explains the presence in the center of SB of gas and young stars which are usually absent in the center of ordinary spirals. S-shape SB galaxies have no clusters at the ends of the bar and we may expect that there is no pronounced streaming in their bars in the outward direction. It is more probable that there are inward motions at the ends of the bar since the tension of magnetic lines in spiral arms slows down the rotation of the ends.

Many barred spirals have a ring, and the bar is its diameter. The arms which are tangent to the ring usually extend from the ends of the bar. Galaxies with a ring structure were statistically studied by B.A. Vorontzov-Veljaminov. He showed that a ring does not consist of wound spiral arms, but is a special type of structure. In accordance with our hypothesis, formation of these rings may be imagined in the following way. After the formation of a shell, magnetic lines are pressed into it. A part of the shell with a low momentum, which remains after the formation of stars, returns to the center and to the inner parts of a bar. The outer part of a shell, which was far from the rotational axis, has a rather large momentum and can move far from the center. It is contracted to the galactic plane and forms a ring which is rather dense and self-gravitation can maintain it. The magnetic field makes the ring stable as it does in spiral arms. It does not allow the gas to shrink to the axis of the circular filament. A scheme of magnetic lines of the bar and two half-rings is shown in figure 6. In the places where the magnetic lines issue from the bar they are shrunk into a narrow bunch by the gas clouds which are found in clusters at the ends of the bar. The field was shrunk in a period of condensation of these clouds.

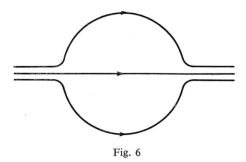

Fig. 6

To check this picture that we have described, special observations are necessary. It is desirable to study the distribution of old stars in SB galaxies. If the distribution is as shown in figure 5, we must see a faint ring, circular in shape in every projection. There must be scarcely any intermediate subsystems and no globular clusters in the central region. There should be no clusters at the ends of bars which abruptly transform into spiral arms. In the inner parts of the bars there should be a slow motion of the gas towards the center.

Ideas on magneto-gravitational waves and on the explosions which occur in the earliest stages of the evolution of galaxies or in later periods may be useful in the interpretation of other types of galaxies, for instance the S0 and SB0. However, we must have more detailed information on these galaxies in order to make such interpretations.

The interpretation of barred spirals may be useful in studying the cause of explosions which take place in galactic nuclei and in powerful radiosources.

A great number of SB, which are comparable in number with the common spirals, prove that in a short period of initial contraction of a protogalaxy the probability of explosion is very high. We must deduce that explosions are connected with a large amount of gas which has contracted to the galactic center. This means that explosions are the result of a condensation of a great mass of gas as supposed by F. Hoyle and W. Fowler. Other possibilities —explosions of superdense bodies (V. A. Ambartsumian) and a concentration of stellar clusters seems less probable. The mechanism which transforms the gravitational energy of shrinking mass into energy of an explosion is so far unknown.

Problems related to the rectification of spiral galaxies

Paris Pişmiş

Observatorio Astronómico, Universidad Nacional de México

In discussing observational data related to flattened galaxies (spirals) it is useful to know the orientation of their plane of symmetry with respect to the observer. Only by the help of this piece of information is it possible to arrive at a more objective representation of the structural and kinematical features of the galaxy. It becomes, thus, necessary to reconstruct the face on view of it, in other words "to rectify" the galaxy.

This problem of orientation cannot be solved in all generality so that simplifying assumptions have to be made. The procedures, or methods, employed to rectify a galaxy fall broadly into two categories which may be termed *structural* and *kinematical*, respectively. Here we propose to examine each of these methods in some detail and discuss their implications. A basic assumption to start with, in both procedures, is that spiral features are coplanar.

Method 1 is based on simple geometrical considerations. Rigorously, the apparent figure of the spiral is compared to the figure in its plane of symmetry, whereby the line of the nodes and the projection angle are determined. One serious shortcoming is that the real figure of the spiral is unknown!

Attempts in the past have been made to obtain the equation of the curve that best represents spiral features of galaxies. von der Pahlen [1911], Groot [1925], Reynolds [1925] and Danver [1942] have discussed the problem. Although no single equation of spiral fits all cases considered, the general conclusion is reached that a logarithmic spiral is a fair approximation in many cases and that this may be used in the determination of orientation. However, since no general agreement exists as to the origin and maintenance of spiral forms we may ask if it is justified to force a single spiral curve to fit a galaxy. Evidently evolution affects the shape of the spiral and since it is reasonable to expect that the spirals we observe are at different stages of evolution there should be no single equation of spiral to represent all of them. Even within the same galaxy at a given instant the curve shown by the details may be much too complicated to attempt an analytic expression for it.

Gauthier-Villars, Paris - Modern Astrophysics - 1967.

A common practice in the rectification of spirals is to adopt as the line
of the nodes the direction of the "apparent major axis". The latter is determined by visual inspection of photographs or in the most favorable case from
isophotes. The ratio of the minor to major axis thus estimated gives φ, the
angle between the plane tangent to the sky and the plane of the galaxy.
In this procedure it is implit, that the approximation of a circular outline
of the arms is valid so that the projected contours of the arms are sensibly
elliptical. This approximation is, doubtless, a crude one.

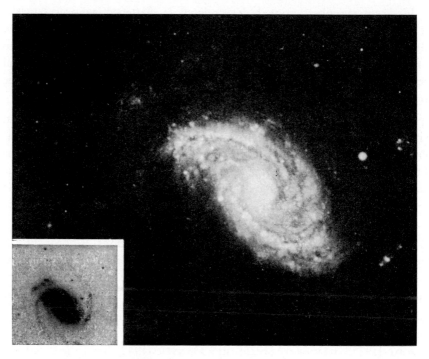

Fig. 1 — The spiral galaxy NGC 5248 (Sc) where a progressive deviation of the apparent
major axis is noted. The deviation is in the same sense as the opening of the arms.
Reproduced from the Hubble Atlas.

STOCK [1954] has shown that for a spiral seen inclined, the line of the
nodes, determined as above, deviates from the true one by an angle α which,
for the logarithmic spiral:

(1) $\bar{\omega} = a \exp(b\theta)$

is given by the expression:

(2) $$\operatorname{tg} \alpha = \frac{b \cos \varphi}{\sin^2 \varphi}$$

In general α is a small angle (reckoned in the plane of the sky) and is constant over all the convolutions of the logarithmic spiral, since b and φ are constants. The apparent major axes determined from the successive convolutions of an inclined logarithmic spiral should thus lie on the same straight line, and this line makes an angle α with the line of the nodes.

Fig. 2 — The spiral galaxy NGC 5364 (Sc) where the progressive deviation of the apparent major axis is in the opposite sense to the opening of the spiral. Reproduced from the Hubble Atlas.

Yet in a number of galaxies where spiral forms can be reliably followed one sees a progressive deviation of the apparent major axes corresponding to the different turns of the spiral; α evidently is not constant throughout such a galaxy which implies: that either b, or φ, or both are not constant. This peculiarity is mentioned as a curious fact in the literature without an explanation (BURBIDGE, 1962). Some galaxies that exhibit this phenomenon are: 1068 (Sb), 3623 (Sa), 5248* (Sc), 5364* (Sc). Those marked with an asterisk are reproduced in figures 1 and 2.

In the present discussion it will be shown that a deviation of the major axes of the kind described is testimony that the corresponding spiral is not logarithmic.

Take the spiral given by the equation:

(3) $\bar{\omega} = a \exp{(b\theta + c\theta^2)}$

where $b > 0$ and $|c| \ll b$.

Clearly for $c = 0$ we have a logarithmic spiral. Assume, again, that the inclination of the spiral is φ. To fix ideas we show, in figures 3 and 4, two logarithmic spirals with $\varphi = 0°$ and $75°$, respectively. X, Y and x, y are the cartesian coordinates in the respective figures. The X-axis is the line of the nodes which corresponds to the x-axis of figure 4. The line of sight is perpendicular to the paper.

We have $x = \bar{\omega} \cos \theta$

$\quad\quad\quad y = \bar{\omega} \sin \theta$

θ increases in the direction of the opening of the spiral.

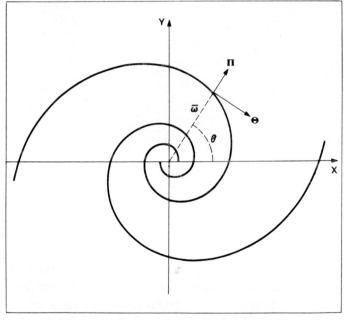

Fig. 3 — Two identical logarithmic spirals drawn in the (X, Y)-plane represent an idealized spiral galaxy seen face on ($\varphi = 0$). $\bar{\omega}$ and θ are the polar coordinates while Π and Θ are the components of velocity in the radial and transverse directions, respectively.

The direction of the "apparent major axis" is evidently that for which the radius vector of the projected spiral is maximum. The angle θ of this direction for which the expression:

(4) $$(x^2+y^2)^{\frac{1}{2}}$$

is maximum will be given by the roots of the equation:

(5) $$\cot g\ \theta + \text{tg}\ \theta\ \cos^2\varphi = \frac{\sin^2\varphi}{b+2\ c\theta}$$

this can be written as:

(6) $$\cot g^2\ \theta - \frac{1}{b+2\ c\theta}\ \sin^2\varphi\ \cot g\ \theta + \cos^2\varphi = 0.$$

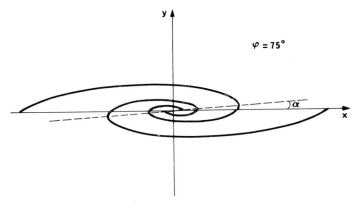

Fig. 4 — The same pair of logarithmic spirals, as in figure 3, seen at an inclination of $\varphi = 75°$. The x-axis is the line of the nodes. The direction of the major axis is shown by the dotted line.

All throughout this discussion the value of the parameter φ will naturally be restricted by the condition:

$$0 \leqslant \varphi \leqslant \frac{\pi}{2}.$$

Two cases will be distinguished:

Case 1. $c = 0$. At first we take φ to be very close to $\pi/2$. The term with $\cos^2\varphi$ being negligible, equation (5) is of the first degree and yields,

$$\text{tg}\ \theta = \frac{b}{\sin^2\varphi}$$

where θ is reckoned in the plane of the galaxy. If α is this angle in the plane of projection one has:

$$\text{tg } \alpha = \frac{b \cos \varphi}{\sin^2 \varphi}$$

this is the relation (2) given by STOCK.

α is thus an increasing function of b, the pitch angle.

For any other value of φ equation (6) giving cotg θ is of the second degree and its roots are as follows:

(7)
$$\frac{1}{2b} \sin^2 \varphi \pm \tfrac{1}{2} \left(\frac{1}{b^2} \sin^4 \varphi - 4 \cos^2 \varphi \right)^{\tfrac{1}{2}}$$

The positive sign is to be taken for the maximum of the radius vector. It is clear that θ is again constant all throughout the convolutions.

An interesting consequence of expression (7) may be pointed out here. Cotg θ and hence θ will be imaginary when:

(8)
$$\left(\frac{1}{b^2} \sin^4 \varphi - 4 \cos^2 \varphi \right) < 0.$$

There will be no real value for θ. Thus for a logarithmic spiral with a given b there is a limiting φ_0 such that for $\varphi < \varphi_0$ the projected spiral will not show a "major axis". This limiting φ_0 is obtained by equating the discriminant to zero; this condition leads to the following second degree equation in cos φ_0:

(9)
$$\cos^2 \varphi_0 + 2 b \cos\varphi_0 - 1 = 0$$

the roots of this are:

(10)
$$- b \pm (b^2 + 1)^{\tfrac{1}{2}}$$

cos $\varphi_0 \geqslant 0$ since $0 \leqslant \varphi \leqslant \pi/2$.

and $(b^2 + 1)^{\tfrac{1}{2}} > b$ therefore the positive sign of the radical is to be taken. The physically significant value of cos φ_0 is thus:

(11)
$$\cos \varphi_0 = (b^2 + 1)^{\tfrac{1}{2}} - b$$

It is clear then, that φ_0 increases as b increases.

We can thus conclude that very open logarithmic spirals with small inclination will not show an apparent major axis if their φ is less than arc cos $(b^2 + 1)^{\tfrac{1}{2}} - b$. In practice, however, this impossibility to determine a major axis will set in for larger inclinations, that is, before one reaches the theoretical limit.

Case 2. $c \neq 0$

Consider the spiral up to $\theta \approx (b/2\,c)$. For $b \approx 50\,|c|$ the spiral will show 4 convolutions and this should cover nearly all spirals observed so far (the reason underlying this restriction will be discussed in the appendix). Now equation (6) is transcendental; we shall not attempt its general solution. Instead we shall consider approximate solutions when φ is close to $\pi/2$. For φ approaching $\pi/2$ equation (6) takes the form:

$$\text{(12)} \qquad\qquad \cotg\,\theta = \frac{\sin^2 \varphi}{b+2c\,\theta}$$

Let the successive roots of this equation (as θ increases) be as follows:

$$\text{(13)} \qquad\qquad \theta_1, 2\pi + \theta_2, ..., (k-1)\,2\pi + \theta_k$$

For $c > 0$ clearly,

$$\text{(14)} \qquad\qquad \theta_1 < \theta_2 < ... < \theta_k$$

This means that for the successive outward turns of the spiral, of which the pitch increases compared to the logarithmic one, *the apparent major axis deviates* gradually *in the sense of the opening of the arms*; NGC 1068 and NGC 5248 exhibit this peculiarity.

When $c < 0$ the successive roots are as follows:

$$\text{(15)} \qquad\qquad \theta_1 > \theta_2 > ... > \theta_k.$$

This result implies that for a spiral of decreasing pitch angle the *deviation of the major axis is opposite to the opening of the spiral arms*. Good examples of such spirals are NGC 3623 and NGC 5364.

Method 2 is used when radial velocity measurements are available, at several position angles, of the flat component of a galaxy. In the few instances where this method is used it is assumed that the field of motions is that of axial rotation only. The maximum observed radial velocity in this case should occur in the direction of the line of nodes. However accumulating observational evidence points to the existence of motions in the radial direction (and probably even in the z-direction) in spiral galaxies.

We shall consider here the flat sub-system of a galaxy where motions are axis-symmetric (and those in the z-direction are negligibly small). We show in what follows, that if these motions consist of circular as well as radial components, Π and Θ respectively, the observed radial velocity will not obtain its extremal values along the nodal line.

Take the galaxy as given in figure 3 and its projection as in figure 4 where the nodal line is the x-axis. Vectors Π and Θ are also represented in figure 3; in the most general case they are functions of $\bar{\omega}$. The plane containing the line of sight is perpendicular to the x-axis. The resultant of Π and Θ projected on the line of sight is:

(16) $$V(\bar{\omega}, \theta) = (\theta \cos \theta - \Pi \sin \theta) \sin \varphi$$

where $V(\bar{\omega}, \theta)$ is the observed radial velocity.

We now seek the value of θ for which expression (16) is maximum or minimum for a given $\bar{\omega}$. From the condition:

$$\frac{\partial V}{\partial \theta} = 0$$

one obtains:

$$\text{tg } \theta_0 = -\frac{\Pi}{\Theta}$$

where θ_0 is reckoned in the plane of the galaxy. In the projection plane we have:

(17) $$\text{tg } \beta = -\frac{\Pi}{\Theta} \cos \varphi.$$

If Π and Θ are both positive as in the figure (expansion and rotation) one finds from (17) that V is minimum at $\theta = -\theta_0$ and maximum at $\theta = \pi - \theta_0$. Thus the observed radial velocity obtains its maximum not at the nodal line but displaced from it by the angle-θ_0. The larger the ratio Π/Θ the larger the absolute value of this angle, for a given φ. When $\Pi \gg \Theta$ the maxima and minima will be very near the minor axis of the projected galaxy, θ_0 tending to $\pi/2$ as a limit. For $\Pi = 0$, $\theta_0 = 0$. The latter is the simplest case and the conventional one where there is only rotation; the maxima and minima of V occur along the nodal line which they define.

However instead of the determination of the nodal line it is more useful to turn the problem around and determine $\Pi(\bar{\omega})$ and $\Theta(\bar{\omega})$ from the observed $V(\bar{\omega}, \theta)$. Once the line of the nodes and φ are determined by the structural method, one has, for a given $\bar{\omega}$, and equation (16) for each of the position angles along which velocities are measured. A least squares solution of (16) gives Π and Θ, the velocity of expansion (or contraction, and the circular velocity, for distance $\bar{\omega}$. This procedure maybe repeated for different $\bar{\omega}$'s and one obtains the variation of Π and of Θ throughout the galaxy.

General Discussion. We have confined the foregoing treatment to the two-dimentional approximation both as regards the structure and the kinematics of the flat component of a galaxy. (The effect of absorbing matter is neglected.) Spiral details are assumed to lie in the plane of symmetry. This means that φ = constant throughout the system. Actually in "normal" spirals the arms appear to be coplanar at least in regions intermediate between the nucleus and boundary(!). Galaxies seen edge-on support this statement. However the outermost sections of spirals may deviate from the plane of symmetry as in NGC 4762, where the two edges curl up and down respectively. This characteristic is observed in our Galaxy as well[1].

In some spirals outer faint arms seen on long exposure photographs seem to belong to a category different from the inner ones, particularly as regards curvature. This phenomenon is manifested in NGC 1068 and 3504, to mention only two. In some cases the deviation of the apparent major axis changes its sense in the outer faint arm as compared to the inner convolutions. In a galaxy like NGC 2685 the outer rings, encircling the spindle shaped system, appear nearly orthogonal to it. But in the majority of cases it is not possible to decide whether the overall shape of arms are projections of space curves (φ not constant) or of plane spirals of different curvatures (of varying b, the pitch angle) or both.

The general assumption made in the kinematical method is that the z-motions of the flat component are negligible as well. The latter assumption is not valid for the central region of galaxies; high resolution spectra taken with image tubes yield evidence of gas clouds moving away from their centers with very high speed. Such is the case with M 31, with our own galaxy and NGC 1068 (WALKER, private communication). In fact the hypothesis is advanced (HUANG and PIŞMIŞ, 1960) that spiral arms are formed as a consequence of ejection of matter from the nucleus of a galaxy. It is conceivable also that far from the nucleus expanding motions will decay so that the dominating motion, there, will be the circular one. At these regions the kinematical method may be indeed applicable to determine the inclination of the galaxy.

We may say, in concluding, that neither the structural not the kinematical method alone are sufficient to determine unambiguously the angle φ and therefore the inclination of a spiral, if high accuracy is pursued.

Appendix

Consider the spiral:

(18)
$$\bar{\omega} = a \exp (b\theta - c'\theta^2)$$

where $-c' = c$.
And again $b \gg c'$.

---

[1] A possible cause of this phenomenon is suggested earlier by this author (PIŞMIŞ, 1961).

It is clear that as θ increases $\bar{\omega}$ will increase until the exponential reaches a maximum; that is when:

$$\theta = \frac{b}{2\,c'}\,.$$

This maximum will occur for

(19) $$\bar{\omega}_{max} = a\,\exp\frac{b^2}{4\,c'}\,.$$

Thus as θ increases the curve represented by equation (3) or (18) will spiral out with a pitch angle decreasing gradually with respect to that of the logarithmic spiral

$$\bar{\omega} = a\,\exp\,(b\theta)$$

until $\bar{\omega}$ reaches the value given in (19). After this maximum is attained, as θ increases $\bar{\omega}$ will diminish.

It is the spiral before $\bar{\omega}$ reaches a maximum that we have taken into account in the foregoing discussion. Although for $c > 0$ no such restriction exists, for the sake of uniformity we have applied the same limit of θ for that case as well. This limit of θ for $b = 50\,|c|$, as adopted earlier, will yield nearly four convolutions until the spiral starts to curl inwards. The spiral with $c < 0$ will always remain within the circle of radius $\bar{\omega}_{max}$.

REFERENCES

BURBIDGE, E. M., 1962, *Symp. on Stellar Evolution*, 283, La Plata.
DANVER, C. J., 1942, *Lund. Obs. Annal.*, **10**.
GROOT, H., 1925, *M. N. R. A. S.*, **85**, 535.
HUANG, S. S. and PIŞMIŞ, P., 1960, *Bol. Obs. Tonantzintla y Tacubaya* **19**, 7.
PIŞMIŞ, P., 1961, *Bol. Obs. Tonantzinla y Tacubaya* **21**, 6.
REYNOLDS, J. H., 1925, *M. N. R. A. S.*, **85**, 1014.
STOCK, J., 1954. *A. J.*, **60**, 216.
VON DER PAHLEN, E., 1911, *A. N.*, **188**, No. 4503.

Acicular Galaxies

K. F. OGORODNIKOV

Leningrad University

1 — A brief outline of theoretical results

An application of the methods of Statistical Physics to the problem of equilibrium figures of rotating stellar systems (OGORODNIKOV, 1958) has led to the conclusion that there are only three essentially different types of rotating systems. The first type consists of moderately flattened spheroids which in a first approximation differ very little from the well known in the classical theory of rotating homogeneous fluid masses Maclaurin spheroids. On the other hand, the second type of the stellar systems is much flattened and resembles another variety of Maclaurin spheroids, the disk-shaped one. Finally the third type consists of highly elongated systems the prototypes of which are homogeneous threeaxes Jacobi ellipsoids.

More precisely, the theory predicts the following general properties of rotating stellar systems;

(1) If the mass of the stellar system is sufficiently large it will assume an equilibrium figure of one of the above three types. If, however, its mass is too small, the gravitation will not be able to counterbalance the tendency for dissipation of the stars. The system then will never consolidate into a regular form and will remain all the time more or less irregular.

(2) The main body of every regular system is surrounded by a diffuse corona (or halo). Corona always has a symmetric spherical form independent of the type of the main body of the system. Within the main body the stellar system behaves much like a continuous medium, while within the corona its properties are largely those of a discrete assembly of masspoints.

(3) In general, especially during early stages of evolution, the density in the main bodies is approximately uniform and proportional to the square of the angular velocity.

(4) The angular velocity within the main body is constant, i.e. its rotation is a rigid-body one.

(5) Only the systems of the first type are dynamically stable, the other two being unstable. The last ones have, however, the property of forming,

through the action of gravitation, of central nuclei. This is driving them away from the critical state of disruption owing to a dangerous approach to the Poincaré lower limit of density.

The smaller is the angular velocity the less the first type systems differ from exact spheres. At the same time the systems of the second and third types tend respectively toward infinitely thin and flat discs, on the one hand, and toward infinitely long and thin rods, on the other, whence the name "acicular" of the latter type.

We may identify the above theoretical figures with the galaxies of different kinds observed on the sky. The first, slightly flattened type we shall identify with E-galaxies. They not only have a suitable form but also have the required rigid body law of rotation. The second, highly flattened type we may identify with the normal SA-galaxies, though it is known that their law of rotation is not a rigid body one. Their density is also not uniform. But this inconsistency appears to be more apparent than real if we bear in mind that the curve $V = f(R)$, where V is the linear speed of rotation and R—the distance from the axis, has two different sections: the one, for small values of R, is ascending almost rectilineously until it reaches a maximum point at R_0, and a second section where the curve is descending. Thus, if we identify the part of the system for $R \leqslant R_0$ with the main body then within it both requirements of the theory on the uniformity of the density and of the rotation will be approximately fulfilled.

2 — What are the acicular galaxies?

There remains only the third type of elongated theoretical figures to be identified. And we now may ask ourselves what kind of existing galaxies can we associate with them? The first thing which comes to the mind are the "bars" of the barred SB-spiral galaxies. As a matter of fact, many of them have the form of elongated ellipsoids as e.g. is the case with NGC 7741. Here the density is apparently uniform. In other barred galaxies a central nucleus is apparent. It has probably absorbed an appreciable part of the mass of the bar and therefore the density distribution in the latter is no more uniform as it is the case e.g. of NGC 4725. But nevertheless, the rotation, if any, must be always a solid body one. Otherwise the main body would be twisted during the first of its revolutions. Now let us assume that the main bodies (bars) of the SB-spiral galaxies are the realizations of the third type of theoretical equilibrium figures. But in the SB-spirals we do not find the bars in equilibrium since there is an outflow of matter from their extremities.

As a matter of fact this is exactly how the spiral arms of the SB-galaxies are originated. The SB-galaxies are nothing but acicular bars in state of disruption resulting from a rapid rotation of the bar around its smallest axis. But then we must expect to find somewhere else acicular galaxies in their integrity, i.e. before the process of disruption has developed itself. We should not expect to find them in great profusion since, as we have already pointed out before, the acicular galaxies are inherently unstable and are always "ready" to disintegrate. As soon as the own gravitation begins to draw the matter toward the center of the bar the angular velocity of rotation increases and the disintegration sets in at the two most vulnerable points at both extremities. The subsequent evolution of the SB-galaxy will proceed in one of two ways: if the efflux of matter is violent as e.g. in NGC 7741, then after a couple of revolutions the mass of the bar will be exhausted and the SB-galaxy will cease to exist. On the other hand, if the efflux is quiescent then almost all of the matter will be concentrated in the nucleus. The ejection of matter will continue as a thin streaming and will form one or several intermittent rings. In both cases the acicular bar will cease to exist. Thus, we can expect to observe an intact acicular galaxy only shortly after its formation before the acceleration of rotation has induced an outflow of matter from its end points.

However a more careful examination of the available photographs of the galaxies shows that there are quite different cases having nothing in common with the formation of SB-galaxies when acicular galaxies do exist notwithstanding their instability. This is, namely, the case when rotation is around the longest axis of the acicular body. Below we give an example of such a case. It is interesting insofar as it shows that in Metagalaxy objects may exist which are "doubly" unstable, since unstable is not only the very figure but is dynamically unstable its rotation around the longest axis.

Below are three photographs of intact acicular galaxies which illustrate what has been said above.

The first is the well known Seyfert group (reproduction from *P.A.S.P.*, **63**, 72, 1951). It consists of six galaxies which, except perhaps one, are interconnected by a single filament of diffuse matter which is most clearly seen in the upper part of the picture (near the arrow). The acicular galaxy is the lowest one on the picture. It shows signs of slow rotation in the counterclockwise direction which is revealed by a corresponding slight twisting of the ends. Seyfert group is a nice example of the formation of the newly born galaxies as condensations in the long intergalactic filaments of matter.

Figure 2 is a reproduction of item 52 of the VORONTSOV-VELYAMINOV, *Atlas of interacting galaxies* [1959]. Here we see two acicular galaxies connected by a short and diffuse filament. The absence of ordinary characteristic features of the normal spirals seen edgewise (no nuclear bulge at the centre, no dark lane along the equator, no sharp edges) as well as a small curvature of the galaxies both give evidence against their being two normal SA-spirals.

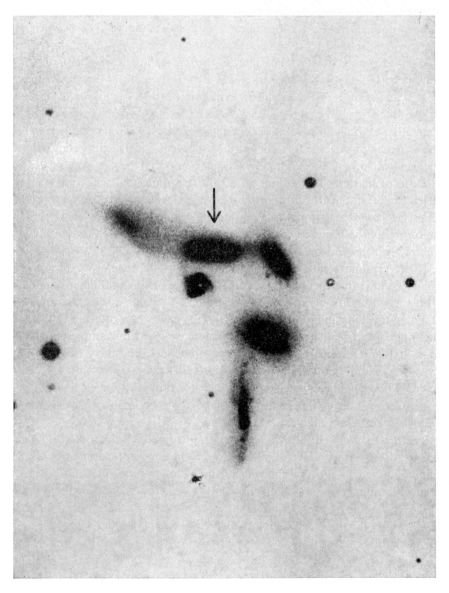

Fig. 1

On the other hand the existence of a short link between them is not so easy to put into accord with any kind of their rotation. But this link together with the peculiar tandem mutual disposition of the galaxies gives support to the supposition that they were formed from a single filament of matter.

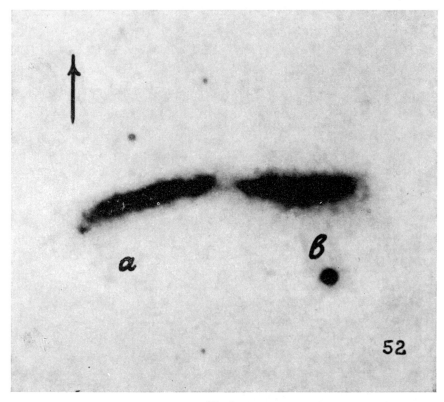

Fig. 2

Figure 3 shows a very interesting case of an acicular galaxy which apparently rotates around its longest axis and an allusion to which was made above. This is NGC 2685 taken from the Sandage " HUBBLE, *Atlas of galaxies*" (1961). In a rather detailed note which accompanies this photograph in the Atlas the possibility of it being "an ellipsoid like a cigar" is indicated. At a first glance it looks like an ordinary S0 galaxy seen edgewise. But the helical filaments which surround the galaxy at right angles to the longest axis of the latter betray rotation around that axis. If our reasoning is true, we have here an instance of a double instability mentioned above.

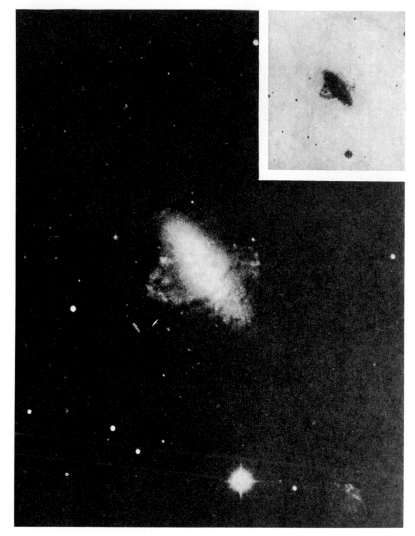

Fig. 3

3 — A few cosmological conjectures

We have seen that acicular stellar systems may be ordinarily considered as present or future bars of SB-spirals. The question now arises what are the factors in the Metagalaxy which provide conditions necessary for the formation of these bodies. That such factors really exist shows not only the case of SB-galaxies but also some of the irregular galaxies which like e.g.

the LMC, NGC 3109, NGC 3034 and others have the form of a diffuse and long shafts. Now we can suggest that the reason why new galaxies have sometimes elongated forms is connected with their formation in the long intergalactic filaments of matter first discovered by F. ZWICKY [1953].

From the theoretical point of view it appears possible that acicular galaxies in some cases may transform themselves into normal spiral SA-galaxies. We shall assume that the intergalactic filaments consist at first of plasma kept back by long intergalactic magnetic force-tubes. Gradually there appear condensations of matter accompanied by the formation of chemical elements and stars. These condensations are the future new galaxies. Some of the condensations are acicular in form. If such a condensation is a massive one then it will evolve into a SB-galaxy. But if its mass is small and the length is large then the stars will rapidly dissipate from it and form a diffuse halo around the galaxy. At the same time the main body after having lost its stars will be twisted like an empty umbrella case, the diffuse matter in it being kept together by the magnetic forces. And out of this matter the star formation will continue. But this time it will be a second generation of stars. They will have small peculiar velocities and they will fill out a volume of a round flat disc circumscribed by the rotating twisted main body. The pattern of the twisted main body will continue to be observable long afterwards as spiral arms.

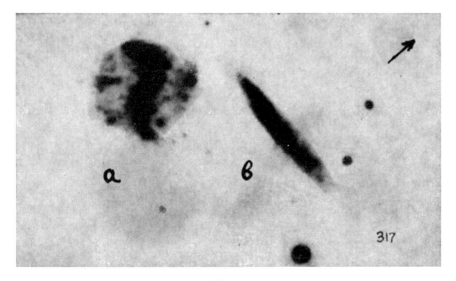

Fig. 4

The process of transformation just described must be rather quick and therefore the number of galaxies in state of transformation seen on the sky must be very small. But a few of them do appear on our photographs. The one example of these objects is NGC 7479 which has been referred to elsewhere (OGORODNIKOV, 1965). On figure 4 is another such example which is VV 317 from Vorontsov's Atlas. Here we see two acicular galaxies. The one denoted by b is a plain specimen of these systems while the a-galaxy is apparently in a state of transformation into a normal SA-spiral.

It may be noted that the above process of the formation of normal spirals is in general agreement with J.H. Oort's conception of the history of our Galaxy exposed by him in his Discourse at the XII Hamburg Assembly of the IAU. And now a final remark. In this connection the spiral arms should be considered as remnants of former intergalactic filaments thus having an intergalactic origin which is in accordance with the views expressed by F. HOYLE and J.G. IRELAND [1960].

REFERENCES

HOYLE, F. and IRELAND, J.G., 1960, *M.N.R.A.S.*, **120**, 173.

OGORODNIKOV, K.F., 1958, *Dinamika zvezdnych sistem. Gosud. Izdatel'stvo fiz.-mat. literatury*, Moskva, 1965. English translation by J.B. SYKES: *Dynamics of Stellar Systems*, Pergamon Press, Oxford.

SANDAGE, A., 1961, *The Hubble Atlas of Galaxies* (Carnegie Institution of Washington).

VORONTSOV-VELYAMINOV, B.A., 1959, *Atlas i Katalog vzaimodejstvujustshich galaktik. Izd. Gosudarstvennyj Astronomitsheskij Institut imeni P.K. Shternberga pri Moskovskom Gosud. Universitete*, (Moskva). *Atlas and Catalogue of interacting Galaxies*, Part I, (Ed. Moscow Sternberg Institute).

ZWICKY, F., 1953, *Phys. Blätter*, **9**, 406.

Dwarf galaxies in clusters

Gibson REAVES

Department of Astronomy, University of Southern California

1 — Introduction

Because studies of the various kinds of stars that compose galactic clusters have provided us with a great deal of knowledge about stellar evolution, we may expect—by analogy—that studies of the population of clusters of galaxies will provide us with insights into the origin and evolution of galaxies. With this in mind, let us consider here one aspect of this problem, namely: the dwarf galaxy population of some clusters of galaxies.

It is first necessary to answer the question: what is a dwarf galaxy? Basically, the answer is: an underluminous one. But it is not yet possible significantly to refine this answer and to specify unequivocally a range of absolute magnitude within which an aggregation of stars should be called a dwarf galaxy. Specifically, a discontinuity in the run of physical properties of galaxies, from the brightest to the faintest, has not yet been established. In general, underluminous galaxies have relatively low surface brightnesses and low center-to-limb luminosity gradients, yet these characteristics also pertain to some of the very brightest (radio) galaxies.

Is it true that dwarf galaxies, though outnumbering normals (by any definition of the term dwarf), make an insignificant contribution to the aggregate mass in—or the density of—space ? We may turn this around to *define* dwarf galaxies as those galaxies not sufficiently massive to make a significant contribution to the mass density of space. On this basis a reasonable borderline between dwarf and normal galaxies is at absolute magnitude -15; with almost any estimate of a luminosity function and mass-luminosity law for galaxies, objects fainter than this do not appear to make a significant contribution to the mass density of space. Further, a division at absolute magnitude -15 is compatible with the qualitative observation that as one looks at fainter and fainter galaxies, the classifiability within Hubble's "tuning fork" sequence becomes less and less.

Gauthier-Villars, Paris - Modern Astrophysics - 1967.

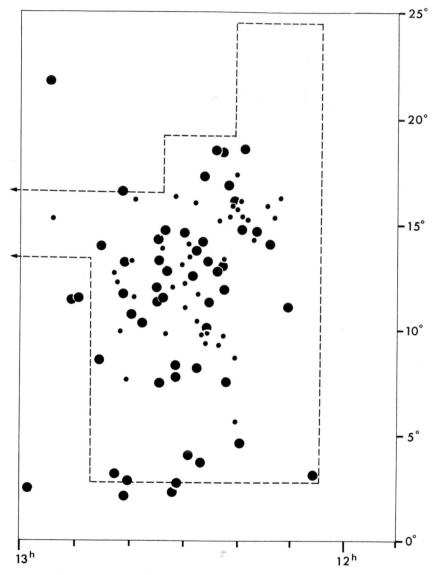

Fig. 1(a) — The Virgo Cluster.

2 — Observations

(a) Local group

It would be logical to begin with a survey of the dwarf members of the Local group. But this group is quite small, and very poorly searched for

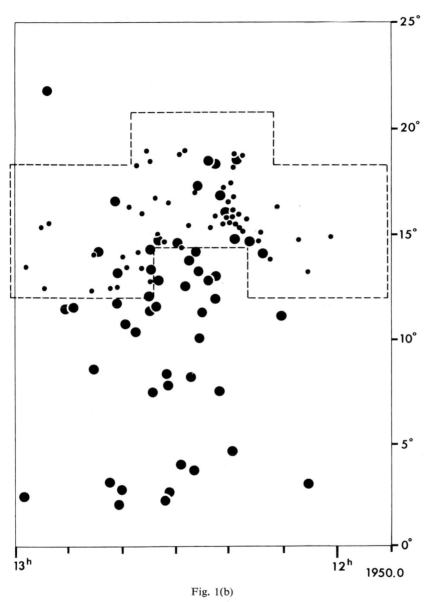

Fig. 1(b)

dwarfs, not only in depth, but also in the southern celestial hemisphere. Moreover, the Zone of Avoidance includes, perhaps, some of the most revealing parts of it.

(b) Virgo cluster

The first investigation of the dwarf galaxies in the Virgo cluster was made by REAVES [1952, 1956], and was based on plates taken with the blue-corrected lens of the Lick Observatory Carnegie 20-inch astrograph, 103a-0 emulsion. A revision was made in 1960 and 1961 using the paper prints of the National Geographic Society-Palomar Observatory *Sky-Survey*; all of the Virgo dwarfs with revised diameters $\geqslant 0\rlap{.}'6$ are shown as small dots in figure 1(a). These are between 3 and 5 kpc in extent, have absolute magnitudes between -16 and -14, and belong to the NGC 205-185-147-Sculptor dwarf sequence (REAVES, 1962); the dashed line encloses the area searched for dwarfs. Plotted as large dots are all normally bright galaxies in VAN DEN BERGH's [1960a] reclassification of the Shapley-Ames catalog, except that those listed by HOLMBERG [1961] as suspected foreground or background galaxies, and NGC 4826, also probably foreground, are omitted. Note how very closely the surface distribution of the dwarfs matches that of the normally bright galaxies.

In the spring of 1962, a region of the Virgo cluster was again surveyed for dwarfs, this time using three Palomar Observatory 48-inch schmidt plates (103a-D through a yellow filter) made available to me by W. A. BAUM. The 53 dwarfs found in that survey are plotted in figure 1(b). These objects are comparable in every way to those plotted in figure 1(a), except that here the survey is carried to much fainter limits. Note that even so, the general character of the distribution is unchanged, though a few discrepancies in individual cases are apparent.

(c) Canes Venatici cluster

A clustering of dwarfs in the Canes Venatici cluster was first noted by VAN DEN BERGH [1959] in his analysis of his catalog of dwarf galaxies. Later [1960b], he published a discussion of the Canes Venatici cluster in which the close association of the dwarfs with the normals was illustrated. Figure 2 shows the Canes Venatici cluster in detail; all of van den Bergh's dwarfs in the area are plotted: dwarf spheroids represented by dots and dwarf irregulars by crossed dots. All probable normal members according to VAN DEN BERGH are plotted except NGC 4182: circles represent Sb galaxies, triangles Sc or Irregulars. Notice that here, as in Virgo, the association of dwarfs with normals is very close and detailed.

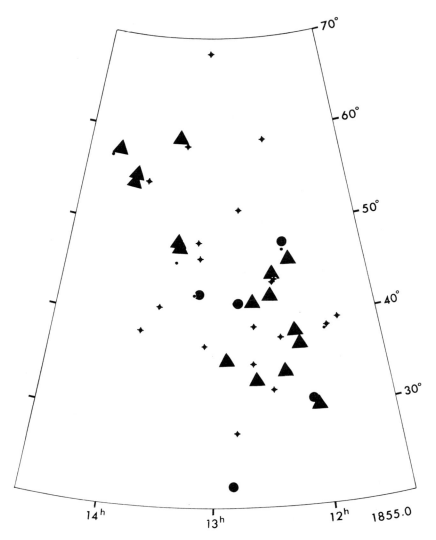

Fig. 2 — The Canes Venatici Cluster.

(d) Fornax cluster

The Fornax cluster was first surveyed for dwarfs by HODGE [1959, 1960] on the basis of three ADH schmidt plates. He found 17 dwarfs, recognizing them by their low surface brightnesses and luminosity gradients, and the fact that such objects were not found in three control areas located 10° from the cluster. Inspection of Hodge's map of the area suggested that here the

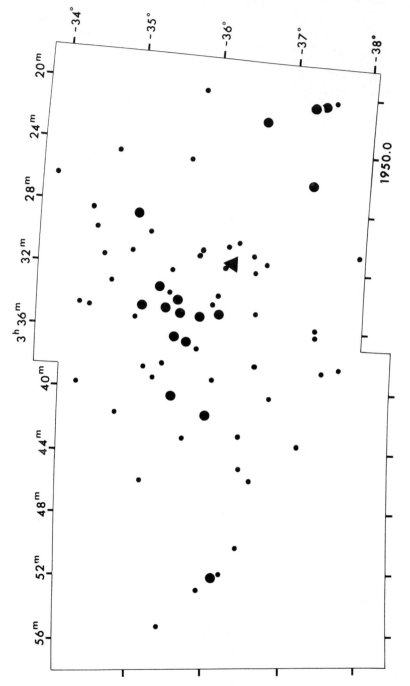

Fig. 3 — The Fornax Cluster.

association between dwarf and normal galaxy might be different from that in Virgo and Canes Venatici, but it was clear that a survey over a larger area of the sky would be desirable. Figure 3 shows the results of such a survey (REAVES, 1964). It is based on an examination of Palomar Observatory 48-inch schmidt plates (103a-D through a yellow filter) made available to me by F. ZWICKY. The large circular dots represent normally bright E, S0, and Sa galaxies in the area; the large triangle represents the giant southern SBc, NGC 1365. The small dots represent 51 dwarf galaxies in the NGC 205-185-147-Sculptor sequence. (About 5 dwarfs presumably similar to IC 1613 and NGC 6822—i.e., containing population I material—were found; these are not shown.) Some of the dwarfs plotted here were listed and measured for magnitude by HODGE; using his values as a basis, the dwarfs shown here are probably between apparent magnitudes 17 and 18. These correspond to absolute magnitudes -14 and -15. The apparent angular extents (usually imprecisely termed angular "diameters") correspond to about 3 kpc. Thus these seem to be similar to the early type dwarfs found in the Local group and in the Virgo cluster.

The detailed association between dwarfs and cluster normals characteristic of the Virgo and Canes Venatici clusters does not appear to obtain here. Yet this is perhaps an illusion: if we find the median projected distance from each dwarf to the nearest normal shown in the figures, the value is essentially the same for all three clusters studied—about 140 kpc. The Fornax cluster differs from the others not because its dwarfs are farther away, but because its normals are closer together. It is more dense.

(e) Other clusters

Although the presence of dwarfs among several other groups and clusters of normal galaxies has been mentioned in passing by numerous investigators, to my knowledge, no special studies of their arrangement other than those cited here have been published.

3 — Conclusions and Speculations

We seek now to use these observations to shed some light on the problems concerning the origin and evolution of galaxies and clusters of galaxies. On the basis of these observations of the Virgo and Canes Venatici clusters, it is tempting to generalize and conclude that in all irregular (late type) clusters of galaxies, the spatial association of dwarfs with normal galaxies is close and detailed. In expanding on this point, AMBARTSUMIAN [1961] wrote that these observations bear, "... testimony to the fact that equipartition of energies between the bright and the faint members of the irregular clusters is out of the question, and that the phenomena of instability are expressed in irregular clusters much more sharply than in spherical ones". While the significance of a lack of equipartition of energies to questions relating to the stability and evolution of clusters of galaxies is clouded because of our present lack of knowledge of cluster dynamics, it has been common to regard regular clusters—denser and composed predominantly of early type galaxies—as having greater evolutionary ages than irregular clusters. If so, then why are not the dwarfs in the Fornax cluster more spread out—more than in Virgo or in Canes Venatici? Could it be that dwarf galaxies, as independent systems, are relatively short-lived, and that they are more or less continuously being ejected (spewed off) by normal galaxies? Certainly there is a continuous transition from knots and condensations in spiral arms, on one extreme, to isolated dwarf galaxies on the other.

It may be more realistic, however, to conclude that equipartition of energies between dwarf and normal galaxies simply does not obtain in either irregular *or* regular clusters. A similar conclusion in regard to the Coma cluster has been reached by others; see the excellent summary by ROOD [1965].

The observational bases for the above comments are so meager that these comments should be regarded as speculations, not as conclusions. The great problem of the internal dynamics of clusters of galaxies remains quite unsolved.

REFERENCES

AMBARTSUMIAN, V. A., 1961, *A. J.*, **66**, 536.

HODGE, P.W., 1959, *P.A.S.P.*, **71**, 28.

HODGE, P.W., 1960, *Ibid*, **72**, 188.

HOLMBERG, E., 1961, *A. J.*, **66**, 620.

REAVES, G., 1952, *Dissertation* (University of California: Berkeley).

REAVES, G., 1956, *A. J.*, **61**, 69.

REAVES, G., 1962, *P. A. S. P.*, **74**, 392.

REAVES, G., 1964, *A. J.*, **69**, 556.

ROOD, H. J., 1965, *Dissertation* (University of Michigan: Ann Arbor).

VAN DEN BERGH, S., 1959, *Publ. David Dunlap Observatory*, **II**:5.

VAN DEN BERGH, S., 1960a, *Ibid.*, **II**:6.

VAN DEN BERGH, S., 1960b, *Ap. J.*, **131**, 558.

Note added in proof, 1966 August 1: The following papers relating to dwarf galaxies in clusters were published after this article was written:

AARSETH, S. J., 1966, "Dynamical evolution of clusters of galaxies, II" in *M. N. R. A. S.*, **132**, 35.

HODGE, P. W., 1966, "Radii, orbital properties, and relaxation times of dwarf elliptical galaxies" in *Ap. J.*, **144**, 869.

HODGE, P. W., PYPER, D. M. and WEBB, C. J., 1965, "Dwarf galaxies in the Fornax cluster" in *A. J.*, **70**, 559.

REAVES, G., 1966, "Dwarf galaxies in the Coma cluster" in *P. A. S. P.*, **78**, *in press*.

New morphological types of galaxies

B. Vorontsov-Velyaminov

Sternberg Astronomical Institute, Moscow

From the study of structure of some 10,000 galaxies (ellipticals excluded) reproduced from the Palomar Sky Atlas it is argued that the existing classifications are not adequate to the enormous variety of structures. The "peculiar" galaxies are also too numerous to be left out of scope of the classification. Rings and disc are often the most prominent features of structure. They have different degrees of resolution and deserve to be isolated in separate sequences. Some new morphological types of galaxies are reproduced together with the additional illustrations of the forms which cannot be explained by purely mechanical processes.

We are indebted to E. Hubble for the first reasonable classification of galaxies which he developed and improved twice. No wonder that the subsequent classifications were closely related to it. His division of galaxies into ellipticals, ordinary and barred spirals and classes intermediate between the true spirals and ellipticals will remain probably forever. For flattened systems most important was his introduction of the degree of resolution of spiral arms which now is interpreted as the difference of population. However, now it is more and more felt that at present his scheme is unsufficient for the classification as more and more galaxies are studied, but no other generally accepted classification exists. No distinction exists between the supergiant, giant and dwarf ellipticals. Besides the dwarf ellipticals belong to the two opposite species—very condensed (as M 32) and very loose ones.

Excluding the ellipticals, Hubble had at his disposal some 300 structural galaxies in 1925 and three times more for his latest classification. *The Palomar Sky Atlas* brings to light tens of thousands galaxies hitherto unknown. The author has compiled a collection of 10,000 enlarged reproductions of structural galaxies from this Atlas. They are to be compared to some two or three hundreds published so far. Of them only one or two dozens still are mentally conceived by those, who do not study their morphology in detail. These by no means exhaust the infinite variety of forms existing in nature. There are no two structural galaxies exactly of the same form. So far all efforts have been directed to put the known forms into the least possible number of classes. Our aim is on the contrary to show the real variety of

Gauthier-Villars, Paris - Modern Astrophysics - 1967.

these forms. Having a definite number of classes chosen by some investigator the latter forcibly tries to drag the real objects into these classes. Every object drastically objecting to this procedure he calls peculiar or irregular. It is said often that I reproduce the "peculiar" galaxies—a kind of exceptions. The point is however that the number of such peculiarities is too considerable to ignore them. Even in the HUBBLE *Atlas*, which intends to show the prototypes, some 10% of galaxies are peculiar, which often is noted by Sandage himself. I am often asked what is the percent of peculiar galaxies. This cannot be answered primarily because there is a gradual transition of the strongly pronounced peculiarities to the "normal" objects. Were not the majority of galaxies badly overexposed on the *Palomar Atlas*, the number of "peculiar" galaxies in my collection could be enlarged manyfold. Many of the peculiarities are of basic importance. So I have reproduced [1964] many galaxies which demonstrate the impossibility that the spiral and other forms can originate by mechanical causes, in particular by the outflow of matter from the nucleus or bar. Possibly the magnetic phenomena are responsible there.

One has also to remember that HUBBLE's classification was under the influence of idea of evolution of ellipticals into spirals or vice versa. Now more and more astronomers come to the conclusion that there are different ways of evolution.

We present here the reproductions of some galaxies from the Palomar Atlas. The majority of them were never reproduced and were even unknown. They are enlarged to a scale 4″ per mm. As a rule we quote only the MCG (*Morphological Catalogue of Galaxies*) numbers. When sometimes an NGC number for them exists it will be in most cases of no value and it is time to pass from the obsolete NGC to the MCG.

With appropriate comments we reproduce here, besides the new morphological types, some ordinary galaxies which present some special interest.

1 — New Morphological Types

(a) Nρ; H! *galaxies*

In 1962, in part III of MCG we finally established the existence of specific type of super giant galaxies which often are seen as the principal members of clusters. They are described there on many occasions. For instance MCG 2-8-44 has a note: "Irregular nucleus surrounded by tremendous halo.

Such galaxy often dominates in a cluster and differs strongly from the galaxies E and N; H by the dimension of its halo and by gradient of luminosity. References to the other representatives of this type are added to the descriptions of 2-7-17, 2-17-4, 2-39-20, 2-58-81, 2-59-35, 1-39-9, 5-38-5, 3-41-78 in clusters and of isolated galaxies apparently of the same type: 1-8-16, 1-33-40, 1-39-9, 7-20-36, 5-35-20, 4-8-5. MCG 2-59-35 = NGC 7649 15 mag has a red shift $+12727$ km/sec, $M = -20.5$ and diameter $> 40,000$ pc. The halo apparently is not flat but roughly spherical and the nucleus in different cases may have different structure. Sometimes it seems to be multiple like in radiogalaxy NGC 6166—also the leader of a cluster. Such galaxies decidedly form a new morphological type and must be classified separately. In plate I are reproduced some of these galaxies: MCG 2-39-20 and 3-41-78 in clusters and isolated 5-30-96 and 7-26-4, the latter with hot spots in the nucleus according to W. Morgan. Probably they are of the same type.

(b) Sharp spirals

It is believed that the diameters of all galaxies drastically vary with the effective exposure. In M 31 and 33 the surface brightness falls off gradually and merge into sky background. Holmberg's and Vaucouleurs' proposition to measure all galaxies to a definite isophote is most correct but difficult for mass measurement of diameters.

From morphological point of view we proposed [1960a] that the diameters of spirals must be compared only within the distinctly visible spiral structure. In plate II are reproduced five spirals of late type, ordinary and barred with very sharp boundary. Their diameters will be practically the same for all exposures, for the eye and from the microphotometric tracing. This must be physically significant. Is it not reasonable to differentiate in a classification the two different morphological types: sharp galaxies and spirals with very diffuse borders ? 2-28-5 = NGC 3367 with its inner structure is reproduced in the Hubble Atlas where nothing allows us to suspect so sharp borders.

(c) Some asymmetric galaxies

In plate II are four galaxies with extreme asymmetry related to the equatorial dark belt, and 2-5-11, where there is some possibility of two overlapping galaxies. In all four cases the further side of a galaxy beyond the central lens is not seen, as well as its prolongations in the principal plane, though the Palomar Atlas shows very faint surface brightness in general. Exactly of the same kind is the reproduction of the underexposed photograph of NGC 1947 (VAUCOULEURS, 1959), which Vaucouleurs classifies as SA 0 "peculiar." We see that such "peculiar galaxies" form a definit morphological type.

(d) On the criteria for classification

In the former Hubble's classification the correlation between the relative size and brightness of the central formation, the degree of tightness of the arms, the resolution of the arms, was adopted as established. Thus his types Sa, Sb, Sc were really the types and the symbols describing all the main features of a galaxy. From the study of the Palomar Atlas we made a revelation that no such strict correlation exists. It is but a tendency. On the other hand there are innumerable galaxies where different details (arms, rings etc.) have different resolution. Therefore in MCG we note, when possible, the resolution of every detail separately using the HUBBLE's symbols a, b, c supplemented by d and i. We were much pleased to see that in the Hubble Atlas Sandage writes: "the three classification criteria are not always consistent." He segregates quite a set of Sa galaxies with small nucleus. In MCG are described many galaxies with smooth but widely open arms (2-30-18 plate IV) and well resolved arms wound tightly around a considerable nucleus. Examples are in plate II.

SANDAGE writes also: "The assignment of galaxies to the Sa, Sb or Sc type is based here primarily on the characteristics of the arms." Thus, it is now not such a definite classification of a galaxy as a whole, which was possible for Hubble formerly. It is closer to our description in MCG, though it remains often unknown to which structure of the galaxy it is related. In principle it means that from the true classification the Hubble Atlas tends to pass to descriptions (as in MCG), only not by symbols, but by words. It is to be interpreted as a conclusion practically unanimous with ours—the classification of galaxies must be wholly revised.

As a result of classification mostly of the flat component, instead of the galaxy as a whole, many inconsistencies arise. Take for instance NGC 4762 in the Hubble Atlas: "undoubtedly an S 01" system. It has apparent axial ratio 1:10. The S 01 systems are considered as the intermediate between Sa and E and closest to the latter. But can such a flat system be considered as the nearest to an elliptical ? However, the insert photograph shows there clearly that NGC 4726 is a counterclock spiral of some variety. If S 0 galaxies really represent a transition form from E to flat spirals it seems nevertheless conflicting that in the Hubble Atlas NGC 4215 S 0_2 is more flat than S 0_3 NGC 5866.

In this respect and generally very interesting is the galaxy 5-38-17 (plate III). It is thick with dark equatorial belt which is the best illustration of the ring of dark matter described by Sandage in S 0 galaxies. The flat component is here very narrow and the bulge very large. The form of 5-38-17 is nearest to ellipticals.

Progressing from SB 0 to SBb(r) we return to the short bright bars which in NGC 2950 SB $0_{\frac{1}{2}}$ and in NGC 3351 SBb(rs) are much alike, but it is said about 2950: "Since the bar is nearly as thick as the nucleus, the galaxy is... between SB 0_1 and SB 0_2."

When we come to the spirals with complicated nucleus or several sets (stories) of outer structures the situation is still more arbitrary. For instance NGC 4736 has several subsequent spiral arms of very different resolution. It is classified as Sb by Sandage and as SAab by Vaucouleurs apparently from the averaged resolution of different arms. NGC 210 is classified in the Hubble Atlas as Sb. The outer arms are wide open, thin, with numerous bright knots. Their resolution is rather c. The inner arms detached from the outer ones are very smooth—resolution a. So here the inner structure is completely neglected for classification.

NGC 1068 is classified as Sb according to the inner structure. Here on the contrary the outer spiral arms of *amorphous texture*, as says SANDAGE, are neglected. Such cases are very numerous even among the bright galaxies classified in the Hubble Atlas and by Vaucouleurs. (We emphasize that here is given the criticism not of the astronomers but of the efforts to adopt a simplified classification to a very complicated nature...)

In the cases mentioned above the structure neglected was quite evident on the photograph. The nuclei of most galaxies are yellow and remind the condensed ellipticals. But some flat systems contain in the lens or in the bar a hot structure in a form of a ring, of small spiral, of spots (NGC 4314, 4321, 1097, etc.). This is most important, it concerns the distribution of population, it differs morphologically. The classification gives no indication upon such nuclei. Sometimes they are considered to define the type of a galaxy, sometimes they do not. NGC 4314 in the Hubble Atlas is classified as SBa(s) pec. But the spiral in the centre which forms the "nucleus" is Sc, it is the brightest detail of the galaxy and not too small. Why should it be an SBa system ?

(e) *Ring and disc galaxies*

NGC 3081 in the Hubble Atlas is classified as Sa, as Sb$^+$ III by van den Bergh, as (R) SAB(r)0$^+$ by VAUCOULEURS. It has a bright small inner part in a disc *Da*, which is well seen in plate III and is bordered by a ring of *b* structure. It is reproduced also by RANDERS [1940]. Here the structure of the ring completely detached from the nucleus is neglected. The ring is considered as an appendix that helps to classify the small nucleus whose structure is barely distinguishable. SANDAGE speaks of a very faint bar crossing the disc. Nothing is said upon the nucleus. Vaucouleurs' classification [1959] is based on the nucleus where he apparently recognizes a short bar as in NGC 4262. In *plate IV* by RANDERS the nucleus appears rather as a bulge with two very short, bright and tight arms thus resembling the central part of 5-56-2. The latter represents a very frequent new morphological type where such a small bright structure is inside a large detached ring. The structure of the later may be *a*, *b* or *c*. 5-56-2 has a thin ring with many so outstanding condensations (HII regions) that its resolution in our notation would be *d*. Apparently such objects as NGC 3081 and 5-56-2 (very numerous) have nothing to do with the So and SB0 objects "intermediate between E and Sa, SBa spirals." We suspect that the nucleus of NGC 4262 (VAUCOULEURS, 1959) is also not a stubby bar, but is of the kind just described.

It is to be remembered, that in all small galaxies the structure of the nuclear part is not resolved even by the largest telescopes. Therefore the classification perhaps will be more homogeneous if based on the outer structures. If so, one has still more right to name as a new morphological type the ring and disc galaxies. We have drawn attention to this already in 1960 (VORONTSOV-VELYAMINOV, 1960*b*). On PA are seen hundreds of galaxies where besides the overexposed nucleus, which may have structure and which may not, the most prominent detail is the disc, or detached ring or both. In Vaucouleurs classification the introduction of SAB galaxies and the attention to the rings was important, but the rings were regarded only as additional detail even when much brighter than the barely visible bar. Of crucial significance is that discs and rings exist having the same variety of resolution as the spiral arms — *a*, *b*, *c*, *d*. We note the perfect circle with sharp edge and a *c*—structure NGC 2976. Discs in combination with other formations are presented in plates III and V.

In NGC 3393 the central formation is exactly as in 5-56-2 (plate III). 12-4-1 (plate III) is a disc with a small sharp nucleus and only the trace of a bar. Nothing of the kind is reproduced in the Hubble Atlas. -4-49-10 (plate V) is a disc with a nucleus in a detached ring of *d* structure. It cannot be classified among the S 0 galaxies. Other "early" and "late" discs and rings are shown in plates III and V. They can form a sequence parallel to that of S and SB galaxies.

We distinguished [1964] the independent structural elements: nucleus, disc, ring, spiral, arc.

Here we note that these elements can be transformed from one to another and form intermediate structures. This complicates the classification.

In plate III 1-37-31 presents a γ-form which transforms into a massive Rc ring. No other spiral arms. The object is quite different from the usual SBc galaxies. In 13-7-40 we see the contrary winding arms. In -4-32-3 one arm changes its direction. 5-38-17 probably is a ring galaxy with dark equatorial belt. The bulge is large, the ring tight and narrow. 7-28-58 is a ring with complicated nucleus. In 7-30-38 the incomplete massive ring Rc is brighter than the nucleus. 5-30-102 (not shown) is an exact small copy of this "peculiar" galaxy. NGC 3393 is apparently a bright ring nebula or a spiral (like in 5-56-2) within a disc. 12-17-23 is a bright disc, one of the largest representatives of this morphological type. Distinct boundary discriminates this types from the S0 and SB0 galaxies with diffuse boundaries. 12-4-1 has very faint but long bar. It is intermediate between the disc galaxies and SB0, where the bar is very bright. The object does not fit any of the descriptions describing the SB 0 subclasses in the Hubble Atlas. All the galaxies mentioned above are in plate III.

2 — Galaxies of Special Interest

a) Plate IV gives some additional illustrations to our paper [1964] upon the magnetic-like phenomena in spiral galaxies. In IC 4538 the strips connecting the arms form lacy patterns which are not possible to produce by gravitation. In 1-31-8 one arm intersects the half ring. The same is seen in 3-31-96 and 1-35-31. In 2-27-21 two arms intersect each other and the loops are seen. This also is another instance of the arms winding in opposite directions, one more demonstration of relative independence of their winding from the sense of rotation. In 2-60-7 we see the γ-form of the same significance. In 2-32-54 the sole arm apparently intersects the main body. In 4-35-14 one arm starts from the middle of the bar and not from its end. This important fact is present in some other galaxies. In 2-58-41 we see again the two pairs of contrary arms. The same in a γ-form is in 3-5-28. In 13-4-4 the central body is again a nucleus with short bright and wide arms. The bright parts of the bar are far from the nucleus and are not diametrically opposed.

The nucleus is not in the centre of the disc and ring. 3-5-28 has a nice $\gamma \rightarrow R$ form. 2-30-18 is an Sa galaxy with wide open arms in contradiction to the belief that in Sa galaxies the arms are tightly wound. In MCG are noted many such galaxies.

In plate V are galaxies with sharp discs sometimes tending to show the ring effect and galaxies with Rc rings. Note the similarity of the "peculiar" galaxies -4-49-10 and 9-32-7, as well as 9-18-86 with a Rd or Ri ring. 5-18-14 has an arc convex toward the centre!

4-22-25 is once more a close pair with similar direction of winding. (Another such pair was shown by the author in 1964.) 6-7-16 is a disc with two perfect loops. Its resolution is a! 7-6-2 is a very enigmatic object. In red light two of starlike objects in it seem to be sharp galaxies.

(b) Flat systems

In the Hubble atlas Sandage says that NGC 4762 "is one of the flattest galaxies known." Its axial ratio is 1:10. In plate I we reproduce MCG 4-29-60 and 7-30-11 with axial ratio 1:35 and 1:25 respectively. No bulge or nucleus is apparent and no equatorial belt of dark matter. The resolution of the first one appears to be b, that of the second-c. They may be S or SB spirals or discs with very small nuclei.

In plate I MCG 2-58-37 has the axial ratio of the disc 1:25 but with an enormously thick, nearly spherical bulge and no prominent dark lane. 4-37-34 has a c resolution with a heavy equatorial belt and a spherical nucleus enormous for an Sc galaxy. 8-15-52 represents an analogy with NGC 2188 reproduced in volume II of the Vistas in Astronomy (p. 1559) (EVANS, 1956), which by some theoretical astronomers are considered as possible "needles" or "sticks". Of the same kind, with blunt edges, are 6-28-15, 6-29-38, 4-20-16, 3-41-138, 0-53-7 and others. So far we have had few possibilities to reproduce on good paper many illustrations of the variety of morphological forms. Besides many objects from the Palomar Atlas are difficult to reproduce owing to their small size, over-exposure or faintness. However in our papers (1960a, 1964) and here we presented already more than 100 galaxies which illustrated sufficiently the suggestions exposed in these papers. . . .

It is urgent to direct the large telescopes to the study of new morphological types with complicated structure.

REFERENCES

EVANS, J.W., 1956, *Vistas in Astronomy*, II, p. 1559 (ed. A. Beer, Pergamon Press, London).

RANDERS, G., 1940, *Ap. J.* **92**, 235.

VAUCOULEURS, G., 1959, *Handbuch der Physik*, **53**.

VORONTSOV-VELYAMINOV, B., 1960a, *Astr. Zh.*, **37**, 778; *Sov. Astron.* **4**, 735.

VORONTSOV-VELYAMINOV, B., 1960b, *Astr. Zh.*, **37**, 381; *Sov. Astron.* **4**, 365.

VORONTSOV-VELYAMINOV, B., 1964, *Astr. Zh.* **41**, 814; *Sov. Astron.* **8**, 649.

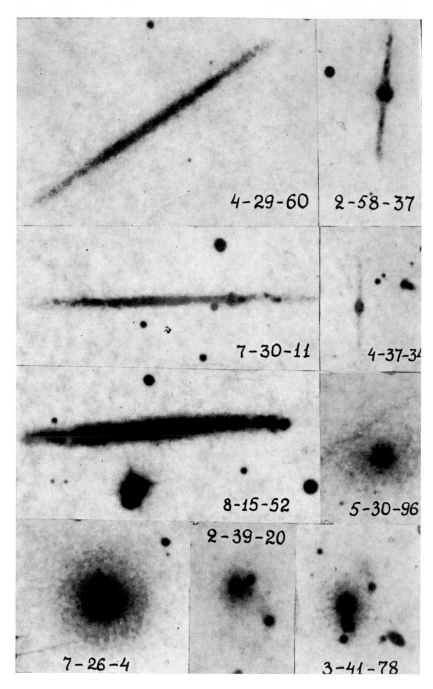

Plate I

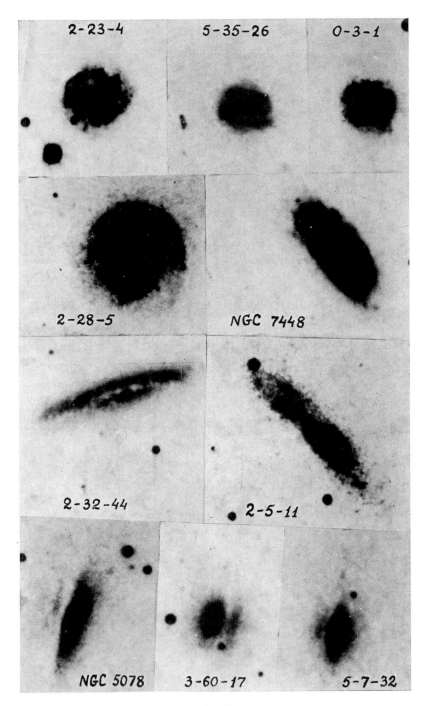

2-23-4   5-35-26   0-3-1

2-28-5   NGC 7448

2-32-44   2-5-11

NGC 5078   3-60-17   5-7-32

Plate II

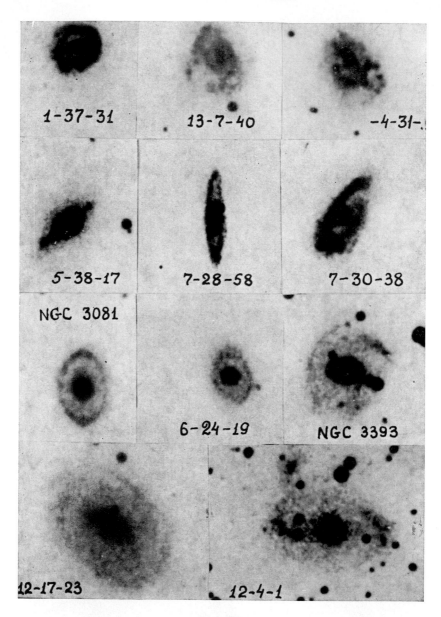

Plate III

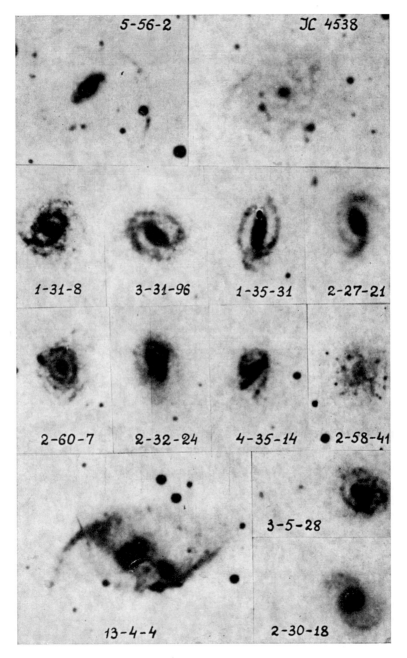

Plate IV

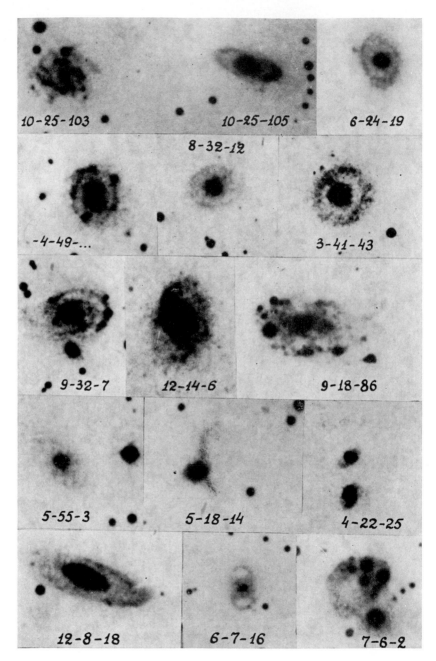

Plate V